THE CREATION
ANSWERS
BOOK

D0017464

ANSWERS OVER 60 COMMONLY-ASKED
QUESTIONS IN 20 CATEGORIES!

Don Batten (Contributing editor)
David Catchpoole
Jonathan Sarfati
Carl Wieland

ISBN: 978-0-949906-62-5

Scripture quotations from the Modern King James Version
or King James Version (AV).

Cover design by Sarah Sercombe

First printing: December 2006
Second Edition: June 2008
Third Edition: March 2009
Fourth Edition: May 2012

Printed by Creation Book Publishers
www.creationbookpublishers.com
CREATION
BOOK PUBLISHERS

Please visit our website for further information on the Christian
world-view and the creation/evolution issue.

CREATION.com

Acknowledgments

Many people helped in the production of this book. Dr Andrew Snelling, one of the authors of the original *Answers Book*, made helpful suggestions at various points in the expanded edition. Dr Werner Gitt provided much of the text of Chapter 9. Dr John Baumgardner helped with parts of the chapter on continental drift. Michael Oard also contributed significantly to the chapter on the Ice Age. Dr Russell Humphreys helped with various aspects of the chapters on distant stars in a young universe and carbon dating.

Dr Len Morris, Rev. Jock Butterss and Warren Nunn checked the first draft and made many helpful suggestions. Russell Grigg and Dr Tas Walker proof-read a later pre-publication draft and made helpful suggestions and corrections. We also appreciated Dave White's checking of the revised parts of the updated edition (2006).

Brendon O'Loughlin created many of the special figures and images used in the book. Special thanks to Robert Smith for his charcoal drawings. Other people who have helped with advice on various points are: David Jolly and Professors Douglas Kelly and David Menton.

Abbreviations

CMI: *Creation Ministries International*
ICC: *International Conference on Creationism*
Ma: *mega annum,* or millions of years

Note: *Journal of Creation* has previously been published as *TJ, CEN Tech.J.,* and *Creation Ex Nihilo Technical Journal.*

Metric conversions

1 centimetre (cm)	0.4 inches
1 metre (m)	3.3 feet
1 kilometre (km)	0.62 miles
1 square kilometre (km^2)	0.39 square miles
1 cubic kilometre (km^3)	0.24 cubic miles
1 tonne	0.98 tons or 1.1 US ('short') tons
0 °C	32 °F
30 °C	86 °F
-20 °C	-4 °F

Contents

Memorize

... always be ready to give an answer to everyone who asks you to give the reason for the hope that you have. But do this with gentleness and respect ...
1 Peter 3:15–16

Chapter 1
Does God exist?

- Is there objective evidence that God exists?
- What are the consequences of atheism?
- Where did God come from?
- Can we know God personally?

THE Bible begins with the statement: *'In the beginning God created the heavens and the earth'* (Gen. 1:1). God's existence is assumed, self-evident. In Psalm 14:1 we are told, *'The fool has said in his heart, There is no God! They acted corruptly; they have done abominable works, there is none who does good.'*

Here we see that the Bible connects corrupt thoughts about God—especially denying His very existence—with corrupt morals. And it is true that, if there is no God, no Creator who sets the rules, then we are set adrift morally. When the children of Israel forgot their Creator in the times of the Judges, when they had no one leading them in being faithful to God, *'... every man did that which was right in his own eyes'* (Judges 21:25), and chaos reigned.

We see the same thing happening today. Countries where the people once honoured God, recognizing that *'God was in Christ reconciling the world to Himself'* (2 Cor. 5:19), experienced unprecedented security and prosperity. Those same countries today are crumbling as people turn their backs on God. *'Righteousness lifts up a nation, but sin is a shame to any people'* (Prov. 14:34).

As nations turn their backs on God, living as if He does not exist, sin abounds—political corruption, lying, slander, public displays of debauchery, violent crime, abortion, theft, adultery, drug-taking, drunkenness, gambling and greed of all kinds. Economic woes follow as taxes increase and governments borrow money to pay for bigger and bigger police forces, jails, and social security systems to patch up the problems.

Romans chapter one reads like a commentary on today's world:

[18]For the wrath of God is revealed from heaven against all ungodliness and unrighteousness of men, who by their unrighteousness suppress the truth. [19]For what can be known about God is plain to them, because God has shown it to them. [20]For his invisible attributes, namely, his eternal power and divine nature, have been clearly perceived, ever since the creation of the world, in the things that have been made. So they are without excuse. [21]For although they knew God, they did not honor him as God or give thanks to him, but they became futile in their thinking, and their foolish hearts were darkened. [22]Claiming to be wise, they became fools, [23]and exchanged the glory of the immortal God for images resembling mortal man and birds and animals and reptiles. [24]Therefore God gave them up in the lusts of their hearts to impurity, to the dishonoring of their bodies among themselves, [25]because they exchanged the truth about God for a lie and worshiped and served the creature rather than the Creator, who is blessed forever! Amen.

[26]For this reason God gave them up to dishonorable passions. For their women exchanged natural relations for those that are contrary to nature; [27]and the men likewise gave up natural relations with women and were consumed with passion for one another, men committing shameless acts with men and receiving in themselves the due penalty for their error. [28]And since they did not see fit to acknowledge God, God gave them up to a debased mind to do what ought not to be done. [29]They were filled with all manner of unrighteousness, evil, covetousness, malice. They are full of envy, murder, strife, deceit, maliciousness. They are gossips, [30]slanderers, haters of God, insolent, haughty, boastful, inventors of evil, disobedient to parents, [31]foolish, faithless, heartless, ruthless. [32]Though they know God's decree that those who practice such things deserve to die, they not only do them but give approval to those who practice them. (ESV)

Many of those in the highest positions in government and education in the once great Christian nations the Bible would call 'fools'. They claim to be wise. But by denying the very existence of God, or His relevance to them today, they have become 'fools'.

Underpinning this abandonment of faith in God is the widespread acceptance of evolutionary thinking—that everything made itself by natural processes; that God is not necessary. There is 'design', such people will admit, but no Designer is necessary. The designed thing designed itself! This thinking, where the plain-as-day evidence for God's existence (Rom. 1:19–20) is explained away, leads naturally to atheism (belief in no god) and secular humanism (man can chart his own course without God). Such thinking abounds in universities and governments today.

Some of the greatest evil seen has been perpetrated by those who have adopted an evolutionary approach to morality—Lenin, Hitler, Stalin, Mao Zedong, Pol Pot. Atheistic evolutionist Sir Arthur Keith acknowledged of Hitler:

'The German Führer ... is an evolutionist; he has consciously sought to make the practice of Germany conform to the theory of evolution.'[1]

Many millions have suffered terribly and lost their lives because of this atheistic way of thinking. Atheism kills, because without God there are no rules—anything goes! Atheists are at the forefront of efforts to legitimize abortion, euthanasia, drug-taking, prostitution, pornography and promiscuity. All these things cause misery, suffering and death. Atheism is the philosophy of death.

Now atheists love to point to atrocities committed by supposed 'Christians'— the Crusades and Northern Ireland are favourites.[2] If the people committing these terrible deeds were indeed Christians, they were/are being **inconsistent** with their own standard of morality (e.g., *'do not murder'*, *'love your enemies'*). However,

1. Keith, A., 1947. *Evolution and Ethics,* Putman, New York, p. 230.
2. The Crusades were a response to Islamic oppression. See Spacer, R., 2005. The politically incorrect guide to Islam (and the Crusades). ISBN: 0895260131.

Stalin, for example, was being **consistent** with his, because, being an atheist (after reading Darwin), he had no objective basis for any standard of morality. Keith (p. 9) admitted that Hitler was also consistent with his evolutionary philosophy.

Christianity says *'God is love'*, *'love one another'* and *'love your enemies'*. Such love is self-sacrificing. Consequently, Christians have been at the forefront in helping the sick, looking after the orphaned and the aged, feeding the hungry, educating the poor, and opposing exploitation through such things as child labour and slavery.

Atheism, with its evolutionary rationale, says 'love' is nothing more than self-interest in increasing the chances of our genes surviving in our offspring or our close relatives. In the 'struggle for survival of the fittest',

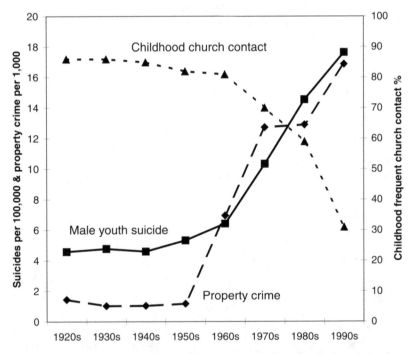

Some social statistics for Australia, showing a relationship between decline of church involvement of children and increased social problems. Other statistics, such as divorce, rape, etc., show similar trends. Church influence declined dramatically with the introduction of evolution into schools in the 1950s and 60s. Statistics for other 'Christian' countries show similar relationships.[3]

3. Sources of data: Childhood church contact from *Why don't people go to church?* National Church Life Survey (2002). Social stats from *State of the Nation: a century of change*, The Centre for Independent Studies, St Leonards, NSW (2001) <www.cis.org.au>

where is the basis for compassion? Hitler's death camps grew out of his desire for the 'Aryan race' to win the battle for 'the preservation of favoured races in the struggle for life' (the subtitle to Darwin's *Origin*).

However, not only is atheism destructive, it is logically flawed at its very roots because there must be a Creator, as we shall see.

Biblical evidence for the existence of a divine author

The Bible, as well as proclaiming the existence of God, also bears witness that God exists, because only divine inspiration can explain the existence of this most remarkable of books. The characteristics that point to divine authorship are:[4-6]

The Bible's amazing unity. Despite being penned by more than 40 authors from over 19 different walks of life over some 1,600 years, the Bible is a consistent revelation from the beginning to the end. Indeed the first and last books of the Bible, Genesis and Revelation, dovetail so perfectly—telling of 'Paradise Lost' and 'Paradise Regained' respectively—that they speak powerfully of their divine authorship (compare, for example, Gen. 1–3 and Rev. 21–22).

The Bible's amazing preservation. In spite of political and religious persecution, the Bible remains. The Roman Emperor Diocletian, following an edict in AD 303, thought he had destroyed every hated Bible. He erected a column over the ashes of a burnt Bible to celebrate his victory. Twenty-five years later, the new emperor, Constantine, commissioned the production of 50 Bibles at the expense of the government! In the eighteenth century, the noted French infidel, Voltaire, forecast that within a century there would be no Bibles left on the Earth. Ironically, 50 years after he died, the Geneva Bible Society used his old printing press and his house to produce stacks of Bibles. The Bible is today available in far more languages than any other book.

The Bible's historical accuracy. Nelson Glueck, famous Jewish archaeologist, spoke of what he called 'the almost incredibly accurate historical memory of the Bible, and particularly so when it is fortified

4. The basic concept for this section comes from Willmington, H.L., 1981. *Willmington's Guide to the Bible,* Tyndale House Publishers, Wheaton, IL, USA., pp. 810–824.
5. Geisler, N.L. and Nix, W.E., 1986. *A General Introduction to the Bible,* Moody Press, Chicago.
6. McDowell, J., 1972. *Evidence that Demands a Verdict,* Vol. 1, Campus Crusade for Christ, San Bernadino, CA.

by archaeological fact'.[7] William F. Albright, widely recognized as one of the great archaeologists, stated:

'The excessive scepticism shown toward the Bible by important historical schools of the eighteenth and nineteenth centuries, certain phases of which still appear periodically, has been progressively discredited. Discovery after discovery has established the accuracy of innumerable details, and has brought increased recognition to the value of the Bible as a source of history.'[7]

Sir William Ramsay, regarded as one of the greatest archaeologists ever, trained in mid-nineteenth century German historical scepticism and so did not believe that the New Testament documents were historically reliable. However, his archaeological investigations drove him to see that his scepticism was unwarranted. He had a profound change of attitude. Speaking of Luke, the writer of the *Gospel of Luke* and the *Acts of the Apostles,* Ramsay said, 'Luke is a historian of the first rank ... he should be placed along with the greatest of historians.'[8]

At many specific points archaeology confirms the Bible's accuracy.[9] There are many particulars where sceptics have questioned the Bible's accuracy, usually on the basis of there being no independent evidence (the fallacy of arguing from silence), only to find that further archaeological discoveries have unearthed evidence for the biblical account.[6]

The Bible's scientific accuracy. Some examples: that the Earth is round (Isa. 40:22); the Earth is suspended in space without support (Job 26:7); the stars are countless[10] (Gen. 15:5); the hydrologic cycle;[11] sea currents;[11] living things

---

7. Cited in Ref. 5, p. 68.
8. Ramsay, W., 1953. *Bearing of Recent Discoveries on the Trustworthiness of the New Testament,* Baker Books, Grand Rapids, Michigan, p. 222.
9. For comprehensive information on the Bible and archaeology, see <http://www.christiananswers.net>.
10. People of old thought that the stars could be counted—there were about 1200 visible stars. Ptolemy (AD 150) dogmatically stated that the number of stars was exactly 1056. See Gitt, W., 1997. Counting the stars. *Creation* **19**(2):10–13.
11. Sarfati, J., 1997. The wonders of water. *Creation* **20**(1):44–46; <creation.com/water>.

reproduce after their kind;[12] many insights into health, hygiene,[13] diet,[14] physiology (such as the importance of blood, e.g. Lev. 17:11); the first and second laws of thermodynamics (e.g. Isa. 51:6), and many other things.[15]

The Bible's prophetic accuracy. The Bible states that the accurate foretelling of events is the province of God. God said:

I have foretold the former things from the beginning; and they went out of My mouth; and I made them hear; I acted suddenly; and they came about. ... I declared it to you from the beginning. Before it happened I revealed it to you; lest you should say, 'My idol has done them, and my graven image, and my molten image, has commanded them.' (Isa. 48:3, 5)

One will search in vain for one line of accurate prophecy in other religious books, but the Bible contains many specific prophecies. McDowell[6] documents 61 prophecies regarding Jesus alone. Many of these, such as His place, time, and manner of birth, betrayal, manner of death, burial, etc., were beyond His control. McDowell also thoroughly documents 12 detailed, specific prophecies regarding Tyre, Sidon, Samaria, Gaza and Ashkelon, Moab and Ammon, Petra and Edom, Thebes and Memphis, Nineveh, Babylon, Chorazin-Bethsaida-Capernaum, Jerusalem and Palestine. He shows how these prophecies were not 'post-dictions' (that is, written after the event).

The probability of all these things coming to pass by chance is effectively zero. Only the wilfully ignorant (2 Peter 3:5) could deny this evidence that God must have inspired these prophecies.

The Bible's civilizing influence. The Bible's message elevated the blood-drinking 'barbarians' of the British Isles to decency. It is the basis of English common law, the American Bill of Rights and the great democracies such as the United Kingdom, the United States, Canada, Australia and New Zealand.

The Bible has inspired the noblest of literature—from Shakespeare, Milton, Pope, Scott, Coleridge and Kipling, to name a few—and

12. Batten, D., 1996. Dogs breeding dogs? That's not evolution. *Creation* (2):20–23; <creation.com/dogs>

13. Wise, D.A., 1995. Modern medicine? It's not so modern! *Creation* 17(1):46–49; <creation.com/modern-medicine>

14. Emerson, P., 1996. Eating out in Eden. *Creation* 18(2):10–13; < creation.com/eating-out-in-eden>.

15. See Morris, H.M., 1984. *The Biblical Basis of Modern Science*, Baker Book House, Grand. Rapids, Michigan.

the art of such as Leonardo da Vinci, Michelangelo, Raphael and Rembrandt. The Bible has inspired the exquisite music of Bach, Handel, Haydn, Mendelssohn and Brahms. Indeed, the decline in acceptance of the biblical world-view in the West has been paralleled by a decline in the beauty of art.[16]

Today the message of the Bible still transforms. Animistic tribal groups in the Philippines are today still being delivered from fear, and former cannibals in Papua New Guinea and Fiji now live in peace, all because of the Gospel.

The Gospel has transformed the lives of animistic people.

The Bible's absolute honesty. Someone has said 'The Bible is not a book that man could write if he would, or would write if he could.' The Bible does not honour man, but God. The people in the Bible have feet of clay; they are shown 'warts and all'. Against the backdrop of their sinfulness and unfaithfulness, God's holiness and faithfulness shine through.

Even the heroes of the faith (Heb. 11) have their failures recorded, including Noah (Gen. 9:20–24), Moses (Num. 20:7–12), David (2 Sam. 11), Elijah (1 Kings 19), and Peter (Matt. 26:74). On the other hand, the enemies of God's people are often praised—for example, Artaxerxes (Neh. 2), Darius the Mede (Dan. 6), and Julius (Acts 27:1–3). These are clear indications that the Bible was not written from a human perspective.

The Bible's life-transforming message. In San Francisco, a man once challenged Dr Harry Ironside to a debate on 'Agnosticism[17] versus Christianity'. Dr Ironside agreed, on one condition: that the agnostic first provide evidence that agnosticism was beneficial enough to defend. Dr Ironside challenged the agnostic to bring one man who had been a 'down-and-outer' (a drunkard, criminal, or such) and one woman who

---

16. Schaeffer, F., 1968. *Escape from Reason*, Inter-Varsity Press, London.
17. Agnosticism is another form of unbelief that denies the truth of God's Word by claiming that we cannot know if God exists. It is in practice little different from atheism.

had been trapped in a degraded life (such as prostitution), and show that both of these people had been rescued from their lives of degradation through embracing the philosophy of agnosticism. Dr Ironside undertook to bring 100 men and women to the debate who had been gloriously rescued through believing the Gospel the agnostic ridiculed. The sceptic withdrew his challenge to debate Dr Ironside.

The message of the Bible mends lives broken by sin, which separates us from our holy Creator. In contrast, agnosticism and atheism, like all anti-God philosophies, destroy.

Other evidence for the Creator-God of the Bible[18]

The universal tendency of things to run down and to fall apart shows that the universe had to be 'wound up' at the beginning. It is not eternal. This is totally consistent with *'In the beginning God created the heavens and the earth.'* (Gen. 1:1).

The changes we see in living things are not the sorts of changes that suggest that the living things themselves came into being by any natural, evolutionary process. Evolution from molecules to man needs some way of creating new complex genetic programs, or information. Mutations and natural selection lead to loss of information.

The fossils do not show the expected transitions from one basic kind of organism to another. This is powerful evidence against the belief that living things made themselves over eons of time.

Evidence that the universe is relatively 'young' also contradicts the belief that everything made itself over billions of years. Because the events are so improbable, lots of time is thought to help the cause of the materialists.

The traditions of hundreds of indigenous peoples from around the world—stories of a global Flood, for example—corroborate the Bible's account of history, as does linguistic and biological evidence for the closeness of all human 'races'.

The explosion in knowledge of the intricate workings of cells and organs has shown that such things as the blood clotting system could not have arisen by a series of accidental changes. The instructions, or information, for specifying the complex organization of living things is

---

18. For more details on these evidences, see the Appendix to this chapter.

not in the molecules themselves (as it is with a crystal), but is imposed from outside. All this demands an intelligent Creator who vastly exceeds our intelligence.

The myth of atheism and science

Many today think that science is anti-God. Atheists encourage this view by claiming that their way of thinking is 'scientific'. In claiming this, they are merely redefining science to exclude God. In fact, science began to flourish only when the biblical view of creation took root in Europe as the Reformation spread its influence. The presuppositions that enabled a scientific approach to investigating the world—that the created universe is real, consistent, understandable, and possible to investigate, for example—came from the Bible. Even non-Christian historians of science such as Loren Eiseley have acknowledged this.[19] Consequently, almost every branch of science was either founded, co-founded, or dramatically advanced, by scientists who believed in the Bible's account of Creation and the Flood.[20,21] And there are many scientists today who believe the Bible.[22]

Is it science?

Science has given us many wonderful things: men on the moon, cheap food, modern medicine, electricity, computers, and so on. All these achievements involve doing experiments in the present, making inferences from these results and doing more experiments to test those ideas. Here, the inferences, or conclusions, are closely related to the experiments and there is often little room for speculation. This type of science is called process, or operational, science, and has given us many valuable advances in knowledge that have benefited mankind.

However, there is another type of science that deals with the past, which can be called historical, or origins, science. When it comes to working out what happened in the past, science is limited because we cannot do experiments directly on past events, and history cannot be

19. Eiseley, L., 1969. *Darwin's Century: Evolution and the Man who Discovered it*. Doubleday, New York, p. 62.
20. Morris, H.M., 1982. *Men of Science, Men of God*, Master Books, USA.
21. Wieland, C. (Ed.). 2004. *The Genesis Files*, Master Books, USA and <creation.com/bios>.
22. Ashton, J., 1999. *In Six Days: Why 50 Scientists Choose to Believe in Creation*, New Holland Publishers, Sydney, Australia.

repeated. In origins science, observations made in the present are used to make inferences about the past. The experiments that can be done in the present that relate to the past are often quite limited, so the inferences require a deal of guesswork. The further in the past the event being studied, the longer the chain of inferences involved, the more guesswork, and the more room there is for non-scientific factors to influence the conclusions—factors such as the religious belief (or unbelief) of the scientist. So, what may be presented as 'science' regarding the past may be little more than the scientist's own personal world-view. The conflicts between 'science' and 'religion' occur in this historical science, not in operational science. Unfortunately, the respect earned by the successes of operational science confounds many into thinking that the conjectural claims arising from origins science carry the same authority.

When it comes to historical science, it is not so much the evidence in the present that is debated, but the inferences about the past. Scientists who believe the record in the Bible, which claims to be the Word of God,[23] will come to different conclusions from those who ignore the Bible. Wilful denial of God's Word (2 Peter 3:3–7) lies at the root of many disagreements over 'historical science'.

---

23. Psalm 78:5, 2 Timothy 3:14–17, 2 Peter 1:19–21. God, who inspired the Bible, has always existed, is perfect and never lies (Titus 1:2). See also Psalm 119 to understand the importance of God's Word.

Who created God?[24]

Sceptics often taunt Christians with 'If God created the universe, then who created God?' (and many genuine thinkers ponder similar ideas). But the Bible defines God as the *uncreated* (i.e. eternal) creator of the universe, and what applies within the universe need not apply to God, so the question 'Who created God?' becomes illogical, just like 'To whom is the bachelor married?'

So a more sophisticated questioner might ask, 'If the universe needs a cause, then why doesn't God need a cause? And if God doesn't need a cause, why should the universe need a cause?' The following reasoning stands up to scrutiny:

- Everything **which has a beginning** has a cause.[25]
- The universe has a beginning.
- Therefore the universe has a cause.

It is important to stress the words in **bold type**. The universe requires a cause because it had a beginning, as will be shown below. God, unlike the universe, had no beginning, so does not need a cause. In addition, Einstein's general relativity, which has much experimental support, shows that time is linked to matter and space. So time itself would have begun along with matter and space at the beginning of the universe. Since God, by definition, is the creator of the whole universe, He is the creator of time. Therefore He is not limited by the time dimension He created, so He has no beginning in time. Therefore He does not have, or need to have, a cause.

In contrast, there is good evidence that the universe had a beginning. This can be shown from the *Laws of Thermodynamics,* the most fundamental laws of the physical sciences.

- 1st Law: The **total** amount of mass-energy in the universe is **constant**.
- 2nd Law: The amount of energy in the universe **available for work** is running down, or *entropy*[26] is increasing to a maximum.

If the total amount of mass-energy is limited, and the amount of usable energy is decreasing, then the universe cannot have existed forever,

---

24. This section is based upon Sarfati, J., 1998. If God created the universe, then who created God? *Journal of Creation* **12**(1):20–22; <creation.com/whomadeGod>.
25. Actually, the word 'cause' has several different meanings in philosophy. But here the word refers to the efficient cause, the chief agent causing something to be made.
26. Entropy is a measure of disorder, or of the decrease in usable energy.

otherwise it would *already* have exhausted all usable energy and reached what is known as 'heat death'. For example, all radio-active atoms would have decayed, every part of the universe would be the same temperature, and no further work would be possible. So the best solution is that the universe must have been created with a lot of usable energy, and is now running down.[27]

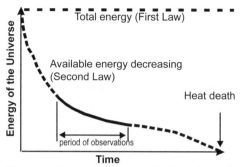

The amount of available energy in the universe is always decreasing, clear evidence that it had a beginning.

Now, what if the questioner accepts that the universe had a beginning, but not that it needs a cause? But it is self-evident that things that begin have a cause—no one really denies it in their heart. All science, history and law enforcement would collapse if this law of cause and effect were denied.[28] Also, the universe cannot be self-caused—nothing can create itself, because it would need to exist before it came into existence; a logical absurdity.

In summary

• The universe (including time itself) can be shown to have had a beginning.

---

27. Oscillating (yoyo) universe ideas were popularized by atheists like the late Carl Sagan and Isaac Asimov, solely to avoid the notion of a beginning, with its implications of a Creator. But the laws of thermodynamics undercut that argument—as each one of the hypothetical cycles would exhaust more and more usable energy. This means every cycle would be larger and longer than the previous one, so looking back in time there would be smaller and smaller cycles. So the multicycle model could have an infinite future, but can only have a finite past. Also, there is far too little mass to stop expansion and allow cycling in the first place, and no known mechanism would allow a bounce back after a hypothetical 'big crunch'.

28. Some physicists assert that quantum mechanics violates this cause/effect principle and can produce something from nothing, but this is not so. Theories that the universe is a quantum fluctuation must presuppose that there was something to fluctuate—their 'quantum vacuum' is a lot of matter-antimatter potential—not 'nothing'. Also, if there is no cause, there is no explanation why this particular universe appeared at a particular time, nor why it was a universe and not, say, a banana or a cat which appeared. This universe can't have any properties to explain its preferential coming into existence, because it would not have any properties until it actually came into existence.

- It is unreasonable to believe something could begin to exist without a cause.
- The universe therefore requires a cause, just as Genesis 1:1 and Romans 1:20 teach.
- God, as creator of time, is outside of time. Therefore, He had no beginning in time, has always existed, and so does not need a cause.[29,30]

Whichever way you look at it—the evidence from the Bible, the incredibly complex, organized information in living things, or the origin of the universe—belief in an all-powerful, all-knowing Creator God, as revealed in the Bible, not only makes sense, but is the only viable explanation.

The Christian knows God!

To one who is a genuine Christian, there is no doubt about God's existence. The Bible says,

For as many as are led by the Spirit of God, they are the sons of God. For you have not received the spirit of bondage again to fear, but you have received the Spirit of adoption by which we cry, Abba, Father! The Spirit Himself bears witness with our spirit that we are the children of God. (Rom. 8:14–16)

The Bible here says that Christians have a personal relationship with God. This is the testimony of those who have realized their sinfulness in the sight of Almighty God and the dire consequences of their sin, have repented of their sin, and have accepted the forgiveness of God made possible through Jesus' death and resurrection. All such genuine Christians have received the Holy Spirit of God and so have assurance that they are 'children of God'. They can indeed know that they have eternal life (1 John 5:13).

Appendix: Non-biblical evidence for the Creator God of the Bible

1. Natural law

There is a universal tendency for all systems of matter/energy to run down.[31] Available energy is dissipated and order is lost. Without either

---

29. See Craig, William L., 1984. *Apologetics: An Introduction*, Moody, Chicago, and The Existence of God and the Beginning of the Universe, at <http://www.leaderu.com/truth>.
30. Geisler, N.L., 1976. *Christian Apologetics*, Baker Books, Grand Rapids, Michigan. But beware of the unfortunate (and unnecessary) friendliness towards the unscriptural 'big bang' theory.
31. This is an aspect of the Second Law of Thermodynamics—see pp. 18–19.

a programmed mechanism or intelligent action, even open systems[32] will tend from *order to disorder*, from information to non-information, and towards less availability of energy. This is the reason why heat flows from hot to cold, and why the sun's energy will not make a dead stick grow (as opposed to a green plant, which contains specific, preprogrammed machinery to direct the energy to create a special type of order known as *specified complexity*).

Applied to the origin of the first life, this denies that such specified complexity can possibly arise *except* from *outside information* impressed on to matter (see pp. 25–26). Applied to the whole universe, which is acknowledged as winding down to 'heat death' (that is, 'cosmos to chaos'), this implies a fundamental contradiction to the 'chaos to cosmos, all by itself' essence of evolutionary philosophy.[33,34]

So, the universe had to be 'wound up' at the beginning and it could not have existed eternally. This requires some agent outside the universe to wind it up—just as a clock cannot wind itself!

2. Living things

Observed changes in living things head in the wrong direction to support evolution from protozoan to man (macro-evolution).

Selection from the genetic information already present in a population (for example, DDT resistance in mosquitoes) causes a net *loss* of genetic information in that population. A DDT-resistant mosquito is adapted to an environment where DDT is present, but the population has lost genes present in the mosquitoes that were not resistant to DDT because they died and so did not pass on their genes. So natural selection and adaptation involve *loss* of genetic information.

From information theory and a vast number of experiments and observations, we know that mutations (copying mistakes) are incapable of causing an ***increase*** in information and functional complexity.[35] Instead, they cause 'noise' during the transmission of genetic information, in accordance with established scientific principles of the effect of random

32. Those able to exchange energy/matter with their surroundings.
33. Thaxton, C.B., Bradley, W.L. and Olsen, R.L., 1984. *The Mystery of Life's Origin*, Lewis and Stanley, Dallas, Texas. These experts in thermodynamics show that thermodynamics is a huge problem for the naturalistic origin of life.
34. Wilder-Smith, A.E., 1981. *The Natural Sciences Know Nothing of Evolution*, Master Books, USA.
35. Spetner, L., 1997. *Not by Chance! Shattering the Modern Theory of Evolution*, The Judaica Press, Inc., Brooklyn, NY.

change on information flow, and so destroy the information.[36] Not surprisingly, over a thousand human diseases are now linked to mutations.

This decrease in genetic information (from mutations, selection/adaptation/speciation and extinction) is consistent with the concept of original created gene pools—with a large degree of initial variety—being depleted since.

Since observed 'micro' changes—such as antibiotic resistance in bacteria and insecticide resistance in insects—are informationally downhill, or at best horizontal, they cannot accumulate to give the required (up-hill) changes for 'macro' evolution, regardless of the time period.[37]

These small changes are erroneously used as 'proofs of evolution' in biology courses, yet they cannot be extrapolated to explain ameba-to-man evolution. Such extrapolation is like arguing that if an unprofitable business loses only a little money each year, given enough years it will make a profit. The observed changes do, however, fit a Creation/Fall model well.

3. Fossils

Although Darwin expected millions of transitional fossils to be found, none have been found, except for a mere handful of disputable ones. Evolutionist Dr Colin Patterson of the British Museum of Natural History responded as follows to a written question asking why he failed to include illustrations of transitional forms in a book he wrote on evolution:

'... I fully agree with your comments on the lack of direct illustration of evolutionary transitions in my book. If I knew of any, fossil or living, I would certainly have included them. You suggest that an artist should be used to visualize such transformations, but where would he get the information from? I could not, honestly, provide it, and if I were to leave it to artistic licence, would that not mislead the reader?

'I wrote the text of my book four years ago. If I were to write it now, I think the book would be rather different. Gradualism is a concept I believe in, not just because of Darwin's authority, but because my understanding of genetics seems to demand it. Yet Gould and the American Museum people are hard to contradict when they say there are no transitional fossils. As a palaeontologist myself, I am much occupied with the philosophical problems of identifying ancestral forms in the fossil record. You say that I should at least "show a photo of the fossil from which each type of organism was derived." I will lay it on the line—there is not one such fossil for

---

36. This is similar to the noise added in the copying of an audio cassette tape. The copy is never better than the master. See <creation.com/infotheory>.

37. Lester, L.P. and Bohlin, R.G., 1989. *The Natural Limits of Biological Change*, Probe Books, Dallas, Texas.

which one could make a water-tight argument.'[38]

Even *Archaeopteryx*, often claimed as the transition between reptiles and birds, shows no sign of the crucial scale-to-feather or leg-to-wing transition. While it is always possible to maintain faith in evolution by belief in unobservable mechanisms,[39] the evidence of such a *systematic* paucity of the anticipated evolutionary 'links' on a global scale is powerful, positive support for biblical creation, regardless of any argument about how and when fossils may have formed.

Image by Steve Cardno

An artist's impression of Archaeopteryx

4. The age of things

The evidence for a 'young' Earth/universe is, by definition, evidence for biblical creation, as naturalistic evolution, if it were at all possible, would require eons. There is much evidence that the universe is relatively young,[40] such as the decay of the Earth's magnetic field, including rapid paleomagnetic reversals,[41] fragile organic molecules in fossils supposedly many millions of years old,[42] not enough helium in the atmosphere,[43] not enough salt in the sea,[44] carbon-14 in coal and oil supposedly millions of years old (see Chapter 4), polystrate fossils that extend through strata supposedly representing many millions of years, inter-tonguing of non-sequential geological strata,[45] small number of

38. Letter (written April 10, 1979) from Dr Colin Patterson, then Senior Palaeontologist at the British Museum of Natural History in London, to Luther D. Sunderland, as quoted in Sunderland, L.D., 1984. Darwin's Enigma, Master Books, San Diego, USA, p. 89. Patterson subsequently tried to play down the significance of this very clear statement.

39. Such as 'punctuated equilibrium', or other secondary assumptions.

40. Morris, J.D., 1994. *The Young Earth*, Master Books, USA.

41. Sarfati, J., 1998. The Earth's magnetic field: evidence that the Earth is young. *Creation* **20**(2):15–17; <creation.com/magfeld>

42. For example, Wieland, C., 1997. Sensational dinosaur blood report. *Creation* **19**(4):42–43; <creation.com/dino_blood>

43. Sarfati, J., 1998. Blowing old-Earth beliefs away. *Creation* **20**(3):19–21; <creation.com/blowing-old-earth-belief-away>

44. Sarfati, J. 1998. Salty seas. *Creation* **21**(1):16–17. <creation.com/salty>.

45. That is, where there are 'missing' layers in between, according to the standard geologic column and the millions of years' time-scale, suggesting that the missing layers do not represent the many millions of years claimed. See Snelling, A., 1992. The case of the missing geologic time. *Creation* **14**(3):31–35 <creation.com/the-case-of-the-missing-geologic-time>

supernova remnants,[46] magnetic fields on 'cold' planets, and much more (see pp. 80–82).

Elapsed time extending back beyond one's own lifetime cannot be directly measured, so all arguments for either a long or a short age are necessarily indirect and must depend on acceptance of the assumptions on which they are inevitably based.

Young-Earth arguments make sense of the fact that many fossils show well-preserved soft parts. This requires rapid deposition and rapid hardening of the encasing sediment for such fossils to exist. Observations of multiple geologic strata and canyons, for example, forming rapidly under catastrophic conditions in recent times, indicate that the entrenched slow-and-gradual, vast-age thinking may well be markedly in error.[47,48]

5. Cultural-anthropological evidence

Hundreds of world-wide traditions among indigenous peoples about a global Flood, each with features in common with the biblical account, provide evidence of the reality of that account. Also widespread, but less so, are accounts of a time of language dispersal. Linguistic and biological evidence has recently revealed a hitherto unrealized genetic closeness among all the 'races' of people (see Chapter 18), consistent with a recent origin from a small population source. This denies the previously widely held belief that human races evolved their characteristic features during long periods of isolation. Molecular studies suggest that, relatively recently, one woman provided the mitochondrial DNA which gave

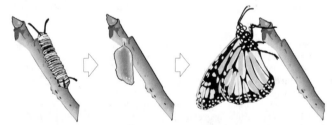

The highly integrated transformation of a caterpillar to a pupa to a butterfly defies evolution's (small) step-wise change as an explanation for its existence.

46. Sarfati, J., 1997. Exploding stars point to a young universe. *Creation* **19**(3):46–48; <creation.com/exploding-stars-point-to-a-young-universe>
47. Mount St Helens: *Explosive Evidence for Catastrophe in Earth's History*, Video featuring Dr Steve Austin, Creation Videos.
48. See Chapter 4, What about carbon dating?

rise to the sequences in all people alive today.[49] Such evidence may be squeezed into an evolutionary model, but it was not a direct prediction of it. However, it is directly consistent with biblical creation.

6. Design and complexity

Incredibly complex coordinated biological systems are known in which no conceivable part-coordinated, part-functioning, simpler arrangement would be other than a liability.[50] Some examples are the blood-clotting mechanism, the bacterial flagellum (used for propulsion), the photosynthetic apparatus, and the pupal transformation of caterpillars to butterflies. Examples abound in living things.

The immense complexity of the human brain, its creativity and power of abstract reasoning, with capacities vastly beyond that required for sheer survival, is perhaps the most 'obvious' evidence for intelligent creation.

At the molecular level, the organization that characterizes living things is inherently different from, for example, a crystal arrangement.

Image by Steve Cardno

49. Wieland, C., 1998. A shrinking date for 'Eve'. *Journal of Creation* **12**(1):1–3; <creation.com/a-shrinking-date-for-eve>.
50. Behe, M.J., 1996. *Darwin's Black Box*, The Free Press, New York.

The function of a given protein, for instance, depends upon the *assembly sequence* of its constituents. The coded information required to generate these sequences is *not* intrinsic to the chemistry of the components (as it is for the structure of a crystal) but extrinsic (imposed from outside).

During reproduction, the information required to make a living organism is impressed upon material substrates to give a preprogrammed pattern, by systems of equal (or greater) complexity (in the parent organism/s) which themselves had the same requirement for their formation. Without preprogrammed machinery, no spontaneous, physico-chemical process is known to generate such information-bearing sequences—this requires the operation of outside intelligence.

The most reasonable inference from such observations is that outside intelligence was responsible for a vast original store of biological information in the form of created populations of fully functioning organisms.[51] Such intelligence vastly surpasses human intelligence—again consistent with the concept of God as revealed in the Bible.

---

51. Gitt, W., 1997. *In the Beginning Was Information,* Christliche Literatur-Verbreitung, Bielefeld, Germany (the German edition was published in 1994).

Chapter 2

Six days? Really?

- Are the days of creation ordinary days?
- Could they be long periods of time?
- Why six days? Is Genesis poetry?
- Does the length of the days really affect the Gospel?
- How can there be 'days' without the sun on the first three days?
- Does Genesis 2 contradict Genesis 1?
- What about the framework hypothesis?

Why is it important?

DOES it really matter if the days of creation in Genesis 1 are real, approximately 24-hour days? Many would say it doesn't matter. In fact, the view that the days should be understood as 'ordinary' days is probably a minority view in churches today, although in the past this was not the case.

Some say that the days can be understood as eons of time, but that God stepped in to do some of the more incredible things at various times—like making pine trees and people. This so-called 'progressive creation' view has God creating *progressively* over eons of time.[1]

---

1. See *Refuting Compromise* for a thorough refutation.

Others claim that Genesis is a mere literary device, a framework upon which hangs important theological teaching—like clothes hanging on a clothesline. They argue that the clothes are the important thing, not the clothesline, so we should not be worried about trying to connect Genesis to the history of the world (this is the 'framework hypothesis').[2]

Yet others say God used evolution to make everything ('theistic evolution') and that Genesis has no relevance to understanding the history of the universe; it is some sort of 'myth'. Science tells us when and how the universe came into being; the Bible tells us why. They are two separate domains of knowledge.[3]

The above views tend to overlap in a fuzzy way in the minds of many who have not thought logically about the effect of these views on the Gospel.

All such 're-interpretations' derive from an attempt to harmonize the Bible's Creation-Fall-Flood account (Genesis 1–11) with the claim of modern historical science that the universe is billions of years old. In this view, rocks containing fossils on Earth formed over eons of time, mostly before people appeared.

The fossil record, so *interpreted*, speaks of death and suffering on a massive scale—which mostly happened before people were created (or evolved). However, this view has serious repercussions for the rest of the Bible, because it:

1. Undermines the goodness of God

Non-Christians object, 'How can you believe in a loving God when there is so much suffering in the world?' They cite animal suffering as part of the problem. According to the history in Genesis, God created everything and He described it as 'very good' after he finished creating the first people, Adam and Eve (Genesis 1:31). It was so good that the people and animals were vegetarian (Genesis 1:29–30)—it is hard to imagine a world like that. It was human sin (rebellion against the Maker and Sustainer of the universe) that brought death and suffering into God's good creation (Genesis 3).

Romans 8:18–25 affirms that the whole creation (not just people)

---

2. Meredith Kline and Henri Blocher promote this view.
3. This view is promoted by organizations such as the American Scientific Affiliation, Christians in Science (U.K.) and the Institute for the Study of Christianity in an Age of Science and Technology (ISCAST; Australia), strangely paralleling the view of the late atheist Stephen Jay Gould on NOMA (non-overlapping magisteria) <creation.com/noma>.

has been *'subjected to futility'* and is now *'groaning'* and in *'bondage to decay'*, waiting for its redemption. Leading commentators on Romans such as F.F. Bruce, C.E.B. Cranfield and James Dunn agree that Paul here refers to the Fall.[4] This is consistent with the real history of Genesis 3, where the creation, not just the people, was cursed because of the man's sin. For example, the ground would now bring forth thorns and thistles (Genesis 3:18). There are thorns preserved in the fossil record, supposedly some 300 million years before man came on the scene. If this is really so, as the above 're-interpretations' maintain, then the Bible misleads.

In reality, we live in a corrupt creation because of man's sin; it was not created this way. Christians have had this view from the beginning. John Milton's classic poems, *Paradise Lost* and *Paradise Regained*, reflect this Christian worldview that was once accepted almost without question.[5] But if God created over billions of years, He is most decidedly *not* 'good'. In such a view, He would have sanctioned and overseen death, disease, cruelty and suffering for billions of years—before sin entered the universe—and called his death-ridden creation 'all very good'.

2. Undermines the Gospel

The New Testament clearly teaches that the reason for Jesus' death and Resurrection depends on the real historical events of Genesis 1–3, that death entered the creation through the sin of the first man:

> For since by a man came death, by a man also came the resurrection of the dead. For as in Adam all die, so also in Christ all will be made alive. (1 Corinthians 15:21, 22; see also Romans 5:12–21).

Jesus is called the 'last Adam' (1 Corinthians 15:45) because he came to undo the work of the first Adam. He took upon himself, in His body on the Cross, the curse of death for the lost race of Adam (Galatians 3:13; Colossians 1:22).

Clearly, the teaching about the reason for Jesus' death depends upon the events in Genesis being real: that physical death originated with

4. For more information, see Sarfati, J., 2005. The Fall: a cosmic catastrophe—Hugh Ross's blunders on plant death in the Bible, *Journal of Creation* **19**(3):60–64; <creation.com/plant_death>; Smith, H., 2007. Cosmic and universal death from Adam's Fall: An exegesis of Romans 8:19–23a, *Journal of Creation* **21**(1):in print, 2006.
5. See Batten, D., and Sarfati, J., 2006. *15 Reasons to Take Genesis as History, Creation Ministries International.*

Adam's sin and that it was not already a part of the created order. Those who devalue the history of Genesis often claim that Adam's death was only 'spiritual' (separation from God). But it was also physical death: *'from dust you came and to dust you will return'* (Genesis 3:19). Thus Jesus also died a physical death on the Cross. He also rose from the dead, bodily, victorious, having dealt with the curse of death that came through Adam.

If death was always a part of 'creation', how can it be *'the last enemy'* (1 Corinthians 15:26) and why did Jesus die?

3. Undermines eschatology (end-times doctrines)

The Bible speaks of a future where the present order will be destroyed and God will make a new heavens and Earth where there will be no more suffering and pain—the former things will have passed away (2 Peter 3:10–13; Revelation 21:4–5). But if God 'created' things much as we see them, with death and suffering intrinsic to the created order, which the previously mentioned views of Genesis suppose, why would God want to destroy the existing order and create a new one?

Why does Revelation equate the removal of the Genesis Curse with the removal of death and pain (Revelation 21:4, 22:2), if the Curse did not bring those things into the world in the first place? It does not make sense.

It also undermines the teaching about the future restoration (Romans 8:21, Acts 3:21)—restoration means return to a former state, so are Christians supposed to be encouraged by a return to millions of years of death and suffering?[6]

4. Undermines hermeneutics (how we understand the Bible)

If Genesis cannot be understood as history, as it is meant to be (as we will show), then how should we understand the rest of the Bible? Perhaps the account of the Exodus or the Exile in Babylon did not actually happen (it is the same form of literature); maybe these writings are just theological arguments (the framework idea)? Perhaps the accounts in the New Testament of Jesus' teaching, death and Resurrection is not actually history (although it seems like it is)?

---

6. See also Verderame, J, 1998. Theistic evolution: future shock? *Creation* **20**(3):18. Grigg, R., 2003. The future—some issues for 'long-age' Christians, *Creation* **25**(4):50–51. <creation.com/future>.

Furthermore, any view that disconnects Genesis from history:

- **Undermines confidence in the rest of the Bible**

If Genesis cannot be understood as straight-forward history, where does history begin? Many accept that Abraham (Genesis 12) was a real person, but refer to some of his ancestors as metaphors (especially Adam). But Jesus' genealogy goes back to Adam (Luke 3) — so where do metaphors begin and end?

Jesus took Genesis as history.[7] Was the Son of God mistaken? 'Darwin's Bulldog', Thomas Huxley, put his finger on the problem when he commented long ago,

'I soon lose my way when I try to follow those who walk delicately among "types" and allegories. A certain passion for clearness forces me to ask, bluntly, whether the writer means to say that Jesus did not believe the stories in question, or that he did? When Jesus spoke, as of a matter of fact, that "the Flood came and destroyed them all," did he believe that the Deluge really took place, or not?'[8]

- **Undermines other doctrines that are based on Genesis**

For example, doctrines relating to marriage, moral law, the wearing of clothing, and the meaning and purpose of our existence are all based on the history of events in Genesis.

Why not believe they are ordinary days?

Many theologians admit that Genesis seems like straightforward history, but do not believe it. Why? The following typifies the thinking:

'It is apparent that the most straightforward understanding of Genesis *without regard to all the hermeneutical considerations suggested by science*, is that God created the heaven and earth in six solar days, that man was created on the sixth day, that death and chaos entered the world after the fall of Adam and Eve, and that all the fossils were the result of the catastrophic universal deluge which spared only Noah's family, and the animals therewith.'[9] [our *emphasis*]

Note that the author says: 'without regard to all the hermeneutical considerations suggested by science', he would believe Genesis is a straightforward historical account of real events.

---

7. See also Sarfati, J., 2006. Genesis: Bible authors believed it to be history, *Creation* **28**(2):21–23, <creation.com/gen-hist>.
8. Thomas Huxley, 1897. *Science and Hebrew Tradition Essays 1*, p.232.
9. Pun, P.P.T., 1987. *J. Amer. Scientific Affiliation* **39**:14.

In other words, for many theologians, 'science' is the authority, not the Word of God. We submit that this confidence in 'science' to be able to dictate a 're-interpreting' of Genesis is misplaced. The conjectures of 'historical science' (or origins science) provide no firm foundation for anything, let alone meddling with the Word of the eternal God Who knows everything (see 'Is it science?' pp. 16–17).

Indeed, the widely-respected systematic theologian, Louis Berkhof, recognized that, contrary to historical science interpreting Genesis, we need the Bible to understand natural history:

'Originally God revealed Himself in creation, but through the blight of sin that original revelation was obscured. Moreover, it was entirely insufficient in the condition of things that obtained after the fall. Only God's self-revelation in the Bible can now be considered adequate. It only conveys a knowledge of God that is pure, that is, free from error and superstition, and that answers to the spiritual needs of fallen man … Some are inclined to speak of God's general revelation as a second source; but this is hardly correct in view of the fact that nature can come into consideration here only as interpreted in the light of Scripture.'[10]

This aptly states a major objection to those who argue that nature is the 67th book of the Bible and who use that 'book' (as interpreted by the majority of scientists) to in turn interpret the days of creation as long periods of time.

| **Christians should base their thinking on the Bible.** |

How has Genesis been understood in the past?

There are two reasons for looking at the history of how Genesis has been interpreted:

1. Generally: If long-age interpretations had always been popular, then a case could be made for assuming that the Bible hints at this. But if they were absent until they became popular in 'science', it's more likely that such interpretations were motivated by trying to reconcile the Bible with 'science'.

---

10. Louis Berkhof, 1932. *Introductory volume to Systematic Theology*, Eerdmans, p. 96.

2. Specifically for those who advocate 'deep time' within the church: in order to overcome the charge that they are motivated by 'science' and not the biblical text, they often *claim that interpreters throughout history have allowed for long creation days*. Therefore it's important to examine the evidence for this claim.

The church fathers

Basil the Great (AD 329–379), in a series of sermons on the six days of creation, the *Hexaëmeron*, argued that the plain meaning was intended: the days were ordinary days; God's commands instantaneously filled the earth with shrubbery, caused trees to shoot up and suddenly filled the rivers with fish; that animals did not originally eat each other; that the sun was created after the earth; etc. He also spoke against evolutionary ideas of humans springing from animals.[11] Note that Darwin did not invent evolution; such ideas go back to anti-theistic philosophers before Christ—such as Anaximander, Epimenides and Lucretius. It has been a pagan, anti-God idea from its earliest origins.

Some have misconstrued the church fathers' positions because they have not read them carefully. It was usual in the Eastern Orthodox Church (EO) to view the Creation Week as real, but they often, in parallel, viewed it as typologically pointing to a total Earth history of seven thousand years until the end. They most definitely did not regard the days of Creation Week as long periods of time.

The late Seraphim Rose, an EO priest, meticulously documented the views of the church fathers of the EO church, showing that they viewed Genesis the way modern creationists do.[12] Terry Mortenson, who earned a Ph.D. in the history of geology, reviewed the book:

'His [Rose's] primary sources are early "Fathers" who wrote commentaries on Genesis: John Chrysostom (344–407), Ephraim the Syrian (306–372), Basil the Great (329–379) and Ambrose of Milan (339–397). But he also used many other "Fathers" of that and later centuries who wrote on some aspect of Genesis 1–11.'[13]

---

11. Batten, D., 1994. Genesis means what it says: Basil (AD 329–379). *Creation* **16**(4):23. <creation.com/basil>, after Basil, *Hexaëmeron* **2**:8.
12. Fr. Rose's papers were published posthumously in *Genesis, Creation and Early Man*, Platina, CA, 2000.
13. Mortenson, T., 2002. Orthodoxy and Genesis: What the fathers *really* taught. *Journal of Creation* **16**(3):48–53. <creation.com/seraphim>.

Rose showed how the EO church fathers were unanimous in their view of the historicity of Creation Week, the Fall and the global Flood. They also believed that God's creative acts were *instantaneous*. They saw the pre-Fall world as fundamentally and profoundly different from the post-Fall one of today.

Some cite Augustine and Origen to justify the smuggling of 'deep time' into the Bible. These two gentlemen, being of the Alexandrian School, tended to allegorize various passages of Scripture. Their allegorization of the days of creation did not arise from within the text, but from outside influences, namely their adherence to neo-Platonic philosophy (whereby they 'reasoned' that God would not sully himself with being bound by time constraints, etc.). But, contrary to the positions of those who would use Augustine and Origen to prop up their own 'deep time' accommodation, both said that God created everything in an instant, *not* over long periods of time. And they *explicitly* argued for the biblical time-frame of thousands of years, as well as the global Flood of Noah.[14]

Now, some may argue that the church fathers erred in their interpretation, that we now have superior knowledge. But modern academics are not the first who have known about the original languages and cultures of the Bible. The onus is on those proposing a new interpretation to prove their case.

The Reformers

Calvin said: 'The day-night cycle was instituted from Day 1, before the sun was created [commenting on "let there be light"]' and 'Here the error of those is manifestly refuted, who maintain that the world was made in a moment [almost certainly referring to Augustine and Origen]. For it is too violent a cavil to contend that Moses distributes the work which God perfected at once into six days, for the mere purpose of conveying instruction [foreshadowing the

John Calvin

TFE Graphics

---

14. Origen, *Contra Celsum (Against Celsus)* 1.19; Augustine, *De Civitate Dei (The City of God)*, **12**(10).

Martin Luther

framework idea?]. Let us rather conclude that God himself took the space of six days, for the purpose of accommodating his works to the capacity of men.' And, 'They will not refrain from guffaws when they are informed that but little more than five thousand years have passed since the creation of the universe.' And, 'And the flood was forty days, &c. Moses copiously insists on this fact, in order to show that the whole world was immersed in the waters.'[15]

Luther wrote even more explicitly of these issues, clearly stating his acceptance of the historicity of Genesis. He also dealt with sceptics' claims of supposed contradictions between Genesis 1 and 2 (see later).[16]

Opponents of the historicity of Genesis love to refer to Ronald Numbers' book, *The Creationists*. Numbers supposedly showed that young-earth 'creationism' was invented by a Seventh-day Adventist, George McCready Price, in the 1920s. This has to be one of the most incredible examples of historical revisionism, on par with the myth that the ancients in general, and the church in particular, held to a flat earth (which was totally demolished by historian Jeffrey Burton Russell[17]). It is as if Numbers, a historian, knows nothing of history before Price. The above material on the church fathers and reformers is sufficient to show the error of Numbers' work. But there is much more that refutes it. See the research of the earth science historian Terry Mortenson on the geologists of the early 1800s who defended the biblical age of the earth and the global flood of Genesis.[18]

15. Documented in Sarfati, J., 2000. Calvin said: Genesis means what it says. *Creation* **22**(4):44–45. <creation.com/calvin >
16. Bartz, P., 1984. Luther on evolution. *Creation* **6**(3):18–21. <creation.com/luther>
17. Russell, J.B., 1991. *Inventing the Flat Earth: Columbus & Modern Historians*, Praeger. See his summary at <www.asa3.org/ASA/topics/history/1997Russell.html>.
18. See Mortenson, T., 2004. *The Great Turning Point*, based on his Ph.D. thesis at Coventry University; <creation.com/turning_point>).

Why *must* they be ordinary days?[19]

1. Genesis was written as history, not poetry

Hebrew has special grammatical forms for recording history, and Genesis 1–11 uses those. It has the same structure as Genesis 12 onwards and most of Exodus, Joshua, Judges, etc. It is *not* poetry or allegory.

Genesis is peppered with *'And ... and ... and ... '* which characterises historical writing (this is technically called the *vav* (ו), often rendered as *waw*, consecutive).

The Hebrew verb forms of Genesis 1 have a particular feature that fits exactly what the Hebrews used for recording history or a series of past events. That is, only the first verb is perfect *(qatal)*, while the verbs that continue the narrative are imperfects *(vayyiqtols)*.[20] In Genesis 1, the first verb, *bara* (create), is perfect, while the subsequent verbs that move the narrative forward are imperfect.[21] A proper translation in English recognises this Hebrew form and translates all the verbs as perfect (or past) tense.

Genesis 1–11 also has several other hallmarks of historical narrative, such as 'accusative particles' that mark the objects of verbs. Terms are often carefully defined. Also, parallelisms, a feature of Hebrew poetry (e.g. in many Psalms), are almost absent in Genesis.[22]

The rare pieces of poetry (e.g. Genesis 1:27 and 2:23) comment on real events anyway, as do many of the Psalms (e.g. Psalm 78). Even if Genesis were poetic, it would not necessarily make it non-historical.

The strongest *structural* parallel of Genesis 1 is Numbers 7:10–84. Both are structured accounts, both contain the Hebrew word for day (יוֹם *yôm*) with a numeric—indeed both are numbered *sequences* of days. In Numbers 7, each of the 12 tribes brought an offering on the different days:

---

19. For detailed treatment of this whole subject, see Chapter 2 in Sarfati, J., 2004. *Refuting Compromise,* available from CMI.
20. Joüon, P. and Muraoka, T., 1991. *A Grammar of Biblical Hebrew: Part Three: Syntax,* p. 390, Pontifical Biblical Institute, Rome.
21. See also a statistical analysis of the Hebrew verb forms by Hebraic scholar Stephen Boyd, 2004. The biblical Hebrew Creation account: New numbers tell the story. *ICR Impact* 377. <www.icr.org/pdf/imp/imp-377.pdf>.
22. Kaiser, W.C., Jr., 1970. The literary form of Genesis 1–11, in Payne, J.B., *New Perspectives on the Old Testament,* Word Inc., Waco, Texas, USA, pp. 59–60.

The one who brought his offering on the first day was Nahshon, son of Amminadab of the tribe of Judah. ...

On the second day Nethanel son of Zuar, the leader of Issachar, brought his offering ...

On the third day, Eliab son of Helon, the leader of the people of Zebulun, brought his offering. ...

On the twelfth day Ahira son of Enan, the leader of the people of Naphtali, brought his offering. ...

The parallel is even stronger when we note that Numbers 7 not only has each day (יום *yôm*) numbered, but also opens and closes with *'in the day that'* to refer collectively to all the ordinary days of the sequence. In spite of the use of 'in the day that' in verses 10 and 84, no one doubts that the numbered day sequence in Numbers 7 (verses 12, 18, 24, 30, 36, 42, 48, 54, 60, 66, 72, 78) involves anything but ordinary-length days, because these days lack a preposition like 'in'. This refutes the claim that 'in the day that' (ביום *b^e yôm* [23]) in Genesis 2:4, summarizing Creation Week, shows that the Genesis 1 days are *not* normal-length. This is simply a Hebrew idiom for 'when' (see NASB, NIV Genesis 2:4 cf. Numbers 7:10, 84).[24]

In this structured narrative (Numbers 7) with a sequence of numbered days, no one claims that it is merely a poetic framework for teaching something theological and that it is not history. No one doubts that the days in Numbers 7 are ordinary days, so there is no grammatical basis for denying the same for the Genesis 1 days. That is, Genesis 1 is straightforward history.

Hebrew scholars concur that Genesis was written as history. For example, the Oxford Hebrew scholar James Barr wrote:

'... probably, so far as I know, there is no professor of Hebrew or Old Testament at any world-class university who does not believe

---

23. Actually, the verses in Numbers 7 have *bayôm*, where the 'a' represents the definite article, 'the', meaning 'on the day [xth]', unlike *beyôm*, which lacks the article.

24. Sarfati, J., 2005. Hebrew scholar affirms that Genesis means what it says! Interview with Dr Ting Wang, Lecturer in Biblical Hebrew, *Creation* 27(4):48–51. <creation.com/wang>.

that the writer(s) of Gen. 1–11 intended to convey to their readers the ideas that

(a) creation took place in a series of six days which were the same as the days of 24 hours we now experience

(b) the figures contained in the Genesis genealogies provided by simple addition a chronology from the beginning of the world up to later stages in the biblical story

(c) Noah's flood was understood to be world-wide and extinguish all human and animal life except for those in the ark.'[25]

Barr, consistent with his neo-orthodox views, does not *believe* Genesis, but he understands what the Hebrew writer clearly intended to convey. Some criticize our use of the Barr quote, because he does not believe in the historicity of Genesis. But that is precisely why we use his statement: he is a *hostile witness*. With no need to try to harmonize Genesis with anything, because he does not see it as carrying any authority, Barr is free to state the clear intention of the author. This contrasts with some 'evangelical' theologians who try to retain some sense of authority without actually believing it says much, if anything, about history—'wrestling with the text', we've heard it called.

Hebrew scholar Dr Stephen Boyd has shown, using a statistical comparison of verb type frequencies of historical and poetic Hebrew texts, that Genesis 1 is clearly historical narrative, not 'poetry'. He concluded, 'There is only one tenable view of its plain sense: God created everything in six literal days.'[26]

Some other Hebrew scholars who support literal creation days include:

- Dr Andrew Steinmann, Associate Professor of Theology and Hebrew at Concordia University in Illinois.[27]
- Dr Robert McCabe, Professor of Old Testament at Detroit Baptist Theological Seminary in Allen Park, MI.[28]

25. Barr, J., Letter to David C.C. Watson, 23 April 1984.
26. Boyd, S.W., The biblical Hebrew creation account: new numbers tell the story. *Impact* **377**, 4 pp. <http://www.icr.org/pdf/imp/imp-377.pdf>
27. Steinmann, A., 2002. אחד [*echad*] as an ordinal number and the meaning of Genesis 1:5, *JETS* **45**(4):577–584. <http://www.etsjets.org/jets/journal/45/45-4/45-4-PP577-584_JETS.pdf>.
28. McCabe, R.V., 2000. A defense of literal days in the Creation Week, *Detroit Baptist Seminary Journal* **5**:97–123. <www.dbts.journals/2000/mccabe.pdf >.

- Dr Ting Wang, lecturer in biblical Hebrew at Stanford University.[24]

2. The use of 'day' in Genesis 1 compared to other Hebrew Scripture

A basic principle of understanding a Bible passage is to compare the use of words and phrases with other parts of the Bible.

How is the word 'day' used in Genesis 1? This is the context of usage of 'day' (as literally as possible, as per the *New American Standard Bible* here):

And God called the light day and the darkness he called night. And there was evening and there was morning, one day ... and there was evening and there was morning, a second day ... a third day ... a fourth day ... a fifth day ... the sixth day.

It is significant that the standard Hebrew lexicon indicates 'day' in Gen 1:5 as a 'day of twenty-four hours'.[29] This 'day' is defined by an evening and a morning cycle; night and day, as well as a number. There should be no need to go further—it is as plain as day what 'day' means in Genesis 1! As the nineteenth-century liberal, Professor Marcus Dods, New College, Edinburgh, said:

'... if, for example, the word "day" in these chapters does not mean a period of twenty-four hours, the interpretation of Scripture is hopeless.'[30]

Note that *'day'* is used with a number in Genesis 1. It is used as a singular or plural with a number 410 times outside of Genesis and it always means an ordinary day.[31]

'Evening' and *'morning'* are used together without *'day'* 38 times outside Genesis 1 and it always indicates an ordinary day. *'Evening'* or *'morning'* are used 23 times each with *'day'* outside Genesis 1 and it always means an ordinary day. And *'night'* is used with *'day'* 52 times and it always indicates an ordinary day.

29. Koehler, K. and Baumgartner, W. (Eds.), Richardson, M.E.J., (trans.) 2002. *Hebrew-Aramaic Lexicon of the Old Testament*.

30. Dodds, M., 1888, as cited by Kelly, D.F., 1997. *Creation and Change,* Christian Focus Publications, Fearn, U.K., p. 112.

31. The numbers come from Stambaugh, J., 1996. The days of creation: A semantic approach. *Proc. Evangelical Society's Far West Region Meeting,* The Master's Seminary, Sun Valley, California.

Scripture and logic dictate that we have no option but to understand *'day'* in Genesis 1 as an 'ordinary' day.

The Hebrew word for 'day', *yom*, is used in several ways in Genesis 1 that show that the days were ordinary days.

---

3. Creation Week is the basis of the 7-day week

Exodus 20:11 summarizes the Creation Week. It eliminates any possibility of an extended time scale by *any* interpretive scheme (framework hypothesis, day-age idea, all gap theories—see Chapter 3, God's days-not-our-days, days of revelation, etc.), since it is given as the basis for our seven-day week with a day of rest (v.10):

For in six days the LORD made heaven and earth, the sea, and all that is in them, and rested the seventh day. Therefore the LORD blessed the Sabbath day and made it holy.

Note Exodus 20:1: *'And God spoke all these words, saying, ... '*.

These are the very words of God himself, not the ideas of Moses, or some redactor or even one of the imaginary scribes, J, E, D or P, who supposedly lived a millennium after the event (long discredited nonsense taught, sadly, at many theological institutions).[32,33]

God took six days to make *everything*—there is nothing other than the *'heavens and earth, the seas and all that is in them'*. This is an all inclusive statement that emphasises completeness. 'God made the universe' would be an appropriate paraphrase.[34] Then God ceased from his work on the seventh day, the day of 'rest'. God did not need six days to make everything and He did not need to rest (Isaiah 40:28), but He did it in this manner and time frame as a pattern for our week. That's where our 7-day week came from.

---

32. Grigg, R., 1998. Did Moses really write Genesis? *Creation* **20**(4):43–46. <creation.com/jedp>.

33. Holding, J.P., Does Genesis hold up under critic's scrutiny? (response to critic of ref. 32), <creation.com/moses-critic >.

34. It is a figure of speech called a *merism*, in which two opposites are combined into an all-encompassing single concept. In English we have 'open day and night' to mean 'open for the entire 24-hr cycle, as well as 'far and near', 'hill and vale' and 'high and low'. 'Heavens and earth' was used for the totality of creation, because biblical Hebrew had no word for 'the universe'. See Leupold, H.C., 1942. *Exposition of Genesis*, **1**:41, Baker Book House, Michigan. Leupold cites similar usage in Jeremiah 10:16; Isaiah 44:24; Psalm 103:19, 119:91; and Ecclesiastes 11:5.

This Scripture alone counters all attempts to stretch the time frame for the universe's existence.

Other arguments used against six days

1. Sometimes 'day' can mean other than an ordinary day

No one denies that 'day' can have several meanings, as it does in English, but the context of a numbered day with an evening and a morning defines the days in Genesis 1 as ordinary days. 'In the day that …' in Genesis 2:4 is a Hebrew idiom for 'when', as explained earlier, and it does not have a number *or* evening *or* morning to define it as an ordinary day.

Some cite *'with the Lord, a day is as a thousand years'* (2 Peter 3:8) to make each of the days of Creation a thousand years long (or longer). This is a misuse of Scripture. Note that the Bible **compares** the thousand years with a day (it is *as* or *like* a day), not that it *is* a day. The Bible teaches us here simply that what might seem like a long time to us waiting for the second coming of Christ is nothing to the eternal God —He is patient, waiting for people to repent of their sin. This has nothing to do with the meaning of 'day' in Genesis 1. In fact, the figure of speech is so effective precisely because the day is *literal* and contrasts so vividly with 1,000 years—to the eternal Creator of time, a short period of time and a long period of time may as well be the same.

A parallel passage in Psalm 90:4, compares a thousand years to a watch in the night (three or four hours) in God's sight, yet no one claims that the night watch could last a thousand years! This passage again underlines that Scripture here contrasts God's eternal perspective with our temporal one. As the respected commentator John Gill said, 'the words aptly express the disproportion there is between the eternal God and mortal man'. They have nothing to do with the meaning of 'day' in Genesis 1.[35]

2. Genesis 1 and 2 are contradictory accounts of creation, so why should we believe Genesis 1 as history?

Genesis chapters One and Two are not different accounts of creation and they are not contradictory. Genesis 1 deals with the creation of everything, the universe, the 'big picture' (see Genesis 1:31–2:4a).

35. Sarfati, J., 2 Peter 3:8 — 'one day is like a thousand years'. <creation.com/content/view/2424>

Genesis 2 recaps the creation of the man and woman, providing details not provided in the first chapter and particularly their situation in the special garden God prepared for them. Chapter 2 is *not* another creation account: there is no mention of the creation of the earth, sun, moon, stars, seas, land, sky, sea creatures, creeping things, etc.

Some cite an apparent difference in order of creation between chapters one and two, claiming a problem with the plants and herbs in Genesis 2:5 and the trees in Genesis 2:9, which in some English translations seem as though they came into being *after* Adam, supposedly contradicting the order in Genesis 1 (plants on Day 3, people on Day 6).

But Genesis 2 focuses on issues of direct importance to Adam and Eve and the garden, not creation in general. Notice that the plants and herbs are described as 'of the field' in chapter 2 (compare 1:12) and they needed a man to tend them (2:5). These are clearly cultivated plants, not plants in general. Also, the trees (2:9) are only the trees planted in the garden, not trees in general. These events relate to God creating the garden, not creation in general.

The mention of the forming of the 'beasts of the field' and 'birds of the air' in Genesis 2:19, before the creation of Eve, is also supposedly a problem.

The supposed contradictions fall away when we realize that Hebrew has no specific verb form to indicate the pluperfect ('had formed', 'having formed'). A number of Hebrew scholars and commentators, such as Keil & Delitzsch and Leupold, have recognized that the context of Genesis Two suggests the pluperfect tense for these events—they are being recounted for the purposes of Chapter 2. For example:

'Now the Lord God had formed out of the ground all the beasts of the field...' (2:19, NIV). Such a translation, which is valid, removes any hint of contradiction.

There is no need to conclude that Genesis 2 contradicts Genesis 1 and so this is not a valid argument against taking Genesis 1 as straightforward history.[36]

> **Genesis chapter 2 is not a *different* account of creation—
> it is a *more detailed* account of the sixth day of creation.**

---

36. For more, see Genesis contradictions? <creation.com/Genesis_contradictions>

3. Adam could not have named all the animals in one day (Day 6)

Adam did not name every *species* of living thing on Earth today, which *would* be rather difficult—he only had to name the animals that God brought to him. The animals named were '*the cattle, the birds of the sky, and every beast of the field'* (Genesis 2:20)—the creatures relevant to man's macro-environment. The sea creatures and 'everything that creeps upon the earth' were not included. Also, even within the named set, there would not have been hundreds of *species* of parrots to name, but maybe only a single parrot *kind*, or a few, for example. God apparently gave Adam the naming exercise as an act of sovereignty (Adam was to rule—Genesis 1:28—and naming something is an exercise of sovereignty). The naming also emphasized to Adam that he was missing something: a mate. Eve was then created, with Adam being most appreciative!

We need to remember that Adam was created perfect, with language, and would have had no trouble in his unfallen state in naming this subset of creatures in a few hours.[37]

4. The sun was not created until Day 4, so how could the first three days have been ordinary days?

The creation of light before the sun was noted by early Church Fathers and the later Reformers without any problem, but some raise it today as if creationists had never thought of it. E.g. in AD 180, Theophilus of Antioch noted that it made nonsense of sun-worship because God made the plants before the sun, and Basil said the same.[38]

The most basic definition of a day is the 'time for Earth to make a complete rotation on its axis'. All we need for a day is the earth rotating. To demarcate the day with evening and morning, we then need a directional source of light so that the rotating earth causes the night and day cycle that is described for each day in Genesis 1. The Bible says that in the latter part of the first day, following the period of darkness (Genesis 1:1–2) *God said, 'Let there be light' and there was light* (v. 3). So we have a source of light and a rotating Earth and we have days happening: *and there was evening and there was morning, one day.*

37. Grigg, R., 1996. Naming the animals: all in a day's work for Adam. *Creation* **18**(4):46–49. <creation.com/animalnames>
38. Theophilus, *To Autolycus* **2**:15, Basil, *Hexaëmeron* **6**:2.

Those who would claim that the first days had to be a different length have to suppose that God changed the speed of rotation of the earth on its axis, when he created the *greater light* as the light bearer (Genesis 1:14), which is hardly likely.

Scripture gives no hint that the days were any different: the same formula applies for Days 2 and 3 as for Days 4 and 5 (*there was evening and there was morning, a second/third/fourth/fifth day*).

5. The seventh day has not finished, so the other days could be long periods of time

Some claim that because the seventh day (Genesis 2:2, 3) did not have the 'evening' and 'morning' demarcation, it must still be continuing; it is a long period of time, so we can regard the other days as long periods also.

Since there was no eighth day of creation, there was no need for an evening and morning to mark off the seventh day from the eighth. Also, evening and morning marked the beginning and end of a day, so if their absence means that the seventh day has not finished, then it has not begun either.

This specious argument is often coupled with the claim that Hebrews 4 says that the seventh day of creation is a long period of time, so the other days could be also. Here is the argument:

'According to this passage [Hebrews 4:4–11], the seventh day of the creation week carries on through the centuries ... the seventh day of Genesis 1 and 2 represents a minimum of several thousand years and a maximum that is open ended (but finite). It seems reasonable to conclude then, given the parallelism of the Genesis creation account, that the first six days may also have been long time periods.'[39]

But Hebrews 4 does *not* say that the seventh day of creation is continuing to the present; it only says God's *rest* is continuing. If someone says on Monday that he rested on Saturday and he is still resting, it would not mean that Saturday has continued through to Monday.

Furthermore, the rest is for those who are in Christ (see vv. 9–11), those who are in the kingdom of God. In other words, it is a spiritual rest. If the rest being alluded to were a continuation of the seventh day of Creation Week, then *everyone* would be in this rest.

---

39. Ross, H., 1994. *Creation and Time*, Navpress, Colorado Springs, Colorado, p. 49.

This argument also founders on the rock of Exodus 20:10–11, written by God Himself, where God's seventh day of rest is given as the basis for the Sabbath rest commandment, making it clear that God's day of rest, the seventh day, was a day like the other six days of the creation week. It would be a strange *week* where the seventh day had not finished yet.[40]

6. Genesis is poetry / figurative, a theological argument (polemic) and so is not history (The Framework hypothesis)

This is the basis of the 'framework hypothesis', probably the favourite view among seminaries that say they accept biblical authority but not six ordinary days of creation.

It is strange, if the literary framework were the true meaning of the text, that no-one interpreted Genesis this way until Arie Noordtzij in 1924. Actually it's not so strange, because the leading framework exponents, Meredith Kline and Henri Blocher, admitted that their rationale for a bizarre, novel interpretation was a desperation to fit the Bible into the alleged 'facts' of science, which no Bible scholar had thought of until the 20th century.

For example, Kline admitted in his major framework article, 'To rebut the literalist interpretation of the Genesis creation "week" propounded by the young-earth theorists is a central concern of this article.'[41] And Blocher said, 'This hypothesis overcomes a number of problems that plagued the commentators [including] the confrontation with the scientific vision of the most distant past.' And he further admits that he rejects the plain teaching of Scripture because, 'The rejection of all the theories accepted by the scientists requires considerable bravado.' Clearly, the framework idea did not come from trying to understand Genesis, but from trying to counter the view, held by scholar and layman alike for 2,000 years, that Genesis records real events in real space and time.[42]

(a) Are the Genesis 1 days real history?

However, as shown above, Genesis is, without any doubt whatsoever, most definitely written as historical narrative. Advocates argue that

---

40. See Anon, 1999. Is the seventh day an eternal day? *Creation* **21**(3):44–45 <creation.com/seventhday>

41. Kline, M.G., 1996. Space and time in the Genesis cosmology. *Perspectives on Science & Christian Faith* **48**(1):2–15.

42. For critiques of the framework hypothesis, see <creation.com/framework>

because Genesis Two is (they say) arranged topically rather than chronologically, so is Genesis 1. So the days are 'figurative' rather than real days. But this is like arguing that because the Gospel of Matthew is arranged topically, then the Gospel of Luke is not arranged chronologically. And, as we have pointed out above (point 2), it is logical (and in line with ancient near eastern literary practice) to have a historical overview (chapter 1) preceding a recap of the details (chapter 2) about certain events already mentioned. Chapter 2 does not have the numbered sequence of days that chapter 1 has, so how can it determine how we view chapter 1?

(b) Are there triads of days?

One of the supposed major 'evidences' for a poetic structure is an alleged two triads of days. In this view, Moses arranged the days in a very stylized framework with days 4–6 paralleling days 1–3. Kline suggests that Days 1–3 refer to the Kingdom, and Days 4–6 to the Rulers, as per the following table:[41]

Table. A framework idea, which fails scrutiny (see text).

Days of Kingdom		Days of Rulers	
Day 1	Light and darkness separated	Day 4	Sun, moon, and stars (luminaries)
Day 2	Sky and waters separated	Day 5	Fish and birds
Day 3	Dry land and seas separated, plants and trees	Day 6	Animals and man

But even if this is true, it would not rule out a historical sequence—surely God is capable of creating in a certain order to teach certain truths. Also, other theologians argue that the 'literary devices' are more in the imagination of the proponents than the text. For example, the parallels of these two triads of days are vastly overdrawn. Systematic theologian Dr Wayne Grudem summarizes:

'First, the proposed correspondence between the days of creation is not nearly as exact as its advocates have supposed. The sun, moon, and stars created on the fourth day as "lights in the firmament of the

heavens" (Gen.1:14) are placed not in any space created on Day 1 but in the "firmament"… that was created on the second day. In fact, the correspondence in language is quite explicit: this "firmament" is not mentioned at all on Day 1 but five times on day 2 (Gen.1:6–8) and three times on Day 4 (Gen.1:14–19). Of course Day 4 also has correspondences with Day 1 (in terms of day and night, light and darkness), but if we say that the second three days show the creation of things to fill the forms or spaces created on the first three days (or to rule the kingdoms as Kline says), then Day 4 overlaps at least as much with Day 2 as it does with Day 1.

'Moreover, the parallel between Days 2 and 5 is not exact, because in some ways the preparation of a space for the fish and birds of Day 5 does not come in Day 2 but in Day 3. It is not until Day 3 that God gathers the waters together and calls them "seas" (Gen.1:10), and on Day 5 the fish are commanded to "fill the waters in the seas" (Gen.1:22). Again in verses 26 and 28 the fish are called "fish of the sea", giving repeated emphasis to the fact that the sphere the fish inhabit was specifically formed on Day 3. Thus, the fish formed on Day 5 seem to belong much more to the place prepared for them on Day 3 than to the widely dispersed waters below the firmament on Day 2. Establishing a parallel between Day 2 and Day 5 faces further difficulties in that nothing is created on Day 5 to inhabit the "waters above the firmament", and the flying things created on this day (the Hebrew word would include flying insects as well as birds) not only fly in the sky created on Day 2, but also live and multiply on the "earth" or "dry land" created on Day 3.

(Note God's command on Day 5: "Let birds multiply on the earth" [Gen.1:22].)

'Finally, the parallel between Days 3 and 6 is not precise, for nothing is created on Day 6 to fill the seas that were gathered together on Day 3. With all of these points of imprecise correspondence and overlapping between places and things created to fill them, the supposed literary "framework," while having an initial appearance of neatness, turns out to be less and less convincing upon closer reading of the text.'[43]

(c) Genesis 2:5 teaches that normal providence was used?

Another key argument by framework proponents is based on Genesis 2:5.[44] Kline rightly states that God did not make plants before the earth had rain or a man, although this is talking about *cultivated* plants not all plants[45]. So, Kline asks, what's to stop God making them anyway because He could miraculously sustain them? The answer, according to Kline, is that God was working by ordinary providence:

'The unargued presupposition of Gen. 2:5 is clearly that the divine providence was operating during the creation period through processes which any reader would recognize as normal in the natural world of his day.'[46]

Note that Kline admits that this alleged presupposition is *not* argued in the text. This would explain why no exegete saw this for thousands of years. Then he makes another amazing leap to say that there was ordinary providence operating throughout Creation Week:

'Embedded in Genesis 2:5 ff. is the principle that the *modus operandi* of the divine providence was the same during the creation period as that of ordinary providence at the present time.'[47]

But this is desperation. Even if normal providence were operating, it would not follow that miracles were *not*. In fact, there is no miracle in the Bible that does *not* operate in the midst of normal providence. Michael Horton points out that those who reject God acting in the normal course of events do it from an *a priori* philosophical assumption and not from anything in the text.[48]

---

43. Grudem, W., 1994. *Systematic Theology*, Zondervan, Grand Rapids, MI, USA, p. 302.
44. Kline, M.G., 1958. Because it had not rained. *WTJ* **20**:146–157.
45. Kruger, M.J., 1997. An understanding of Genesis 2:5. *Journal of Creation* **11**(1):106–110.
46. Kline, Ref. 44, p. 150.
47. Kline, Ref. 44, p. 151.
48. Horton, M.S., 2002. *Covenant and Eschatology: The Divine Drama*, Westminster John Knox.

A miracle is properly understood not as a 'violation' of providence but an *addition*. So when Jesus turned water into wine (John 2), the other aspects of 'providence' were still operating. Perhaps Jesus created the dazzling variety of organic compounds in the water to make the wine, but gravity still held the liquid in the barrels, taste buds were still working in the guests, their hearts pumped blood without skipping a beat, etc.

Ironically, if we assume the evolutionary timespans that Kline's notion is meant to accommodate, Genesis 2:5 actually argues *against* normal providence. In the evolutionary scenario, there are billions of years between the appearance of the oceans and the first plants on land. Note that the verse indicates that the reason why 'no plant of the field had yet sprung up' was that 'the LORD God had not sent rain on the earth.' I.e. there had not been any rain prior to the appearance of land plants. Given the normal providential operation of evaporation and precipitation, etc., how could there have been no rainfall on the earth in all that vast stretch of time? Such would have been hugely miraculous!

So, in conclusion, Kline incorrectly presupposes normal providence as God's sole *modus operandi* for Genesis 2:5, wildly extrapolates it to the entire Creation Week, and further presumes that normal providence excludes miracles. This error is compounded by failing to note the narrow focus of Genesis 2 on man in the Garden.

(d) Is Genesis merely a theological argument (polemic)?

While Genesis 1 certainly refutes various errant ideas about God, it refutes those ideas precisely because of the real events. For example, it has an implied argument against sun worship *because* God actually created light without the sun (Day 1), before He created the sun (Day 4). The contention depends on the historicity of the events.

Is Genesis 1 an argument for the Sabbath? Exodus 20:10–11, which clearly teaches the Sabbath commandment, cites the historical events of Genesis 1 as the basis for the commandment. That is, the works of God recorded in Genesis presage the commandment. The *history* forms the basis of the commandment.

The writings of the framework advocates are marked by lack of clarity. Take a statement by Blocher, for example: 'It [the framework idea] recognizes ordinary days but takes them in the context of one large figurative whole.'[49] But, cutting through the verbal fog, what they really mean is that they deny that the days occurred in real space-time history.

About the only thing that gives any logical coherence to their views is a clear opposition to the calendar-day understanding of Genesis.

7. God's days not our days?

A few have argued that the days of Genesis 1 are 'God's days' and so we should not worry about taking it literally (i.e. as history).

This idea, which sounds superficially pious, if applied consistently, would make understanding any of the Bible an impossible task. God inspired the Bible's words so that we descendants of Adam could understand the things that God would have us know (about salvation, etc.). That means that the words convey God's thoughts *to us*. If any words have meanings that only God understands, then what is the point of having them in the Bible? Perhaps 'murder' or 'adultery' are 'God words' that do not mean what we understand them to mean—obviously a preposterous idea.

In any case, since God is eternal and is outside of time, as we have discussed earlier, what would 'God's day' be; what would it mean? God does not have days and years (see the earlier discussion of 2 Peter 3:8).

8. Days of revelation?

Yet another attempt to get away from the plain, intended meaning of Genesis 1 is to claim that the days were days when God revealed the creation account to Moses (or someone else). But nowhere does the text give any hint that God is *revealing* things on the days. Proponents of this view try to argue that the Hebrew translated as 'made' (*asah*) can mean 'revealed' or 'showed'. The Hebrew clearly says that God created (Hebrew: *bara*) or made (*asah*) things, not that He revealed them. *Asah* has a broader meaning than *bara*, covering 'to make, manufacture, produce, do' etc., but not 'to show' in the sense of reveal.[50] Where *asah* is translated as 'show'—for example, *'show kindness'* (Gen. 24:12), it is in the sense of 'to do', or 'make', kindness.

Again, Exodus 20:11 emphasises that the *whole creation process* occurred in the time frame of an 'ordinary' week.

---

49. Blocher, H. 1984. *In the Beginning*, IVP, Downers Grove, USA, p. 50.
50. Nothing in the standard Gesenius' *Lexicon* supports the interpretation of *asah* as 'show'. See Taylor, C.V., 1997. Revelation or creation? <creation.com/showdays>).

Other problems with long-age interpretations

1. The order of events

Attempts to stretch the time frame of Genesis 1 by making the days into eras of Earth history fail to accommodate the millions of years anyway—the order of creation contradicts the order claimed by the very same secular historical 'science' that is being accommodated (see following table).

Table. Some contradictions between the order of creation in the Bible and evolution/long ages.

Bible account of Creation	Evolution/long-age speculation
Earth before the sun and stars	Stars and sun before Earth
Earth covered in water initially	Earth a molten blob initially
Oceans first, then dry land	Dry land, then the oceans
Life first created on the land	Life started in the oceans
Plants created before the sun	Plants came long after the sun
Fish and birds created together	Fish formed long before birds
Land animals created after birds	Land animals before whales
Man and dinosaurs lived together	Dinosaurs died out long before man appeared

2. What pollinated the plants?

The plants were created on Day 3, but the pollinators were not created until Day 5 or Day 6. If these days were eras of hundreds of millions of years or more, what pollinated the plants to ensure their survival? Some plants have intricate symbiotic relationships with their pollinators—for example, the yucca plant and its moth pollinator.

3. Adam's age

God created Adam on Day 6. Adam lived through Day 7 and died at an age of 930 years (Genesis 5:5). If each day were an era of time, even (only) thousands of years, or the seventh day was still continuing, it would make no sense of Adam's age at death.

Conclusion

This is a question of authority: is historical 'science' or Scripture the authority? For those who

a) regard Scripture (the Word of God) as the ultimate authority, and

b) take the historical roots of the Gospel seriously, with the reality of Adam and the Fall affecting the created order,

belief in six 'ordinary' days is the only logically consistent position to take.

Attempts to disconnect Genesis from the real history of the universe end up making Christianity into an 'upper storey' irrelevance, where 'faith' is seen as little more than a virus of the mind, or an exercise in wishful thinking, like believing in fairies at the bottom of the garden. Over 100 years ago, Scottish theologian James Denney prophetically said,

'The separation of the religious and the scientific means in the end the separation of the religious and the true; and this means that religion dies among true men.'

That has happened to a large extent in much of the once-Christian 'West'—it has lost its spiritual and moral moorings following capitulation to the billions-of-years foundation of cosmic, geological and biological evolution. The various re-interpretations of Genesis discussed in this chapter have contributed to that capitulation.

Chapter 3

What about gap theories?

- What is the ruin-reconstruction theory?
- Lucifer's flood?
- Is the 'soft gap' idea better?

A S shown last chapter, Bible scholars *who relied on the biblical text itself* consistently taught that the earth was about 6,000 years old. However, around the turn of the 19th century, the unbiblical *philosophy* of uniformitarianism[1] found its way into geology,[2] stretching history to millions of years, and theologians responded in different ways.

Nigel Cameron[3] and Douglas Kelly[4] have each documented the

---

1. Uniformitarianism: the belief that the same processes at the same rates observed today applied from the beginning of everything right up till the present time. This philosophy denies miraculous Creation and the catastrophe of the Flood, for example, neither of which are observable today. See 2 Peter 3:3–7.

2. Mortenson, T., 2004, Philosophical naturalism and the age of the earth: are they related? *The Master's Seminary Journal (TMSJ)* **15**(1):71–92, <creation.com/naturalism-church>.

3. Cameron, N.M.deS., 1983. *Evolution and the Authority of the Bible,* Paternoster, Exeter, Devon, UK.

4. Kelly, D.F., 1997, *Creation and Change: Genesis 1:1–2:4 in the light of changing scientific paradigms*, Mentor (Christian Focus Publications), Ross-shire, UK.

change in Bible commentaries over this period. Before the rise of uniformitarianism, a straightforward view of Genesis was practically unanimous. Cameron and Kelly showed that many conservative commentators were intimidated by 'science' and it was only after the rise of this philosophy that they invented ways to add millions of years to the Bible. Since long ages were not even thought of by conservative Bible scholars before their acceptance by geologists, it is strong evidence that they are not in the biblical text at all.

The conservative theologians were trying to preserve scriptural authority this way, but in adopting this approach, they in effect placed science in authority over the Bible—replacing the biblical and Reformation teaching of *Sola Scriptura* with *Scriptura sub scientia* (Scripture alone with Scripture subservient to science)

In contrast to conservatives, liberal theologians[5] saw no need to try to preserve biblical authority, so they had no need for the conservative's rationalizations. Rather, it suited their purpose that the 'facts of science' undermined the Bible. But they gave not the slightest credence to the compromise views, because they could see that such views didn't line up with the grammar of Scripture. They could also point out that the compromise views were novelties not thought of before the rise of long-ages 'science'.

Typical of such liberals was Marcus Dods (1834–1909), a Scottish theologian and author, who became Professor of New Testament Exegesis and then Principal of New College, Edinburgh. He wrote:

'If, for example, the word "day" in these chapters does not mean a period of twenty-four hours, the interpretation of scripture is hopeless.'[6]

These considerations show that the relatively recent rise of the day-age theory and the framework hypothesis (Chapter 2) are reactions to 'science' rather than arising from sound exegesis (Bible interpretation).

Gap theories

Gap theorists accept that the days of the Creation Week had to be six normal-length creation days, but they also accept 'deep time' (up to billions of years). So instead of stretching the days (as the day-age theory does) or denying that they are days in history (framework

---

5. Those who regard the Bible as merely a human invention, not the Word of God.
6. Marcus Dods, 1907. *The Book of Genesis,* Armstrong, NY, p. 4.

hypothesis), they insert a gap between a supposed initial creation and the six days. The classical gap theory inserts the gap between Genesis 1:1 and 1:2, and this gap includes a great flood catastrophe. After this, God supposedly re-created the earth in six normal-length days.

According to Weston Fields, author of the definitive anti-gap book *Unformed and Unfilled*,[7] the traditional or classical gap theory can be summarized as follows:

'In the far distant dateless past God created a perfect heaven and perfect earth. Satan was ruler of the earth which was peopled by a race of "men" without any souls. Eventually, Satan, who dwelled in a garden of Eden composed of minerals (Ezekiel 28), rebelled by desiring to become like God (Isaiah 14). Because of Satan's fall, sin entered the universe and brought on the earth God's judgment in the form of a flood (indicated by the water of 1:2), and then a global Ice Age when the light and heat from the sun were somehow removed. All the plant, animal, and human fossils upon the earth today date from this 'Lucifer's flood' and do not bear any genetic relationship with the plants, animals and fossils living upon the earth today ... .'

More recently, a new type of gap theory has appeared, sometimes called the 'soft gap'. Its proponents realize the force of the argument in Chapter 2 that death is the result of Adam's sin. So this gap theory has no ruin or reconstruction, and merely has long ages for the earth or the universe, or both, and yet the entire fossil record of death postdates the Fall. It is notable that soft gap theorists normally postulate their gap between Genesis 1:2 and 1:3, contrasting with the ruin-reconstruction gappists, who put it between verses 1 and 2. But if there is so clearly a gap, as both parties claim, why is there no agreement about where to put it?

Soft-gap advocate Gorman Gray[8] claims,

'Earth lay in total darkness ... for an undefined length of time before the first day until God began to clear the envelope of thick darkness'.[9]

According to Gray, the Creation Week begins with verse 3, with Earth's first day of forming and filling the pre-existing matter.

---

7. Fields, W.W., 1976. *Unformed and Unfilled,* Burgener Enterprises, Collinsville, Illinois. In Ch. 8, Fields devastates the day-age view as well.
8. Gray, G., 1997. *The Age of the Universe: What Are the Biblical Limits?* Morningstar Publications, Washougal, Washington.
9. A biblical solution to starlight and other problems, <www.hal-pc.org/~tom/GGray.html>, 22 January 2004.

The classical gap theory

The idea of a gap of millions of years between Genesis 1:1 and 1:2 was virtually unknown until Thomas Chalmers (1780–1847), founder of the Free Church of Scotland and popular evangelical preacher, started promoting it. As a very young pastor in 1804 (seven years before he became an evangelical) he startled his congregation by telling them that millions of years was compatible with Scripture. In response to Cuvier's catastrophist theory in 1813, Chalmers began to argue against the day-age view and for the gap theory and persuaded many Christians.[10] The idea of a gap was 'canonized' for some Christians when C.I. Scofield included it in the footnotes of the *Scofield Reference Bible* in 1909. Arthur Custance defended the gap theory in detail in *Without Form and Void*,[11] and Fields wrote *Unformed and Unfilled*[7] largely to refute this.

But many gap theorists admit that their motivation (as it was for Chalmers) is to find a place in the Bible to fit millions of years. For example, the *Scofield Reference Bible* claims, with incredible wishful thinking:

> 'Relegate fossils to the primitive creation, and no conflict of science with the Genesis cosmogony remains.'

Problems with the classical gap theory

The classical gap or ruin-reconstruction theory postulates a catastrophe between Genesis 1:1 and 1:2—the 'ruin'—followed by the 'reconstruction' of the six-day creation. God originally created a perfect world, but then, in this gap, the anointed cherub fell to become Satan (meaning 'adversary'), and God judged the world by a flood catastrophe, which formed most of the fossils. Thus, gappists translate

---

10. Compare 'Chalmers, Thomas, D.D. (1780–1847)' entry in Stephen, L. and Lee, S., eds., 1917. *Dictionary of National Biography* III:1358 (Oxford University Press) and Francis C. Haber, 1959. *The Age of the World: Moses to Darwin* (Baltimore: John Hopkins Press), pp. 201–203.
11. Custance, A.C., 1970. *Without Form and Void,* self-published, Brookville, Canada.

Genesis 1:2 as 'the earth *became* formless and void'. Then the six Days of Creation are said to be a re-creation of this fallen world.

But this fails on several grounds:[12]

1. Although the gap theory originated out of a desire to accommodate the millions of years of supposed geological time, only the most naïve would think it succeeds. Uniformitarian geologists reject the idea of *any* global Flood, whether the biblical Noah's Flood, or the imagined 'Lucifer's Flood' of the gap theory. The fossils supposedly formed over hundreds of millions of years, not rapidly as in a catastrophic flood (ruin). Students from Christian homes went to secular universities and found that the 'gap theory' made no sense with secular geology anyway, so they saw it for what it is—an ill-informed attempt to make the Bible fit secular science. And since their Christian leaders had effectively made 'science' authoritative over Scripture in this matter, many of these students took the next logical step: since 'science' says that dead men don't rise, virgins don't conceive, adultery and homosexual behaviour are natural, then …

2. It postulates the fall of Satan and wholesale death and suffering in a world that God declared 'very good' in Genesis 1:31 (see Chapter 2) and thus undermines the doctrine of redemption and the need for Jesus' death and resurrection.

3. It contradicts the Sabbath command of Exodus 20:8–11, which is

> **The gap theory undermines the foundations of the Gospel.**

based on the creation of the 'heavens, earth, sea and everything in them' in six ordinary days. In Old Testament Hebrew, the words 'heaven(s) and earth' form a figure of speech called a *merism*, in which two opposites are combined into an all-encompassing single concept.[13] Throughout the Bible (e.g. Genesis 14:19, 22; 2 Kings 19:15; Psalm 121:2) this means the totality of creation, not just

---

12. Grigg, R., 1997. From the Beginning of Creation: Does Genesis have a Gap? *Creation* **19**(2):35–38, <creation.com/gap>.

13. An English example is 'open day and night'. This doesn't simply mean during sunlight and darkness but not dusk; rather, 'day and night' means the whole 24-hour day-night cycle. Other examples are 'high and low', 'far and near' and 'hill and dale'.

Gap theorists, often unwittingly, put death and suffering before Creation week and the Fall.

the earth and its atmosphere, or our solar system alone. It is used because Hebrew has no word for 'the universe' and can at best say 'the all'.[14]

4. '*Vav*' (often rendered *waw*) is the name of the Hebrew letter ו which is used as a conjunction. It can mean 'and', 'but', 'now', 'then' and several other things depending upon the context. It occurs at the beginning of Genesis 1:2 and is translated in the KJV, 'And [*vav*] the earth was without form, and void.' Gappists use this translation to support the gap theory. However, the most straightforward reading of the text sees verse 1 of Genesis 1 as the principal subject-and-verb clause, with verse 2 containing three 'circumstantial clauses', meaning that they describe or explain the condition in verse 1. Hebrew grammarian Gesenius called this a '*vav explicativum*', and compares it to the English 'to wit'. Other grammarians have called it the *vav copulative* or *vav disjunctive* or *explanatory vav*.

A *vav* disjunctive is easy to tell from the Hebrew, because it is formed by *vav* followed by a non-verb. It introduces a parenthetic statement; that is, it alerts the reader to put the passage following in brackets, as it were—a descriptive phrase about the previous noun.

---

14. See Leupold, H.C., 1942. *Exposition of Genesis* 1:41, Baker Book House, Michigan, who cites similar usage in Jeremiah 10:16; Isaiah 44:24; Psalm 103:19, 119:91; and Ecclesiastes 11:5.

It does *not* indicate something following in a time sequence—this would have been indicated by a different Hebrew construction called the *vav consecutive*, where the *vav* is followed by a verb. (The *vav consecutive* is in fact used at the beginning of every day of creation—indeed, the beginning of every sentence. In some cases it is used in the middle of a sentence—from Genesis 1:3 through 2:3—which is strong evidence that this is all straightforward historical narrative).

5. It is grammatically impossible to translate the verb היה (*hayah*) as 'became' when it is combined with a *vav* disjunctive—in the rest of the Old Testament, *vav* + a noun + היה (*qal* perfect, 3rd person) is always translated, 'was' or 'came', but never 'became'. Moreover the *qal* form of היה does not normally mean 'became', especially in the beginning of a text, where it usually gives the setting.[15]

6. Also, the correct Hebrew idiom for 'become' is to attach the verb 'to be' היה (*hayah*), e.g. 'was', to the preposition 'to' (Hebrew ל *le*). The verb 'to be' does NOT mean 'become' without this preposition. Since Genesis 1:2 lacks the preposition, it *cannot* mean 'became'.

> **The gap theory imposes an interpretation upon Genesis 1:1-2 which is unnatural, and grammatically unsound.**

7. The Hebrew phrase *tohu va bohu* (ובהו תהו), translated 'without form and void' in Genesis 1:2, is claimed by gap theorists to indicate a judgmental destruction rather than something in the process of being built. But *tohu* occurs several times in the Bible in which it is used in a morally neutral state, describing something unfinished, and not yet organized, but not necessarily evil. Hebrew scholars and the church have for centuries taken the view that Genesis 1:2 is not a scene of judgment or an evil state created by the fall of angels, but a description of the earth in its undeveloped state. The plain and simple meaning of what Moses says is that on the first day there was a mass covered by water, with no dry land involving features such as hills (*tohu* = 'unformed'), and no inhabitants yet (*bohu* = 'unfilled'). The following verses simply describe the forming and filling.

---

15. den Exter Blokland, A.F., 1995. *In Search of Text Syntax: Towards a Syntactic Text Segmentation Model for Biblical Hebrew*, Applicatio, 14, VU University Press: Amsterdam, p. 52.

8. *Bara* (ברא) and *asah* (עשה) (create and make). Gap theorists overstate the distinction between these words, claiming that *bara* refers only to God's creating out of nothing and *asah* refers to shaping something out of pre-existent material. This is an exegetical fallacy that evangelical New Testament scholar Dr Don Carson called 'Unwarranted semantic disjunction or restriction.'[16]

As in English, there is considerable semantic overlap between 'create' and 'make'. Sometimes *asah* is used to mean 'create *ex nihilo*', e.g. Nehemiah 9:6

*You alone are the LORD. You made (*asah*) the heavens, even the highest heavens, and all their starry host, the earth and all that is on it, the seas and all that is in them. You give life to everything,*

God created **everything** in six days. (Exodus 20:8-11)

and the multitudes of heaven worship you.

Indeed, the two words are often used interchangeably in the O.T., sometimes even in synonymous parallelism, e.g. Isaiah 43:7, *Everyone who is called by my name, whom I created* (bara) *for my glory, whom I formed* (yatsar יצר) *and made* (asah).

See also Genesis 1:26–27.

9. Some have attempted to use Jeremiah 4:23 to teach the gap theory, because it uses the same phrase, *tohu va bohu*, to describe the results of a judgment. Gap theorists like Arthur Custance used this to assert that 'without form and void' must mean 'laid waste by a judgment'—so that use of these words in Genesis 1:2 must mean that the earth suffered a judgment. But this is fallacious—there is nothing in the Hebrew words *tohu va bohu* themselves to suggest that. The only reason they refer to being 'laid waste' is due to the context in which the phrase is found in Jeremiah 4. The

16. Carson, D.A., 1996. *Exegetical Fallacies,* Baker Book House, Grand Rapids, MI, 2nd Ed., p. 55.

words simply mean 'unformed and unfilled'. This state can be due either to nothing else having been created, or some created things having been removed. The context of Jeremiah 4 is a prophecy of the Babylonians attacking Jerusalem, not creation. In fact, Jeremiah 4:23 is known as a literary allusion to Genesis 1:2—the judgment would be so severe that it would leave the final state as empty as the earth before God formed and filled it.

An analogy might help here. When you open your word processor program, your document screen is blank. But if you delete an entire document, the screen would likewise be blank. So 'blank' means 'free from any text'. In some situations, the lack of text is because you haven't written anything, in others it is due to a deletion of text. One would need to know the context to tell which—one couldn't tell from the word 'blank' itself. However, a gappist-type analysis of the word might conclude, '"blank" can refer to a screen with all the text deleted, so the word "blank" itself signifies a text deletion event, even when none is stated.'

This is in line with the common biblical principle where a judgment is a *reversal of creation*. Jeremiah 4:23 is taking the land back to its unformed state, unfit for man to live in. Similarly, the Flood took the world back to its condition on Day 2, before the land and water had separated.

This argument for the gap theory also violates the principle of God's progressive revelation in Scripture. Later texts presuppose the prior revelation of earlier texts, not vice versa. Therefore, Jeremiah 4:23

If 'Lucifer's flood' created this, then what did Noah's Flood do?

cannot be used to interpret Genesis 1:2 as a judgment—that would be completely back-to-front, because an allusion works only one way.

10. Gap theorists often rely on the English word 'replenish' in the KJV translation of Genesis 1:28 (*'... and God said unto them, be fruitful and multiply and replenish the earth'*), since this word today often means *'refill'*. But the original Hebrew means 'fill' *not* 'refill'. Linguist Dr Charles Taylor writes, 'As translated in 1611, it ("replenish") was merely a parallel to "fill", and the prefix "re-" didn't mean "again", but "completely".[17] The same Hebrew word *mālē* is used in Genesis 1:22, and is there translated "fill (the seas)", so there was no need to translate it differently in verse 28.'

Soft gap problems

While the soft gap tries to avoid the problems involving death and suffering before sin, many problems remain. By far the most important one is *authority*, as previously pointed out. The web promotion for Gorman Gray's book claims, 'Light from distant galaxies, isotope dating and other riddles are solved.' Distant starlight and isotope dating supposedly 'prove' billions of years of 'deep time', and Gray claims that he has the solution.

The web promo also says, 'Unique interpretive devices force the issue to a showdown in this controversial but insightful treatise.' If we are to accept the author's claims, for thousands of years readers of Genesis have apparently been in the dark as to its true meaning. Even great Bible scholars such as Basil, Luther, Calvin, John Gill, Matthew Henry and others, missed seeing it. But now, finally, Mr Gray has enlightened us with his unique ('only one of its kind') understanding of what Genesis really means. This is a hugely presumptuous claim, and really an admission that 'science' has been made the authority over the text, just like all the other failed attempts at harmonizing.

1. Did the heavenly bodies merely appear on Day 4?

One problem with all these reinterpretations is that Genesis 1 says that God *made* the sun, moon and stars on Day 4 of the Creation Week (1:14–19). Some, including Gray, try to get around this clear teaching by proposing that the sun, moon and stars merely *appeared*, on Day 4

---

17. Taylor, C., 1996. What does 'replenish the earth' mean? *Creation* **18**(2):44–45, <creation. com/replenish>.

(but who was there, on the earth, to see it?). Gray says:
> 'On Day Four, God cleared the translucent blanket of obscuring cloud to transparency. ... Day Four has nothing to do with the creation of sun, moon and stars but only initiating their function as seasonal markers by clearing the atmosphere to transparency'.

To justify this, Gray claims that the Hebrew word used for God making (Heb. עשה *asah*) things can mean almost anything, including uncovering something.

However, the land animals were 'made' (*asah*, v. 25), as was the sky (v. 6–8) and no-one interprets these passages to mean that they were merely revealed, having been created at some earlier time. Furthermore, Hebrew has a word for 'appear', ראה *ra'ah*, used in Genesis 1:9 where God said, 'Let the dry land appear (*ra'ah*)' (from under the water). God could have inspired the writer of His Holy Word to use this word regarding the sun, moon and stars, if they were only caused to appear (from behind the cloud). But He did not.

2. Does Exodus 20:11 really refer to the whole universe?

Gray proposes a novel translation:
> 'For six days God worked on the atmosphere and the land, the seas and all their hosts ...'

To justify this, Gray argues that the merism of 'the heavens and the earth' (meaning the universe) is 'broken', by the addition of 'and the seas'. Thus he justifies restricting heavens to merely the atmosphere, so he can have billions of years for other parts of the universe (stars, galaxies, etc.).

However, the merism is hardly 'broken'; rather, it is *emphasized*. Even in English, we can say, 'he worked day and night, even during coffee breaks', or 'she looked high and low, even in the kitchen sink'.[18]

3. The soft gap creates new problems of its own

The soft gap, like the older gap idea, does not solve anything anyway. Using igneous inclusions, geologists date rocks that contain fossils using the very same dating techniques used for meteorites, the moon, or rocks without fossils. So if one believes the dating for the age of the

---

18. See also DeRemer, F., 2005. Young biosphere, old universe? A review of Gray, Ref. 8, *Journal of Creation* **19**(2):51–57.

rocks of the earth, as the soft gap proposes, then logically one should also accept it for the age of the fossils buried in those rocks. That then makes fossils millions of years old, older than Adam and Eve, and we now have death and corruption before the Fall—just what the soft gap was trying to avoid!

Also, if we accept such 'dating', then the sedimentary rocks laid down by water all around the world actually formed over hundreds of millions of years, not during the year of Noah's Flood. Thus, the abundant evidence for the global Flood of Noah evaporates—this leads logically to a tranquil flood, an absurdity, or no flood at all. Everything unravels—it's another slippery slide to unbelief.[19]

Conclusion

Compromise on the first chapter of Genesis, as explained in this Chapter and Chapter 2, has caused enormous damage to the church. After all, if we can't trust the first chapter of Genesis to mean what it so plainly says, why should we trust the rest of the Bible? And if the first Adam didn't really bring physical death to a previously deathless world, then why did the Last Adam have to die physically? (See 1 Corinthians 15:21–22.) Or if we should 'reinterpret' Genesis to fit secular science,

why not do the same with the other miracles, and the passages that offend secular morality?

Gap theories have arisen in response to the obvious clash between the long-age interpretations prevalent in the culture of the day and the straightforward implications of the biblical text. But 'gap' solutions have massive textual and scientific problems, much greater than the ones that they purport to solve.

Even though their inventors may have had good motivations, such notions still seriously compromise the authority of the Bible, even if unintentionally.

19. See Batten, D., 2004. 'Soft' gap sophistry, *Creation* **26**(3):44–47, <creation.com/softgap>.

The classical gap theory caused much of Christendom to 'fall asleep on its watch', comforted by the mistaken belief that the scientific problems of uniformitarian geology had been solved for the believer. This left a generation of students to face evolutionary teaching unprepared and defenceless, in effect. Today, as more of the public is educated in such areas, one finds the gap theory (apart from the occasional flirting with new versions like the soft gap) generally 'dying out' as an interpretive framework.

> **The gap theory anesthetized the church for over one hundred years.**

Chapter 4

What about carbon dating?

- How does the carbon 'clock' work?
- Is it reliable?
- What does carbon dating really show?
- What about other radiometric dating methods?
- Is there evidence that the Earth is young?

PEOPLE who ask about carbon-14 (^{14}C) dating usually want to know about the radiometric[1] dating methods that are claimed to give millions and billions of years—carbon dating can only give thousands of years. People wonder how millions of years could be squeezed into the biblical account of history.

Clearly, such huge time periods cannot be fitted into the Bible without compromising what the Bible says about the goodness of God and the origin of sin, death and suffering—the reason Jesus came into the world (see Chapter 2).

Christians, by definition, take the statements of Jesus Christ seriously. He said, *'But from the beginning of the creation God made them male*

---

1. Also known as isotope or radioisotope dating.

and female' (Mark 10:6). This only makes sense with a time line beginning with the creation week thousands of years ago. It makes no sense at all if man appeared at the end of billions of years.

We will deal with carbon dating first and then with the other dating methods.

How the carbon clock works

Carbon has unique properties that are essential for life on Earth. Familiar to us as the black substance in charred wood, as diamonds, and as the graphite in 'lead' pencils, carbon comes in several forms, or isotopes. One rare form has atoms that are 14 times as heavy as hydrogen atoms: carbon-14, or ^{14}C, or radiocarbon.

Carbon-14 is made when cosmic rays knock neutrons out of atomic nuclei in the upper atmosphere. These displaced neutrons, now moving fast, hit ordinary nitrogen (^{14}N) at lower altitudes, converting it into ^{14}C. Unlike common carbon (^{12}C), ^{14}C is unstable and slowly decays, changing back into nitrogen and releasing energy. This instability makes it radioactive.

Ordinary carbon (^{12}C) is found in the carbon dioxide (CO_2) in the air, which is taken up by plants, which in turn are eaten by animals. So a bone, or a leaf of a tree, or even a piece of wooden furniture, contains carbon. When ^{14}C has been formed, like ordinary carbon (^{12}C), it combines with oxygen to give carbon dioxide ($^{14}CO_2$), and so it also gets cycled through the cells of plants and animals.

We can take a sample of air, count how many ^{12}C atoms there are for every ^{14}C atom, and calculate the $^{14}C/^{12}C$

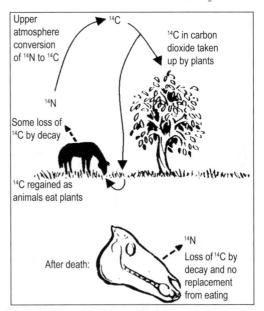

Upper atmosphere conversion of ^{14}N to ^{14}C

^{14}C

^{14}C in carbon dioxide taken up by plants

^{14}N

Some loss of ^{14}C by decay

^{14}C regained as animals eat plants

After death:

^{14}N

Loss of ^{14}C by decay and no replacement from eating

Figure 1. ^{14}C is gained by living things but lost after death.

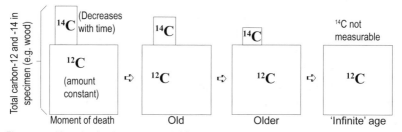

Figure 2. *After death, the amount of ^{12}C remains constant, but the amount of ^{14}C decreases.*

ratio. Because ^{14}C is so well mixed up with ^{12}C, we expect to find that this ratio is the same if we sample a leaf from a tree, or a part of your body.

In living things, although ^{14}C atoms are constantly changing back to ^{14}N, they are still exchanging carbon with their surroundings, so the mixture remains about the same as in the atmosphere. However, as soon as a plant or animal dies, the ^{14}C atoms which decay are no longer replaced, so the amount of ^{14}C in that once-living thing decreases as time goes on (Figure 1). In other words, the $^{14}C/^{12}C$ ratio gets smaller. So, we have a 'clock' which starts ticking the moment something dies (Figure 2).

Obviously, this works only for things which were once living. It cannot be used to date volcanic rocks, for example.

The rate of decay of ^{14}C is such that half of an amount will convert back to ^{14}N in 5,730 ± 40 years. This is the 'half-life'. So, in two half-lives, or 11,460 years, only one-quarter will be left. Thus, if the amount of ^{14}C relative to ^{12}C in a sample is one-quarter of that in living organisms at present, then it has a theoretical age of 11,460 years. Anything over about 50,000 years old should theoretically have no detectable ^{14}C left. That is why radiocarbon dating cannot give millions of years. In fact, if a sample contains ^{14}C, it is good evidence that it is *not* millions of years old.

However, things are not quite so simple. Firstly, plants discriminate against carbon dioxide containing ^{14}C. That is, they take up less than would be expected and so they test older than they really are. Furthermore, different types of plants discriminate differently. This also has to be corrected for.[2]

---

2.   Today, a stable carbon isotope, ^{13}C, is measured as an indication of the level of discrimination against ^{14}C.

Secondly, the ratio of $^{14}C/^{12}C$ in the atmosphere has not been constant—for example it was higher before the industrial era when the massive burning of fossil fuels released a lot of carbon dioxide that was depleted in ^{14}C. This would make things which died at that time appear older in terms of carbon dating. Then there was a rise in $^{14}CO_2$ with the advent of atmospheric testing of atomic bombs in the 1950s.[3] This would make things carbon-dated from that time appear younger than their true age.

Measurement of ^{14}C in historically dated objects (e.g. seeds in the graves of historically dated tombs) enables the level of ^{14}C in the atmosphere at that time to be estimated, and so partial calibration of the 'clock' is possible. Accordingly, carbon dating carefully applied to items from historical times can be useful. However, even with such historical calibration, archaeologists do not regard ^{14}C dates as absolute because of frequent anomalies. They rely more on dating methods that link into historical records.

Outside the range of recorded history, calibration of the ^{14}C 'clock' is not possible.[4]

Other factors affecting carbon dating

The amount of cosmic rays penetrating Earth's atmosphere affects the amount of ^{14}C produced and therefore the dating system. The amount of cosmic rays reaching the Earth varies with the sun's activity, and with the Earth's passage through magnetic clouds as the solar system travels around the Milky Way galaxy.

The strength of the Earth's magnetic field affects the amount of cosmic rays entering the atmosphere. A stronger magnetic field deflects more cosmic rays away from the Earth. Overall, the energy of the Earth's magnetic field has been decreasing,[5] so more ^{14}C is being produced now

---

3. Radiation from atomic testing, like cosmic rays, causes the conversion of ^{14}N to ^{14}C.

4. Tree ring dating (dendrochronology) has been used in an attempt to extend the calibration of carbon-14 dating earlier than historical records allow, but this depends on temporal placement of fragments of wood (from long-dead trees) using carbon-14 dating, assuming straight-line extrapolation backwards. Then cross-matching of ring patterns is used to calibrate the carbon 'clock'—a somewhat circular process which does not give an independent calibration of the carbon dating system.

5. McDonald, K.L. and Gunst, R.H., 1965. An analysis of the earth's magnetic field from 1835 to 1965. *ESSA Technical Report IER 46-IES,* U.S. Government Printing Office, Washington, D.C., p. 14.

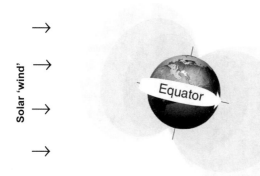

The strength of Earth's magnetic field affects carbon dating.

than in the past. This will make old things look older than they really are.

Also, the Genesis Flood would have greatly upset the carbon balance. The Flood buried a huge amount of carbon, which became coal, oil, etc., lowering the total ^{12}C in the biosphere (including the atmosphere—plants regrowing after the Flood absorb CO_2 which is not replaced by the decay of the buried vegetation).[6] Total ^{14}C is also proportionately lowered at this time, but whereas no terrestrial process generates any more ^{12}C, ^{14}C is continually being produced, and at a rate which does not depend on carbon levels (it comes from nitrogen). Therefore the ^{14}C level *relative to ^{12}C* increases after the Flood. So the $^{14}C/^{12}C$ ratio in plants/animals/ the atmosphere before the Flood had to be lower than what it is now.

Unless this effect (which is additional to the magnetic field issue just discussed) were corrected for, carbon dating of fossils formed in the Flood would give ages much older than the true ages.

Creationist researchers have suggested that dates of 35,000–45,000 years should be recalibrated to the biblical date for the Flood.[7] Such a recalibration makes sense of anomalous data from carbon dating—for

6. Taylor, B.J., 1994. Carbon dioxide in the antediluvian atmosphere. *Creation Research Society Quarterly* **30**(4):193–197.
7. Brown, R.H., 1992. Correlation of C-14 age with real time. *Creation Research Society Quarterly* **29**:45–47. Musk ox muscle was dated at 24,000 years, but hair was dated at 17,000 years. Corrected dates bring the difference in age approximately within the life span of a musk ox. With sloth cave dung, standard carbon dates of the lower layers suggested less than 2 pellets per year were produced by the sloths. Correcting the dates increased the number to a more realistic 1.4 per day.

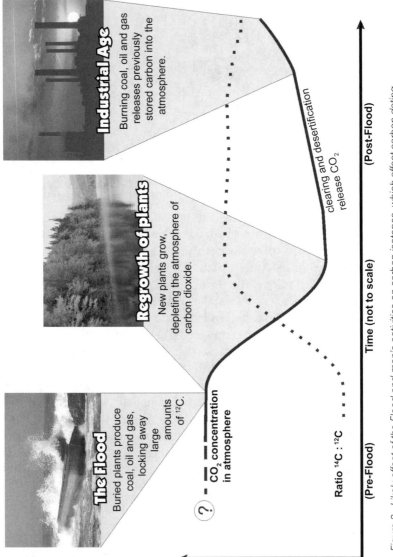

Figure 3. *Likely effect of the Flood and man's activities on carbon isotopes, which affect carbon dating.*

example, very discordant 'dates' for different parts of a frozen musk ox carcass from Alaska and an inordinately slow rate of accumulation of ground sloth dung pellets in the older layers of a cave where the layers were carbon dated.[7]

Also, volcanoes emit much CO_2 depleted in ^{14}C. Since the Flood was accompanied by much volcanism (see Chapters 10, 11, 12, 17), fossils formed in the early post-Flood period would give radiocarbon ages older than they really are.

In summary, the carbon-14 method, when corrected for the effects of the Flood, can give useful results, but needs to be applied carefully. It does not give dates of millions of years and when corrected properly fits well with the biblical Flood (Figure 3).

Other radiometric dating methods

There are various other radiometric dating methods used today to give ages of millions or billions of years for rocks. These techniques, unlike carbon dating, mostly use the relative concentrations of parent and daughter products in radioactive decay chains. For example, potassium-40 decays to argon-40, uranium-238 decays to lead-206 via other elements like radium, uranium-235 decays to lead-207, rubidium-87 decays to strontium-87, etc. These techniques are applied to igneous rocks, and are normally seen as giving the time since solidification.

The isotope concentrations can be measured very accurately, but isotope concentrations are not dates. To derive ages from such measurements, unprovable assumptions have to be made (see hourglass diagram below) such as:

The hourglasses represent radiometric dating. It is assumed that we know the amount of parent and daughter elements in the original sample, the rate of decay is constant, and no parent or daughter material has been added or removed.

1. The starting conditions are known (for example, that there was no daughter isotope present at the start, or that we know how much was there).
2. Decay rates have always been constant.
3. Systems were closed or isolated so that no parent or daughter isotopes were lost or added.

> **Isotope concentrations, or ratios, can be measured very accurately, but isotope concentrations, or ratios, are not dates.**

There are patterns in the isotope data

There is plenty of evidence that the radioisotope dating systems are not the infallible techniques many think, and that they are not measuring millions of years. However, there are still patterns to be explained. For example, deeper rocks often tend to give older 'ages'. Creationists agree that the deeper rocks are generally older, but not by millions of years. Geologist John Woodmorappe, in his devastating critique of radioactive dating,[8] points out that there are other large-scale trends in the rocks that have nothing to do with radioactive decay.

'Bad' dates?

When a 'date' differs from that expected, researchers readily invent excuses for rejecting the result. The common application of such posterior reasoning shows that radiometric dating has serious problems. Woodmorappe cites hundreds of examples of excuses used to explain 'bad' dates.[8]

For example, researchers applied posterior reasoning to the dating of *Australopithecus ramidus* fossils.[9] Most samples of basalt closest to the fossil-bearing strata gave dates of about 23 Ma (*Mega annum*, million years) by the argon-argon method. The authors decided that was 'too old', according to their beliefs about the place of the fossils in the evolutionary grand scheme of things. So they looked at some basalt further removed from the fossils and selected 17 of 26 samples to get an

8. Woodmorappe, J., 1999. *The Mythology of Modern Dating Methods,* Institute for Creation Research, San Diego, California.
9. WoldeGabriel, G., *et al.,* 1994. Ecological and temporal placement of early Pliocene hominids at Aramis, Ethiopia. *Nature* **371**:330–333.

acceptable maximum age of 4.4 Ma. The other nine samples again gave much older dates but the authors decided they must be contaminated, and discarded them. That is how radiometric dating works. It is very much driven by the existing long-age worldview that pervades academia today.

A similar story surrounds the dating of the primate skull known as KNM-ER 1470.[10,11] This started with an initial 212 to 230 Ma, which, *according to the fossils,* was considered way off the mark (humans 'weren't around then'). Various other attempts were made to date the volcanic rocks in the area. Over the years an age of 2.9 Ma was settled upon because of the agreement between several different published studies (although the studies involved selection of 'good' from 'bad' results, just like *Australopithecus ramidus*).

However, preconceived notions about human evolution could not cope with a skull like 1470 being 'that old'. A study of pig fossils in Africa readily convinced most anthropologists that the 1470 skull was much younger. After this was widely accepted, further studies of the rocks brought the radiometric age down to about 1.9 Ma—again several studies 'confirmed' *this* date. Such is the dating game.

Are we suggesting that evolutionists are conspiring to massage the data to get the answers they want? No, not generally. It is simply that all observations must fit the prevailing paradigm. The paradigm, or belief system, of molecules-to-man evolution over eons of time, is so strongly entrenched it is not questioned—it is a 'fact'. So every observation *must* fit this paradigm. Unconsciously, the researchers, who are supposedly 'objective scientists' in the eyes of the public, select the observations to fit the basic belief system.

We must remember that the past is not open to the normal processes of experimental science; that is, repeatable experiments in the present. A scientist cannot do experiments on events that happened in the past. Scientists do not measure the age of rocks, they measure isotope concentrations, and these can be measured extremely accurately. However, the 'age' is calculated using assumptions about the past that cannot be proven.

We should remember God's admonition to Job, *'Where were you when I laid the foundations of the earth?'* (Job 38:4).

10. Lubenow, M., 1995. The pigs took it all. *Creation* **17**(3):36–38.
11. Lubenow, M., 1993. *Bones of Contention,* Baker Books, Grand Rapids, Michigan, pp. 247–266.

Those involved with unrecorded history gather information in the present and construct stories about the past. The level of proof demanded for such stories seems to be much less than for studies in the empirical sciences, such as physics, chemistry, molecular biology, physiology, etc.

Williams, an expert in the environmental fate of radioactive elements, identified 17 flaws in the isotope dating reported in just three widely respected seminal papers that supposedly established the age of the Earth at 4.6 billion years.[12] John Woodmorappe has produced an incisive critique of these dating methods.[8] He exposes hundreds of myths that have grown up around the techniques. He shows that the few 'good' dates left after the 'bad' dates are filtered out could easily be explained as fortunate coincidences.

What date would you like?

The forms issued by radioisotope laboratories for submission with samples to be dated commonly ask how old the sample is expected to be. Why? If the techniques were absolutely objective and reliable, such information should not be necessary. Presumably the laboratories know that anomalous dates are common, so they need some check on whether they have obtained a 'good' date.

Testing radiometric dating methods

If the long-age dating techniques were really objective means of finding the ages of rocks, they should work in situations where we know the age. Furthermore, different techniques should consistently agree with one another.

Methods should work reliably on things of known age

There are many examples where the dating methods give 'dates' that are wrong for rocks of known age. One example is K-Ar 'dating' of five historical andesite lava flows from Mt Ngauruhoe in New Zealand. Although one lava flow occurred in 1949, three in 1954, and one in 1975, the 'dates' ranged from less than 0.27 to 3.5 Ma.[13]

---

12. Williams, A.R., 1992. Long-age isotope dating short on credibility. *CEN Tech. J.* **6**(1):2–5.
13. Snelling, A.A., 1998. The cause of anomalous potassium-argon 'ages' for recent andesite flows at Mt. Ngauruhoe, New Zealand, and the implications for potassium-argon 'dating'. *Proc. 4ᵗʰ ICC*, pp. 503–525.

Lava flows of known age often give wrong radioisotope dates.

Again, using hindsight, it is argued that 'excess' argon from the magma (molten rock) was retained in the rock when it solidified. The secular scientific literature lists many examples of excess argon causing dates of millions of years in rocks of known historical age.[14] This excess appears to have come from the upper mantle, below the Earth's crust. This is consistent with a young world—the argon has had too little time to escape.[15] If excess argon can cause exaggerated dates for rocks of **known** age, then why should we trust the method for rocks of **unknown** age?

Other techniques, such as the use of isochrons,[16] make different assumptions about starting conditions, but there is a growing recognition that such 'fool-proof' techniques can also give 'bad' dates. So data are again selected according to what the researcher already believes about the age of the rock.

14. Ref. 13 lists many instances. For example, six cases were reported by Krummenacher, D., 1970. Isotopic composition of argon in modern surface rocks. *Earth and Planetary Science Letters* **8**:109–117; five were reported by Dalrymple, G.B., 1969. $^{40}Ar/^{36}Ar$ analysis of historic lava flows. *Earth and Planetary Science Letters* **6**:47–55. A large excess was reported in Fisher, D.E., 1970. Excess rare gases in a subaerial basalt from Nigeria. *Nature* **232**:60–61.

15. Ref. 13, p. 520.

16. The isochron technique involves collecting a number of rock samples from different parts of the rock unit being dated. The concentration of a parent radioactive isotope, such as rubidium-87, is graphed against the concentration of a daughter isotope, such as strontium-87, for all the samples. A straight line is drawn through these points, representing the ratio of the parent:daughter, from which a 'date' is calculated. If the line is of good fit and the 'age' is acceptable it is considered a 'good' date. The method involves dividing both the parent and daughter concentrations by the concentration of a similar stable isotope—in this case, strontium-86. See pp. 79–80.

Geologist Dr Steve Austin sampled basalt from the base of the Grand Canyon strata and from lava that spilled over the edge of the canyon.[17] By evolutionary reckoning, the latter should be a billion years younger than the basalt from the bottom. Standard laboratories analysed the isotopes. The rubidium-strontium isochron technique suggested that the recent lava flow was 270 Ma *older* than the basalts beneath the Grand Canyon—an impossibility.

Different dating techniques should consistently agree

If the dating methods are an objective and reliable means of determining ages, they should agree. If a chemist were measuring the sugar content of blood, all valid methods for the determination would give the same answer (within the limits of experimental error). However, with radiometric dating, the different techniques often give quite different results.

In the study of Grand Canyon rocks by Austin,[17] different techniques gave different results (see Table below). Again all sorts of reasons can be suggested for the 'bad' dates, but this is again posterior reasoning. Techniques that give results that can be dismissed just because they don't agree with what we already believe cannot be considered objective.

In Australia, some wood found in Tertiary basalt was clearly buried in the lava flow that formed the basalt, as can be seen from the charring. The wood was 'dated' by radiocarbon (^{14}C) analysis at about 45,000 years old, but the basalt was 'dated' by the potassium-argon method at 45 million years old![18]

Method	'Age'
Six potassium-argon model ages	10,000 years to 117 Ma
Five rubidium-strontium ages	1,270–1,390 Ma
Rubidium-strontium isochron	1,340 Ma
Lead-lead isochron	2,600 Ma

Radiometric 'ages', using different methods, for basaltic rocks most geologists accept as only thousands of years old, from the Uinkaret Plateau of the Grand Canyon (Ma = millions of years).[17]

17. Austin, S.A. (ed.) 1994. *Grand Canyon: Monument to Catastrophe*. Institute for Creation Research, Santee, California, pp. 120–131.
18. Snelling, A.A., 1998. Radiometric dating in conflict. *Creation* **20**(1):24–27.

Isotope ratios of uraninite crystals from the Koongarra uranium body in the Northern Territory of Australia gave lead-lead isochron ages of 841 ± 140 Ma.[19] This contrasts with an age of 1550–1650 Ma based on other isotope ratios,[20] and ages of 275, 61, 0, 0, and 0 Ma from thorium/lead ($^{232}Th/^{208}Pb$) ratios in five uraninite grains.[19] The latter figures are significant because thorium-derived dates should be the more reliable, since thorium is less mobile than the uranium minerals that are the parents of the lead isotopes in the lead-lead system.[19] The 'zero' ages in this case are consistent with the Bible.

More evidence something is wrong

^{14}C in fossils supposedly millions of years old

Fossils older than 100,000 years should have too little ^{14}C to measure, but dating labs consistently find ^{14}C, well above background levels, in fossils supposedly many *millions* of years old.[21,22] For example, no source of coal has been found that lacks ^{14}C, yet this fossil fuel supposedly ranges up to hundreds of millions of years old. Fossils in rocks dated at 1–500 Ma by long-age radioisotope dating methods gave an average radiocarbon 'age' of about 50,000 years, much less than the limits of modern carbon dating[22] (see pp. 65–69 for why even these radiocarbon ages are inflated). Furthermore, there was no pattern of younger to older in the carbon dates that correlated with the evolutionary/uniformitarian 'ages'.[22]

This evidence is consistent with the fossil-bearing rock layers being formed in the year-long global catastrophe of the biblical Flood, as flood geologists since Nicholas Steno (1631–1687) have recognized.

Even Precambrian ('older than 545 Ma') graphite, which is not of organic origin, contains ^{14}C above background levels.[22] This is consistent with Earth itself being only thousands of years old, as a straightforward reading of the Bible would suggest.

19. Snelling, A.A., 1995. The failure of U-Th-Pb 'dating' at Koongarra, Australia. *Journal of Creation* **9**(1):71–92.
20. Maas, R., 1989. Nd-Sr isotope constraints on the age and origin of unconformity-type uranium deposits in the Alligator Rivers Uranium Field, Northern Territory, Australia. *Economic Geology* **84**:64–90.
21. Giem, P., 2001. Carbon-14 content of fossil carbon. *Origins* **51**:6–30.
22. Baumgardner, J.R., Snelling, A.S., Humphreys, D.R., and Austin, S.A., 2003. Measurable ^{14}C in fossilized organic materials: confirming the young earth creation-flood model. *Proc. 5th ICC* pp. 127–142.

It is an unsolved mystery to evolutionists as to why coal has ^{14}C in it,[23] or wood supposedly many millions of years old still has ^{14}C present, but it makes perfect sense in a creationist worldview.

Many physical evidences contradict the 'billions of years'

Of the methods that have been used to estimate the age of the Earth, 90% point to an age far less than the billions of years asserted by evolutionists. A few of them:

- Evidence for rapid formation of geological strata, as in the biblical Flood. Some of the evidences are: lack of erosion between rock layers supposedly separated in age by many millions of years; lack of disturbance of rock strata by biological activity (worms, roots, etc.); lack of soil layers; polystrate fossils (which traverse several rock layers vertically—these could not have stood vertically for eons of time while they slowly got buried); thick layers of 'rock' bent without fracturing, indicating that the rock was all soft when bent; and more. See Chapter 15 (pp. 183–186) and books by geologists Morris[24] and Austin.[17]

Kaibab Upwarp

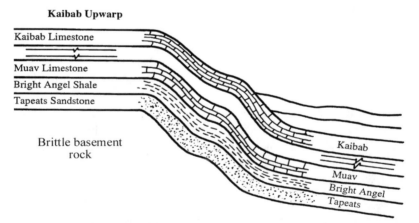

Cross-section of Grand Canyon geology showing the Kaibab upwarp. Plastic folding of strata shows that the layers were still soft when bent, consistent with them all being laid down quickly—as in Noah's Flood (after Morris[24]).

23. Lowe, D.C., 1989. Problems associated with the use of coal as a source of ^{14}C free background material. *Radiocarbon* **31**:117–120.
24. Morris, J., 1994. *The Young Earth.* Creation-Life Publishers, Colorado Springs, Colorado.

- Red blood cells and hemoglobin have been found in some (unfossilized!) dinosaur bone. But these could not last more than a few thousand years—certainly not the 65 Ma since the last dinosaurs lived, according to evolutionists.[25]
- The Earth's magnetic field has been decaying so fast that it looks like it is less than 10,000 years old. Rapid reversals during the Flood year and fluctuations shortly after would have caused the field energy to drop even faster.[26,27]
- A supernova is an explosion of a massive star—the explosion briefly outshines the rest of the galaxy. Supernova remnants (SNRs) should keep expanding for hundreds of thousands of years, according to the physical equations. Yet there are no very old, widely expanded (Stage 3) SNRs, and few moderately old (Stage 1) ones in our galaxy, the Milky Way, or in its satellite galaxies, the Magellanic Clouds. This is just what we would expect for 'young' galaxies that have not existed long enough for wide expansion.[28,29]
- Continents erode so rapidly that they should have worn away completely many times over in billions of years.[30] The problem is more acute in mountainous regions, and there are also huge plains that are supposedly very old with hardly any erosion. The average height reduction for all the continents of the world is about 6.0 mm (0.24 inches) per 100 years.[31] A height of 150 kilometres (93 miles) of continent would have eroded in 2.5 billion years (the uniformitarian age of the cores of the continents). If erosion had been going on for billions of years, no continents would remain on the earth. For example, North America should have been levelled in just 10 million years if erosion has happened at the average rate. Note that this is an upper age limit, not an actual age.

25. Wieland, C., 1997. Sensational dinosaur blood report! *Creation* **19**(4):42–43, based on Schweitzer, M. and Staedter, T., 1997. The real Jurassic Park. *Earth*, June, pp. 55–57.
26. Humphreys, D.R., 1986. Reversals of the earth's magnetic field during the Genesis Flood. *Proc. First ICC* 2:113–126.
27. Sarfati, J.D., 1998. The earth's magnetic field: evidence that the earth is young. *Creation* **20**(2):15–19.
28. Davies, K., 1994. Distribution of supernova remnants in the galaxy. *Proc. 3rd ICC*, pp. 175–184.
29. Sarfati, J.D., 1998. Exploding stars point to a young universe. *Creation* **19**(3):46–49.
30. Walker, T., Eroding ages, Creation 22(2):18–21, March–May 2000; <creation.com/erosion>.
31. Roth, A., 1998. *Origins: Linking Science and Scripture*, Review and Herald Publishing, Hagerstown, p. 271, cites Dott and Batten, *Evolution of the Earth,* McGraw-Hill, NY, USA, p. 155, 1988, and a number of others.

- Salt is entering the sea much faster than it is escaping. The sea is not nearly salty enough for this to have been happening for billions of years. Even granting generous assumptions to evolutionists, such as the sea having no salt to start with, the sea could not be more than 62 Ma old—far younger than the billions of years believed by evolutionists. Again, this indicates a maximum age, not the actual age.[32,33]

Dr Russell Humphreys gives other processes inconsistent with billions of years in the booklet *Evidence for a Young World.*

However, creationists cannot prove the age of the Earth using a particular scientific method, any more than evolutionists can. They realize that all science is tentative because we do not have all the data, especially when dealing with the past. This is true of both creationist and evolutionist scientific arguments—evolutionists have had to abandon many 'proofs' for evolution just as creationists have also had to modify their arguments. The atheistic evolutionist W.B. Provine admitted: 'Most of what I learned of the field [evolutionary biology] in graduate (1964–68) school is either wrong or significantly changed.'[34]

Creationists understand the limitations of dating methods better than evolutionists who claim that they can use processes observed in the present to 'prove' that Earth is billions of years old. In reality, all dating methods, including those that point to a young Earth, rely on unprovable assumptions.

Creationists ultimately date the Earth historically using the chronology of the Bible. This is because they believe that this is an accurate eyewitness account of world history, which bears the evidence within it that it is the Word of God, and therefore totally reliable and error-free (see Chapter 1 for some of the evidences).

Orphan radiohalos

Decaying radioactive particles in solid rock cause spherical zones of damage in the surrounding crystal structure. A speck of radioactive element such as Uranium-238, for example, will leave a sphere of

32. Austin S.A. and Humphreys, D.R., 1990. The sea's missing salt: a dilemma for evolutionists. *Proc. 2nd ICC* pp. 17–33.
33. Sarfati, J.D., 1999. Salty seas: Evidence for a young earth. *Creation* 21(1):16–17.
34. A review of Teaching about Evolution and the Nature of Science (National Academy of Science USA, 1998) by Dr Will B. Provine, online at <http://fp.bio.utk.edu/darwin/NAS_guidebook/provine_1.html>, 18 Feb. 1999.

discoloration of characteristically different radius for each element it produces in its decay chain to lead-206.[35] Viewed in cross-section with a microscope, these spheres appear as rings called radiohalos. Dr Gentry has researched radiohalos for many years, and published his results in leading scientific journals.[36]

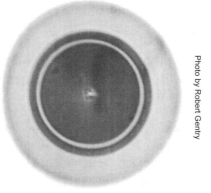

A concentric series of radiohalos

Some of the intermediate decay products—such as the polonium isotopes—have very short half-lives (they decay quickly). For example, ^{214}Po has a half-life of just 164 microseconds. Curiously, rings created by polonium decay are often found without the parent uranium halos. Now, the polonium has to get into the rock before the rock solidifies, but it cannot derive from a uranium speck in the solid rock, otherwise there would be a uranium halo. This suggests the rock formed *very* quickly.[37] There possibly also had to be a period of rapid decay of uranium to produce the amount of polonium that is seen. Orphan halos speak of conditions in the past that do not fit with the uniformitarian view of Earth history, which is the basis of the radiometric dating systems.

Do radiometric 'dates' have any meaning?

Geologist John Woodmorappe, after analyzing 500 papers published on radioisotope dating, concluded that isotope dating was rife with

35. Only those that undergo alpha decay (releasing a helium nucleus) produce a halo.
36. Gentry, R.V., 1986. *Creation's Tiny Mystery,* Earth Science Associates, Knoxville, Tennessee (see references therein).
37. Snelling, A.A. and Armitage, M.H., 2003. Radiohalos—a tale of three granitic plutons. *Proc. 5th ICC* pp. 243–267.

circular reasoning, and story telling to fit the preconceived ideas of the researchers.[8]

The isochron dating technique[16] was once thought to be infallible because it supposedly covered the assumptions about starting conditions and closed systems. Geologist Dr Andrew Snelling reported on 'dating' of the Koongarra uranium deposits in the Northern Territory of Australia, primarily using the lead-lead isochron method.[38] He found that even 113 highly weathered soil samples from the area, which are definitely not closed systems (leaching of parent and daughter isotopes would invalidate the 'dates'), gave a very nice looking 'isochron' line with an 'age' of 1,445±20 Ma. Other methods gave 'ages' ranging from even higher to all the way down to zero years.

Such 'false isochrons' are so common that a whole terminology has grown up to describe them, such as apparent isochron, mantle isochron, pseudoisochron, secondary isochron, inherited isochron, erupted isochron, mixing line and mixing isochron. Zheng wrote:

'… some of the basic assumptions of the conventional Rb-Sr [rubidium-strontium] isochron method have to be modified and an observed isochron does not certainly define valid age information for a geological system, even if a goodness of fit of the experimental results is obtained in plotting $^{87}Sr/^{86}Sr$ against $^{87}Rb/^{86}Sr$. This problem cannot be overlooked, especially in evaluating the numerical time scale. Similar questions can also arise in applying Sm-Nd [samarium-neodymium] and U-Pb [uranium-lead] isochron methods.'[39]

Even with 'isochrons', part of the isochron line is interpreted as not being due to age—how can one part of the line be attributed to age but the other part of the same line be ignored as irrelevant where it cannot be due to age? Furthermore, even non-radioactive elements will give nice straight lines when ratios of concentrations are plotted.[40] Clearly, such patterns are not due to age at all.

Another popular dating method is the uranium-lead concordia technique. This effectively combines the two uranium-lead decay series into one diagram. Results that lie on the concordia curve have the same 'age' according to the two lead series and are called 'concordant'.

38. Snelling, A.A., 1985. The Failure of U-Th-Pb 'Dating' at Koongarra, Australia. *TJ* **9**(1):72–92.
39. Zheng, Y.F., 1989. Influence of the nature of initial Rb-Sr system on isochron validity. *Chemical Geology* **80**:1–16 (p. 14).
40. Walker, T., The Somerset Dam igneous complex, south-east Queensland, Honours thesis [1st class Honours or *Summa cum laude* awarded], Dept of Earth Sciences, Uni. of Queensland, 1998.

However, the results from zircons, for example, generally lie off the concordia curve—they are discordant (disagree). Numerous models, or stories, have been developed to explain such data.[41] However, such story-telling is not objective science that proves an old Earth.

Dr Snelling has suggested that fractionation (sorting) of elements in the molten state in the Earth's mantle could be a significant factor in explaining the ratios of isotope concentrations which are interpreted as ages. This would also explain the prevalence of 'false isochrons'. But how does a geologist tell a false isochron from a 'good' one? Results that agree with accepted ages are considered 'good'. This is circular reasoning and very bad science.

As long ago as 1966, Nobel Prize nominee Melvin Cook, Professor of Metallurgy at the University of Utah, pointed out evidence that lead isotope ratios, for example, may involve alteration by important factors other than radioactive decay.[42] Cook noted that in ores from the Katanga mine there was an abundance of lead-208, a stable isotope, but no Thorium-232 as a source of lead-208. Thorium has a long halflife (decays very slowly) and is not easily leached out of the rock, so if the lead-208 came from thorium decay, some thorium should still be there. Cook suggested that perhaps the lead-208 came about by neutron capture conversion of lead-206 to lead-207 to lead-208. However, a period of rapid radioactive decay could also explain the data (see below). In either case the data are consistent with an age of thousands of years, not millions of years.

Helium and heat: evidence for non-constant decay rates

Physicist Dr Robert Gentry has pointed out that the amount of helium (helium derives from the decay of radioactive elements, such as uranium) in zircons from deep (hot) bores is not consistent with an evolutionary age of 1,500 Ma for the granite rocks in which they are found.[36] The amount of lead corresponds with current rates of decay of uranium acting over the assumed timescale, but almost all the helium formed should have diffused out of the crystals in that time. The diffusion rates of helium have now been measured and they are very high (100,000 times greater than evolutionary geologists had assumed), so the helium should not be there if the radioactive decay had been going on at present rates for

41. Gebauer, D. and Grunenfelder, M., 1979. U-Th-Pb dating of minerals. In Jager, E. and Hunziker, J.C. (eds). *Lectures in Isotope Geology,* Springer Verlag, New York, 105–131.

42. Cook, M.A., 1966. *Prehistory and Earth Models,* Max Parrish, London, 353 pp.

the eons of time claimed by uniformitarians.[43] Indeed, modeling of the diffusion indicates that the '1.5 billion years' worth of radioactive decay occurred, but the rate of helium leakage dates these 'billion-year-old' zircons at $5,700 \pm 2,000$ years.[43] The only sensible explanation for this is that there has been a period of accelerated radioactive decay several thousand years ago. Whatever caused such elevated rates of decay may also have been responsible for the lead isotope anomalies documented by Cook (above).

A period of accelerated decay would also solve the puzzle of the amount of heat emanating from the Earth—an amount consistent with the amount of radioactive decay that has occurred, but not with a billions of years timescale.[44]

So, evidence is mounting to suggest a period of rapid radioactive decay in the past, just thousands of years ago. Interestingly, the accelerated decay seems to have affected the longest half-life isotopes most, and particularly those involving alpha-decay.[45]

Conclusions

There are many lines of evidence that the radiometric dates are not the objective evidence for an old Earth that many claim, and that the world is really only thousands of years old. Although we don't have all the answers, we have lots of answers, and we do have the sure testimony of the Word of God to the true history of the world.

---

43. Humphreys, R.D., Austin, S.A., Baumgardner, J.R. and Snelling, A.A., 2003. Helium diffusion rates support accelerated nuclear decay. *Proc. 5th ICC*, Pittsburg, pp.175–195.
44. Baumgardner, J., Distribution of radioactive isotopes in the earth, ch. 3 in Vardiman, L., Snelling, A.A. and Chaffin, E.F. (eds), 2000. *Radioisotopes and the Age of the Earth*, Institute for Creation Research and Creation Research Society, USA.
45. Vardiman, L., Austin, S.A., Baumgardner, J.R., Chaffin, E.F., DeYoung, D.B., Humphreys, D.R. and Snelling, A.A., 2003. Radioisotopes and the age of the earth. *Proc. 5th ICC* pp. 337–348.

Chapter 5

How can we see distant stars in a young universe?

- If the universe is young and it takes millions of years for light to get to us from many stars, how can we see them?
- Did God create light in transit?
- Was the speed of light faster in the past?
- Does this have anything to do with the 'big bang'?
- Is there evidence that Earth is a privileged planet?
- What about Relativity?

S OME galaxies are billions of light-years away. Since a light-year is the distance travelled by light in one year, and we can see such galaxies, does this mean that the universe is very old? Despite all the biblical and scientific evidence for a young earth/ universe (see *Evidences for a Young Earth*, in this booklet series),[1] this has long been a seemingly intractable problem. However, any scientific understanding of origins will always have opportunities

1. See also: Young age evidence; <creation.com/young>

for research—problems that need to be solved. We can never have complete knowledge and so there will always be things to learn.

The big bang light travel problem

It's important to note that the most widely held cosmology, the standard secular big bang theory has a problem of its own with light travel, called the *horizon problem*. This arises from the universe being thought to be at least ten times bigger than the distance that radiation ('light') could have travelled since the big bang, even with their billions of years timescale.

According to the big bang the universe began in a fireball from which all matter in the universe is ultimately derived. For galaxies to have any hope of forming at all during the expansion process, the fireball must have begun with an uneven distribution of temperatures. However, we see radiation coming from the cosmos, in all directions on the sky and it is very uniformly distributed, wherever we look. This is the cosmic microwave background (CMB) radiation and it has been measured to be uniform to one part in 100,000. But, how could this be so if the radiation has not had sufficient time to traverse the greatest distances in the universe so that it could even out the temperature by transmitting energy from hot regions to cold?

This problem gave rise to hypothetical fudge factors such as faster-than-light 'inflation' being added to the big bang, but there is no known mechanism to start or stop the process in a smooth fashion (it is effectively a naturalistic 'miracle'). Other big bang cosmologists have even suggested that the speed of light (radiation) may have been

Photo by NASA

much faster in the past.[2] So no one can rightly claim this issue as a reason not to believe the Bible, because the standard secular big bang cosmology has a similar problem.[3]

Created light?

A few decades ago, perhaps the most commonly used explanation was that God created the light 'on its way', so that Adam could see the stars immediately without having to wait years for the light from even the closest ones to reach the Earth. While we should not limit the power of God, this has some immense difficulties.

It would mean that whenever we look at the behaviour of a very distant object, what we apparently see happening never really happened at all. For instance, say we see an object a million light-years away which appears to be rotating; that is, the light we receive in our telescopes carries this information, 'recording' this behaviour. However, according to the 'created in transit' explanation, the light we are now receiving did not come from the star, but was created 'en route'.

This would mean, for a (say) 10,000-year-old universe, that anything we see happening beyond about 10,000 light-years is actually part of a gigantic picture-show of things that have not actually happened, showing us objects which may not even exist.

To explain this problem further, consider an exploding star (supernova) at, say, an accurately measured distance of 100,000 light-years. Remember we are using this explanation in a 10,000-year-old universe. As the astronomer on Earth watches this exploding star, he is not just receiving a beam of light. If that were all, then it would be no problem at all to say that God could have created a whole chain of photons (light particles) already on their way. However, what the astronomer receives is also a particular, very specific pattern of variation within the light, showing the changes that one would expect to accompany such an explosion—a predictable sequence of events involving neutrinos, visible light, X rays and gamma-rays. For example, because most neutrinos pass through solid matter as if it were not there, while light is slowed down, we can detect a massive

---

2.   Wieland, C., 2002. Speed of light slowing down after all? *Journal of Creation* **16**(3):7–10; <creation.com/cdk>

3.   Lisle, J., 2003. Light-travel time: a problem for the big bang. *Creation* **25**(4):48–49; <creation.com /lighttravel>

neutrino burst before the light reaches us.

The light and neutrino burst carries information recording an *apparently real event*. The astronomer is perfectly justified in interpreting this 'message' as representing actual reality—that there really was such an object, which exploded according to the laws of physics, brightened, emitted X-rays, dimmed, and so on, all in accord with those same physical laws.

Everything the astronomer sees is consistent with this, including the spectral patterns in the light from the star giving us a 'chemical signature' of the elements contained in it. Yet the 'light created *en route*' explanation means that this recorded message of events, transmitted through space, had to be contained within the light beam from the moment of its creation, or planted into the light beam at a later date, without ever having originated from that distant point. (If it had started from the star—assuming that there really was such a star—the light beam would still be 90,000 light years away from Earth, assuming the universe is 10,000 years old and the speed of light constant.)

To create such a detailed series of signals in light beams reaching Earth, signals which seem to have come from a series of real events but in fact did not, has no conceivable purpose. Worse, it is like saying that God created fossils in rocks to fool us, or even test our faith, and that they don't represent anything real (a real animal or plant that lived and died in the past). This would be a strange deception for a holy God to engage in.

Did light always travel at the same speed?

An obvious solution would seem to be a higher speed of light in the past, allowing the light to cover the same distance in less time. This seems at first glance a too-convenient *ad hoc* explanation. Some years ago, Barry Setterfield raised such a possibility to a high profile by showing that there seemed to be a decreasing trend in the historical observations of the speed of light (c) over the past 300 years or so. Setterfield (and his later co-author, Trevor Norman) produced evidence in favour of their 'cdk' theory.[4] They believed that it would have affected radiometric dating results, and even have caused the

---

4. Norman, T.G. and Setterfield, B., 1990. *The atomic constants, light and time*. Privately published, 88 pp.8.

red-shifting of light from distant galaxies, although this idea was later overturned, and other modifications were made also.

Many attacked the idea on the fallacious grounds that Einstein's special relativity said that the speed of light could not change. It actually just says that the speed of light measured by observers will be invariant regardless of the speed of the source or observer.

Much debate raged to and fro among equally capable people within creationist circles about whether the statistical evidence really supported cdk or not.

The biggest difficulty, however, is with certain physical consequences of the theory. If c has declined the way Setterfield proposed, these consequences should still be discernible in the light from distant galaxies, but they are apparently not. High precision tests of Einstein's theory of general relativity, in our galaxy, using co-orbiting pairs of neutron stars, where at least one is a pulsar, within thousands of light-years distance, indicate the same value for c as we measure locally.[5] In short, none of the theory's defenders have been able to answer all the problems raised. Interestingly, big bang defenders treated the idea of cdk with contempt, but then one of their own, João Magueijo, proposed a similar idea to rescue the big bang from its own light travel problem!

New creationist cosmologies

Nevertheless, the cdk theory stimulated much thinking about the issues. Creationist physicist Dr Russell Humphreys says that he spent a year, on and off, trying to get the cdk theory to work consistently, but without success. However, the thinking inspired him to develop ideas for a new creationist cosmology that appeared to solve the problem of the apparent conflict with the Bible's clear, authoritative teaching of a recent creation.[6] This new cosmology was proposed as a creationist alternative to big bang theory.

5. Creationist physicist Dr Keith Wanser pointed out that the rate of energy loss of a pulsar due to gravitational radiation is proportional to c, according to general relativity (*Radioactive Decay Update: Breaking Down the Old-Age Paradigm* (Video)). The 1993 Nobel Prize in Physics was awarded to Russell Hulse and Joseph Taylor for discovering a binary pulsar and showing that the observed energy loss matched the predictions of general relativity to within 0.4%. But this indicates that c hasn't changed in the thousands of years since light left that pulsar.

6. Humphreys, D.R., 1998. New vistas of space-time rebut the critics. *Journal of Creation* **12**(2):195–212 and see further discussion in *Journal of Creation* **13**(1):49–62, 1999.13.

This sort of development, in which one creationist theory, cdk, is overtaken by another, is a healthy aspect of science. The basic biblical framework, because it comes from the Creator, is non-negotiable, as opposed to the changing views and models of fallible people seeking to understand the data within that framework (evolutionists also often change their ideas on exactly how things have made themselves, but never *whether* they did).

A clue

Let us briefly give a hint as to how the new cosmology seemed to solve the starlight problem. Consider that the time taken for something to travel a given distance is the distance divided by the speed it is travelling. That is,

Time = Distance (divided by) Speed

When this is applied to light from distant stars, the time calculates out to be billions of years. Some have sought to challenge the distances, but that is a very unlikely solution.[7]

Astronomers use many different methods to measure the distances, and no informed creationist astronomer would claim that errors would be so vast that billions of light years could be reduced to several thousand, for example. Even our own Milky Way galaxy is about 100,000 light years across!

If the speed of light (**c**) has not changed, the only thing left in the equation is time itself. In fact, Einstein's relativity theory has been telling the world for decades that time itself is not an absolute concept. Scientists may not know what time is but they do know how to measure it. Nowadays very precise and exact atomic clocks measure the rate or flow of time and it has been measured to vary from place to place.

In fact, two things have been observed to distort the flow of time—one is speed and the other is gravity. Einstein's general theory, the best theory of gravity we have at present, indicates that *gravity distorts time*.

This effect has been measured experimentally, many times. Clocks at the top of tall buildings, where gravity is slightly less,

---

7. Many billions of stars exist, many just like our own sun, according to the analysis of the light coming from them. Such numbers of stars have to be distributed through a huge volume of space, otherwise we would all be fried.

run slightly faster than those at the bottom, just as predicted by the equations of general relativity (GR).[8]

When the concentration of matter is very large, the gravitational distortion can be so immense that even light cannot escape.[9] The equations of GR show that at the invisible boundary surrounding such a concentration of matter (called the event horizon, the point at which light rays trying to escape the enormous pull of gravity bend back on themselves), time literally stands still, as observed by a distant observer.

Using different assumptions ...

Dr Humphreys' new creationist cosmology 'falls out' of the equations of GR, so long as one assumes that the universe is bounded with a unique centre. In other words, that it has a centre and an edge. This means that if you were to travel into space, you would eventually come to a place beyond which there was no more matter. In this cosmology, Earth is near the centre, as it appears to be as we look out into space.

This might sound like common sense, as indeed it is, but all modern secular cosmologies deny this. That is, they make the *arbitrary* assumption (without any scientific necessity) that the universe has no boundary—no edge and no centre—dubbed the 'cosmological principle'. In this *assumed* universe, every galaxy would be surrounded by galaxies spread evenly in all directions and so therefore (on a large enough scale) all net gravitational forces cancel out.

This is a *philosophical* assumption; that is, religious. And it is made to remove Earth from its apparently privileged position near the centre of the Universe (because that's what the Bible implies; that Earth is the focus of God's attention in creating the universe). Note what respected cosmologist George Ellis says:

'People need to be aware that there is a range of models that could explain the observations,' Ellis argues. 'For instance, I can construct you a spherically symmetrical universe with Earth at its center, and you cannot disprove it based on observations.'

8. The demonstrable usefulness of GR in the physics of time-keeping, for example, can be separated from certain 'philosophical baggage' that some have illegitimately attached to it, and to which some Christians have objected, thinking that such relativity in physics in some way supported *relative morality*.
9. Such an object is called a 'black hole'.

Ellis has published a paper on this. 'You can only exclude it on philosophical grounds. In my view there is absolutely nothing wrong in that. What I want to bring into the open is the fact that we are using philosophical criteria in choosing our models. A lot of cosmology tries to hide that.'[10]

Not only can you have such an understanding of the universe, but it actually fits the evidence much better than the no-centre, boundless universe assumed by secularists. There is now powerful evidence that the universe has a centre. For example, the observed radiation from quasars is polarized in a given direction, galaxies have been shown to have a preferred direction of alignment and red-shifts of galaxies are quantized (in distinct groups) rather than random.[11] The quantized light from galaxies suggests that galaxies are organized in concentric shells of the order of a million light years apart, centred on our part of the universe. The probability of Earth being in this privileged position with a naturalistic (non-designed) origin of the universe is less than a trillion to one.[12]

These observations do not fit the materialists' no-centre, unbounded randomly generated universe, but are consistent with a universe designed by a Creator.

The big bang has many other problems,[13,14] so much so that even

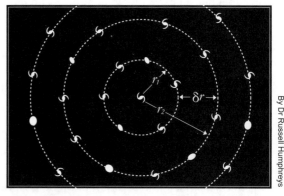

By Dr Russell Humphreys

Galaxies tend to be grouped in concentric spherical shells around our home galaxy. The distance interval between shells is of the order of a million light years. Such a pattern would not be observable if Earth was not near the centre of the Universe.

10. Gibbs, W. W., 1995. Profile: George F. R. Ellis; Thinking Globally, Acting Universally. *Scientific American* **273**(4):28–29.
11. See: Where is the centre of the universe? <creation.com/astronomy#centre>
12. Humphreys, D.R., 2002. Our galaxy is the centre of the universe, 'quantized' redshifts show. *Journal of Creation* **16**(2):95–104; <creation.com/center>
13. Williams, A., and Hartnett, J., 2005. *Dismantling the big bang; God's universe rediscovered.* Master Books.
14. See papers listed under: What are some of the problems with the big bang hypothesis? <creation.com/astronomy#big_bang>

many secularists are calling for a radical re-think:[15]

'Big bang theory relies on a growing number of hypothetical entities—things that we have never observed. Inflation, dark matter and dark energy are the most prominent. Without them there would be fatal contradictions between the observations made by astronomers and the predictions of the big bang theory.'[16]

According to GR, if the universe has a boundary and centre, then there should be a net gravitational force toward the centre. Clocks at the edge should run faster than clocks on Earth, assuming Earth is near the centre. In other words, it is no longer enough to say God made the *universe* in six days. He certainly did, but six days as measured by which clocks? (If we say 'God's time' we miss the point that He created the flow of time as we now experience it; He is outside of time, seeing the end from the beginning.)[17]

There appears to be observational evidence that the universe has expanded in the past, which is consistent with the many phrases God inspired the Bible writers with to tell us that at creation He 'stretched out'[18] (other verses say 'spread out') the heavens.

If the universe is not much bigger than we can observe, and if it was only 50 times smaller in the past than it is now, then scientific deduction based on GR means it has to have expanded out of a previous state in which it was surrounded by an event horizon (a condition known technically as a 'white hole'—a black hole running in reverse, something permitted by the equations of GR).

As matter passed out of this event horizon, according to Humphreys' theory, the horizon itself had to shrink—eventually to nothing. Therefore at one point this horizon would have been touching the Earth. In that instant, time on the Earth (relative to a point far away from it) would have been virtually frozen. An observer on Earth would not in any way 'feel different'. In principle 'billions of years' would be available for light to reach the Earth (in the frame of reference within which it is travelling in deep space), for stars to age, etc.—while less than an ordinary day passes on Earth. Humphreys

15. Wieland, C., 2005. Secular scientists blast the big bang. *Creation* 27(2):23–25; <creation.com/bigbangblast>

16. Eric Lerner and 33 other scientists from 10 different countries, 2004. Bucking the big bang. *New Scientist* 182(2448):20; <www.cosmologystatement.org>

17. Genesis 1:1; Ecclesiastes 3:11; Isaiah 26:4; Romans 1:20; 1 Timothy 1:17; Hebrews 11:3. Interestingly, according to GR, time does not exist without matter, as was discussed in the *Does God Exist?* booklet in this series.

18. For example, Isaiah 42:5; Jeremiah 10:12; Zechariah 12:1.

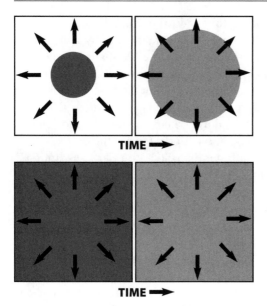

TIME ➡

TIME ➡

Expansion of a bounded (top) and an unbounded (bottom) universe.

suggested that massive gravitational time dilation would seem to be a scientific inevitability if a bounded universe has expanded significantly from a previously denser state.

In one sense, if observers on Earth at that particular time could have looked out and 'seen' the speed with which light was moving toward them out in space, it would have appeared as if it were travelling many times faster than **c**. (Galaxies would also appear to be rotating faster.) However, if an observer in deep space was out there locally measuring the speed of light, he would still only measure **c**.

It is fortunate that creationists did not invent such concepts as gravitational time dilation, black and white holes, event horizons and so on, or we would likely be accused of manipulating the data, or fantasizing, to solve this problem. The interesting thing about Humphreys' cosmology is that it is based upon mathematics and physics accepted by all cosmologists (general relativity), and it accepts (along with virtually all physicists) that there has been expansion in the past (though not from some imaginary dimensionless point). The results 'fall out' so long as one abandons the arbitrary starting point which big bangers use (the unbounded cosmos idea, which could be called 'what the experts don't tell you about the big bang').

This cosmology seems to explain many of the observations used to support the big bang, without compromising the data or the biblical record of a young Earth.

New cosmology solves light-travel problem

All theories of fallible people, no matter how well they seem to fit the data, are subject to revision or abandonment in the light of future discoveries. The white hole cosmology discussed above does not provide the *correct amount* of time dilation, but it is certainly headed in the right direction with encouraging theoretical and observational support. Indeed, the observed anomalous acceleration (towards the sun) of distant *Pioneer* spacecraft is consistent with the essentials of several creationist cosmologies—a cosmic centre of mass, expansion of space, and recent time dilation.[19] Big bang advocates have been unable to explain these observations.

Dr John Hartnett has taken these three concepts further and incorporated *cosmological relativity.* The latter is derived from the development of special relativity theory (the effect of motion on time) for the large scale structure of the universe. The concept was developed by Dr Moshe Carmeli, but Hartnett has shown that it can equally be applied to a universe with a centre of mass (as per Humphreys), and also explains the observations. It also shows how we can see distant starlight as a direct consequence of the way that God stretched out the universe during creation week.[20] The model involves the usual four dimensions (three of space, plus time) but adds a new fifth dimension, the velocity of the expansion of the cosmos, an analogue to the effect that velocity has on time in special relativity. Hartnett's model, for example, explains the structure of galaxies without resorting to unseen 'dark matter', a 'fudge' factor that the big bang model needs. He has published papers showing that Carmeli's fifth dimension ('metric') really works.

Time dilation also results, but not due to a net gravitational effect in a finite bounded universe—it is due to the enormous stretching of the fabric of space. Space is not nothing—there is a lot of energy in the vacuum and, at Creation, God caused space to rapidly expand such that clocks on Earth at the centre of the expansion ran very slowly compared to clocks in galaxies in the expanding cosmos.

---

19. Humphreys, D.R., 2007. Creationist cosmologies explain the anomalous acceleration of Pioneer spacecraft. *Journal of Creation* **21**(2):61–70.
20. See Hartnett, J., 2007. A 5D spherically symmetric expanding universe is young, *Journal of Creation* **21**(1): 69–74 and papers at <creation.com/hartnett>. There is a good technical summary of this model at <http://creationwiki.org/Cosmological_relativity>.

Conclusion

What if no one had ever thought of the possibility of time dilation? Many might have felt forced to agree with those scientists (including some Christians) that there was *no* possible solution—the vast ages are a fact because we can see distant stars, and the Bible must be 'reinterpreted' (massaged) or increasingly rejected. Many have in fact been urging Christians to abandon the Bible's clear teaching of a recent creation because of these 'undeniable facts'.

However, this reinterpretation of Scripture would also mean that Earth is old and the rocks containing fossils under our feet are old. So this also entails (if it is logically thought through) accepting that there were billions of years of death, disease, and bloodshed before Adam, thus eroding the Creation/ Fall/Restoration historical
framework presented in the Bible[21] —the framework in which the gospel makes sense, and upon which western civilisation has been built, with all its many benefits.[22]

However, even without the new ideas that seem to solve the problem, such an approach would still have been wrong-headed. The authority of the Bible should never be compromised by mankind's 'scientific' proposals. One little previously unknown fact, or one change in a starting assumption, can drastically alter the whole picture so that what was 'fact' is no longer so.

This is worth remembering when dealing with other areas of difficulty which, despite the substantial evidence for Genesis creation, still remain. Only God possesses infinite knowledge. By basing our scientific research on the assumption that His Word is true (instead of the assumption that it is wrong or irrelevant) our scientific theories are much more likely, in the long run, to come to accurately represent reality.

---

21. Batten, D.J., and Sarfati, J., 2006. *15 Reasons to take Genesis as history.* Creation Ministries International, Brisbane, Australia.
22. Williams, A., 2004. The biblical origins of science. *Journal of Creation (TJ)* **18**(2):49–52; <creation.com/stark>

Chapter 6

How did bad things come about?

- If God's original creation was 'very good', why is 'nature red in tooth and claw' now?
- Did God create animals with defence-attack structures?
- Or were they redesigned after the Fall? Wouldn't there be a population explosion if animals did not eat each other?

THE world before the Fall had no death, disease or suffering, as God proclaimed the finished creation 'very good' (Gen. 1:31). Consistent with this, God gave plants to the animals to eat (Gen. 1:29, 30).

Nowadays, many creatures have equipment that seems designed for attacking, hurting, trapping, killing, or eating others, or defending themselves against such things—for example, the poison-injecting fangs of snakes, the great meat-eating cats, and the spider's web, to name just a few. So when and how did these things, which are suited to a fallen world but were unnecessary before the Fall, come to be?

There is no single position that would be agreed upon by all creationists in answer to this, so we will briefly look at the merits of a number of possibilities.

First, we need to look at the clear teachings of Scripture which

Some creatures seem designed to kill and eat others.

bear on this question, remembering that the Bible gives us true, but not exhaustive, information. We may then try to fill in the gaps in our knowledge by reasoning, which will have to be somewhat speculative, using what we know about the living world. The Bible teaches:

- People and animals alike were given plants to eat in the beginning (Gen. 1:29–30). There was no meat eating before the Fall, whether by man or animal. The carnivorous part of the present 'food chain' did not exist. And God appropriately described His creation as 'very good' (Gen.1:31).

- The Bible makes a clear distinction between the status of plants and animals. People and animals are described in Genesis as having, or being, *nephesh* (Hebrew)—see Genesis 1:20, 21, 24 where *nephesh chayyah* is translated 'living creatures', and Genesis 2:7 where Adam became a 'living soul' *(nephesh chayyah)*. *Nephesh* conveys the basic idea of a 'breathing creature'. It is also used widely in the Old Testament, in combination with other words, to convey ideas of emotions, feelings, etc. Perhaps *nephesh* refers to life with a certain level of consciousness. Plants do not have such *nephesh,* and so Adam eating a carrot did not involve death in the biblical sense.

- The world will one day be restored (Acts 3:21) to a state in which, once again, there will be no violence and death involving animals. Whether Isaiah 11:6–9 is taken to refer to a millennial kingdom or a new Earth, the point is the same. Lambs, wolves, leopards, children, bears, calves and snakes will all dwell together peacefully. Lions will once again be plant-eaters. Clearly, this vision of future bliss reflects the former paradise lost through sin.

- Clearly there was no disease, suffering or death of animals (*nephesh* creatures) before the Fall. This raises the question of just what is a *nephesh* animal. Do one-celled organisms like bacteria and yeast, or invertebrates like worms, insects and prawns have *nephesh* life? Scripture gives us some clues. It tells us that *'the life* (nephesh) *of the flesh is in the blood'* (Lev. 17:11. See also Gen. 9:4). If we use this to classify organisms into those with or without such *'nephesh* life', it is helpful up to a point—this would exclude microorganisms from having *nephesh*-life. But there are still difficulties as to what counts as blood. For example, insects and crustaceans have a form of blood, although it is somewhat different from the blood of animals with backbones. The presence of hemoglobin cannot be definitive, as it is found even in some plants.

  Adam's naming of the land animals in Genesis 2 may give us further clues. Adam named 'each *living creature* (nephesh chayyah)' (Gen.2:19). What did he name? *'Adam gave names to all the cattle, and to the birds of the air, and to every animal of the field'* (Gen. 2:20).[1] It may be significant at this point that the *remes,* the 'creeping things' of Gen. 1:24, were not included, as Leupold, the respected theologian, noted. If 'creeping things' included insects and worms, for example, then maybe they are not *nephesh* life. However, Scripture is not clear on this, so we should not be dogmatic.

  It can be safely said, however, that there was no violent death, especially that involving bloodshed. In other words, creatures we would normally call 'animals' in everyday speech were not fighting, killing, shedding the blood of others, or eating one another, as many do today.

- Man was permitted to eat meat only after the Flood (Gen. 9:3). This may have been due to the extinction, in the Flood, of many plant species that formerly were able to provide all the protein and vitamin requirements for humans. To be well nourished by a totally vegetarian diet today is difficult, though not impossible. Of course, people may have eaten animals anyway, even before God gave permission. If that did happen, then it was probably not widespread, because

---

1. For a discussion of what Adam named, see Grigg, R., 1996. Naming the animals: All in a day's work for Adam. *Creation* **18**(4):46–49; <creation.com/animalnames>.

Scripture implies that the animals had minimal fear of man before the Flood (Gen. 9:2).

Man and the animals were originally vegetarian.

Animals today have certain biological equipment, which they use either to attack others or to defend themselves. Let's group these together and call them 'defence-attack structures' (DAS). The first question is, 'Are these created structures designed to do harm, for instance?'

The next, related, question is, 'When did they come about?' DAS would seem to have been quite out of place in a pre-Fall world.

The following are some of the possible answers, along with a discussion of some of the difficulties.

Position No. 1

Those things that are now used as DAS were not designed for this purpose, and had a different function, pre-Fall. They reached their present function by degeneration—for example, through mutations.

Different species of bats differ in what they eat, but their teeth are similar.[2]

One can point to the fact that some creatures today have sharp teeth that look as if they would be used to rip meat, but we know they don't use them for that. The fruit bat is a prime example. Some species in the piranha group of fish use their jaws and teeth entirely for plants. So, the argument goes, could not the lion's teeth have been used to

---

2.   Weston, P., 1998. Bats: sophistication in miniature. *Creation* **21**(1):29–31.

chew fruit before the Fall? Viruses that today inject harmful genes into their hosts may have had a useful pre-Fall role.[3]

Perhaps other harmful structures had a different pre-Fall function, which has been lost or modified, either by choice[4] or (the explanation usually given) by degenerate mutations.

The giant panda has sharp teeth and claws, and yet uses them to rip off and eat mainly plant (bamboo) material. Occasionally they have been seen to eat small animals. If, by the time man first observed them, most pandas ate animals, we would find it hard to imagine that their teeth and claws originally were for the purpose of eating plants.

Immune systems basically distinguish 'self' from 'non-self', which would be important for maintaining bodily integrity even in the pre-Fall world. Of course such systems became even more important in the post-

Image by Steve Cardno

Pandas have sharp teeth and claws and eat mainly bamboo.

---

3. Viruses, for instance, could have had a pre-Fall role in transferring genetic information to maintain/increase genetic diversity. It would not take any informational leap upwards in complexity to enable them to cause disease instead. Genes could have been acquired from hosts, even being modified by mutations to make the enzymes less specific (note this is a loss of information due to mutation), thus enabling disease-causing actions. Many disease-causing organisms are even degenerate from their own point of view—they quickly kill their host, thus destroying themselves. Also, the host might have degenerated and lost resistance. See Bergman, J., 1999. Did God make pathogenic viruses? *Journal of Creation* **13**(1):115–125.

4. This raises another problem: how much does an animal choose its way of life, as opposed to having programmed instinct? The only indirect Scriptural support for this seems to be Genesis 6:7, 11–13, which has been understood by some to mean that violence in the animal kingdom was one reason for the eradication of the land animals outside the Ark. However, this does not necessarily mean that God attributes any moral responsibility to the animals. Perhaps He was grieved because man's sin opened the door to the whole post-Fall reign of death and bloodshed.

Fall world, to protect against disease-causing organisms.

Position No. 1 avoids the problem of a good God designing harmful structures.[5] However, difficulties arise if this position is used to explain all occurrences of DAS. Virtually all creatures have some form of DAS, even if only a highly sensitive nervous system for warning of attack. They certainly give every indication of being designed to cope in a fallen world. Most of these DAS show great evidence of complex and specific design.

In fact, most, if not all, of the examples used by creationists to show design in living things involve DAS. If we say that DAS, or at least some aspects of their present function, arose by chance mutations, then we may have seriously undermined the main argument from design. It would mean saying that millions of different, complex and intricate patterns came about by chance (mutations and natural selection). Think of the sophisticated chemistry behind spider silk and the engineering marvel of spiders' webs, some of which are used to trap birds. All the complex

Charcoal by Robert Smith

The design adaptations for meat eating in the great cats are more than just sharp teeth.

5. This raises an old and interesting theological question. Would God, being omnipotent, be any less responsible for DAS by allowing them to happen 'naturally' rather than by actively designing them? An analogy is a doctor who, knowing that he could save a patient with the oxygen in his possession, fails to administer it. Is he less responsible than if he had actively killed the patient with cyanide? Some have pointed out that God is frequently actively involved in judgment without there being any ethical/theological dilemma; for instance, the sending of the great Flood that brought death and destruction to millions.

machinery to make these webs is coupled with programmed instincts (programming of which involves coded information) to tell the spiders where to build them for best hunting results, and when and how to move in for the kill of the trapped prey. In literally millions of examples, since we would maintain that complex, purposive design means intelligent, purposive creation, there is *prima facie* evidence of God having purposely designed the DAS as well.

The other problem with this argument is that in each case of an **observed** DAS, the true (pre-Fall) function was something different. It may be argued that our ignorance of the pre-Fall function does not mean that there wasn't one. This is true, of course, but if used for each and every one of the millions of DAS, it risks stretching credulity to the limit. One should also not overlook the full extent of what is involved in any particular defence-attack mechanism. For instance, discussions on the shape of teeth and claws may overlook the fact that the design features for meat eating in the great cats are more than just sharp teeth. A lion has finely-programmed hunting instincts, and immense muscular power capable of breaking a wildebeest's neck with one blow. Its digestive system is attuned to a diet of fresh meat (though lions can cope with vegetables in a crisis and, since meat is easier to digest, degenerative changes could be responsible for dependence on meat). All this makes it overwhelmingly appear to be a highly designed hunting and killing machine.

Such qualities are very common. Before the Fall, what was the function of the cheetah's blinding speed?[6] What did the bombardier beetle use its highly complex twin cannons for (useful now to blast attackers)? If we could think of a purpose, it would still leave open the question of how and when the programmed instincts to fire at beetle-eaters arose.

The idea that the snake's fangs may have been used to inject a fruit-

---

6. Perhaps it was created to reveal God's glory by running fast (just as an eagle soars at high altitude or a dolphin rides waves, apparently for 'recreation'). Also, many of God's designs have inspired human inventions—e.g., the iris diaphragm in cameras, and Velcro®. This could be part of the providence of God.

softening substance pre-Fall has the same problem. That is, why, how and when (if not by direct creation) did snakes change not only their diet but their behaviour, which appears to be programmed in their genetic code and not a matter of conscious choice?[7]

In any case, snake venom contains complex chemicals that appear to be designed for purposes far removed from fruit eating. One of these chemicals is highly specific in its attack on the central nervous system to arrest breathing; another specifically blocks the clotting mechanism so that the prey bleeds to death internally.

Despite the above problems, this may still be the correct explanation in at least some, if not many, instances. The female mosquito draws blood, as it needs hemoglobin to reproduce. However, the male mosquito only sucks sap from plants. Perhaps both sexes drew sap from plants before the Fall, and with the eventual extinction of some plant species they could no longer get hemoglobin from plants as easily (as already mentioned, some living plants have hemoglobin).

Position No. 2

This essentially looks at complex design as requiring the direct hand of the Designer, whether for DAS or not. There are different possibilities within this, however. For example,

1. There were no creatures with DAS pre-Fall—these creatures were all created afterwards.

This would mean that most creatures alive today would not have had a pre-Fall representative. The Bible makes no mention of such a new creation, and Exodus 20:11 directly contradicts the idea. Not surprisingly, this view is not widely held.

2. The design information for DAS was already present before

---

7. Based on the premise that the pre-Flood world had no desert or cold environments, some have queried the design features in many animals that are only useful in such conditions—e.g. the anti-dehydration equipment of a camel, or the special insulating features of a polar bear's fur. However, the Bible nowhere says that there were no deserts or cold areas before the Flood. In any case, such adaptive design features could have been present in the genes of more generalized created kinds of these creatures. For example, polar bears, which have special adaptations for the cold and are almost exclusively carnivorous, hybridize with brown bears, which do not have special cold adaptations and are mainly vegetarian (75%), suggesting that both derived from an original created bear kind.

the Fall, perhaps in latent or masked form.

This implies that the Fall was foreknown by God, which of course reflects His omniscience, and also is clearly stated in various Bible passages which speak of such things as God choosing us *'in him before the foundation of the world'* (Eph. 1:4). This information was allowed to become expressed, either through direct unmasking at the Fall or through the natural processes of recombination and selection. If the latter were the case, this would again involve the foreknowledge of God, this time that there would be only a short time between creation and the Fall. Otherwise, these DAS would have come to the fore in Eden eventually.

However, it is not easy to imagine genetically how such self-activation could take place for such a vast number of creatures which must also interact ecologically (the appearance of a defence structure must take place very smartly after one's enemy has a new weapon).

3. No new creatures were created, but many existing ones were 'redesigned' after the Fall, with the addition of new design information into their DNA.

This position has some indirect Scriptural support. The Curse placed upon the creation at the Fall involved biological changes to people—they would now die (Gen. 3:19) and pain in childbirth would increase (Gen. 3:16). The ground was also cursed such that thorns and thistles would spring forth (Gen. 3:18)—suggesting that biological changes occurred in plants. And the serpent, at least, appears to have been radically and permanently redesigned by God with the Curse (Gen. 3:14). So changes occurred in man, animals, plants and the soil because of the Fall. The sense suggests that these things resulted from a sovereign directive as a result of Adam's sin; they did not result from something just being 'let go'.[8] This understanding agrees with Scriptures such as Romans 8 where the *'whole creation'* is described as subject to the Curse and awaiting redemption from the consequences of sin.

---

8. In a future restoration, to get meat-eating lions (ML) to become grass-eating lions (GL) would seem to require supernatural rearranging of the DNA so as to make the change permanent. Since ML→GL requires this, and since this is a 're'-storation (i.e. a reversal of the results of the Fall), perhaps this indicates that GL→ML happened by the same route (supernatural DNA reprogramming), only in reverse.

Conclusion

Scripture simply does not provide enough information for Christians to insist dogmatically that one or other of these possible explanations is totally right or wrong. Several of them may apply together.

As fallen creatures in a fallen world, we have difficulty imagining what a pre-Fall world was really like. We are also finite creatures lacking all the information. We therefore need to be particularly careful about arguing from the present to the past.

What is clear from God's Word is that the present 'reign of tooth and claw', of violent death, cruelty, and bloodshed, had no place in the world before Adam sinned, and will have no place in the restored creation.

APPENDIX

Population Explosion?

We see in today's post-Fall world that death, and animals eating others, are useful ways of avoiding overcrowding of the Earth by any one type. Some, therefore, ask how, if there had been no Fall, such overcrowding could have been avoided without death and bloodshed.

This may be a non-question, since Scripture indicates that Adam's rebellion (and thus the need for the shed blood of God's Lamb, Jesus Christ) was foreknown before creation. Even if this were not so, it is surely presumptuous to suggest that the all-powerful Creator would have been unable to devise other means of avoiding such a problem. God gave the command to reproduce to 'fill the earth' (Gen. 1:22, 28), and once that was completed, the command would no longer apply and the filling would stop.

One natural mechanism already exists for limiting population growth, and is well known. Some animals, when subjected to overcrowding, drastically reduce their reproductive rate, only to increase it again if the population density should drop once more.

Chapter 7

What about similarities and other such arguments for evolution?

- Do similarities between creatures prove that they had a common ancestor (evolved)?
- Is human and chimp DNA very similar?
- Do human embryos go through animal stages as they develop?
- Do we have useless left-over bits of animals in us? What about 'ape-men'?

Similarities?[1,2]

WE are similar in many respects to animals, especially the apes, and evolutionists argue that therefore we are related to them; we must have a common ancestor with them.

What does the Bible say? In Genesis 1 we are told that God made mankind, a man and a woman, specially:

---

1. See Chapter 1 for some evidences for creation.
2. Known technically as homologies.

And God said, Let us make man in our image, after our likeness: and let them have dominion over the fish of the sea, and over the fowl of the air, and over the cattle, and over all the earth, and over every creeping thing that creeps on the earth. (Gen. 1:26)

God created mankind in *His* image, not in the image of animals. Furthermore, man was to rule, have dominion, over the animals.

In Genesis 2, we are given more details of the creation process and we find that Adam was created from *'the dust of the ground'* (Gen. 2:7), not from an ape. When God pronounced judgment on Adam, He affirmed that Adam came from the ground:

In the sweat of your face you shall eat bread until you return to the ground, for out of it you were taken. For dust you are, and to dust you shall return. (Gen. 3:19)

Some wish to allegorize the Genesis account of man's creation to make it conform to the current evolutionary fashion that man evolved from the apes. They are countered right here: if the dust Adam was made from represents the ape that he evolved from, then Adam must have turned back into an ape because of his sin! Of course not; the Bible is clear that man is a special creation.

Indeed, various kinds of animals and plants were created individually, not just humans. Plants were to produce seed *'after their kind'* meaning that bean plants were to produce bean seeds; and cattle would give birth to cattle, etc. (Gen. 1:11, 12, 21, 24, 25). So there is no hint in Scripture of any kind of an evolutionary process where one kind of organism would change into another kind.

Evolutionists believe not only that mankind evolved from an ape-like creature, but that ultimately everything evolved from a single-celled organism which happened to arise from non-living matter. They claim that the similarities between living things are proof that they evolved from common ancestors. They cite such things as the similarity between human and chimp DNA, similarities between embryos, claimed vestigial organs, and claimed transitional fossils between different kinds—such as supposed ape-men.

Human / chimp DNA similarity
—evidence for evolutionary relationship?

The idea that human beings and chimps have close to 100% similarity in their DNA is often asserted. Early studies, using crude techniques and based on a small fraction of the genetic code, led to claims of 97%

to 99% similarity, depending on who was telling the story. However, in 2005, decoding of the chimp DNA sequence was announced and a more accurate comparison is now possible. The new similarity is 96%, or less.[3,4] So, do the facts mean that there really is not much difference between chimps and people? Are we just (slightly) evolved apes?

Most importantly, similarity is not evidence for common ancestry (evolution), but rather for a common designer (creation). Think about the original Porsche and the Volkswagen 'Beetle' cars. They both have air-cooled, flat, horizontally-opposed, 4-cylinder engines in the rear, independent rear suspension, two doors, trunk in the front, and many other similarities ('homologies').

Why do these two very different cars have so many similarities? Because they had the same designer! Whether similarity is morphological (shape, form) or biochemical, it is not an argument for evolution over creation. If humans were entirely different from all other living things, or indeed every living thing was entirely different, would this reveal the Creator to us? No, we could think that there must be many creators rather than one. The unity of the creation is testimony to the One True God who made it all (Romans 1:20).

Also, if humans were entirely different from all other living things, then how could we live? We have to eat other organisms to gain nutrients and energy to live. How could we digest them and how could we use the amino acids, sugars, etc., if they were different to the ones we have in our bodies? Biochemical similarity is necessary for us to have food.

DNA in cells contains much of the information necessary for the development of an organism. So, if two organisms look similar, we expect there to be similarities also in their DNA. The DNA of a cow and a whale, two mammals, should be more alike than the DNA of a cow and a worm. If it were not so, then the idea of DNA being the information carrier in living things would have to be questioned.

Organisms descended from the same original created kinds would be expected to be very similar biochemically, showing only downhill changes in the information. Indeed, creationist biologists can use the

3. The Chimpanzee Sequencing and Analysis Consortium 2005. "Initial sequence of the chimpanzee genome and comparison with the human genome," Nature 437:69–87. See comment: 'Chimp genome sequence very different from man' by Dr. David DeWitt at <creation.com/dnachimp>

4. Batten, Don, Chimp/Human DNA—count the differences! <creation.com/DNAdiff>.

data from DNA comparisons in studies to determine the bounds of the original created kinds.[5]

Humans and apes are similar in appearance, so we would expect there would be similarities in their DNA. Of all the animals, chimps are most like humans, so we would expect that their DNA would be most like human DNA.

Certain biochemical capacities are common to all living things, so there is even a degree of similarity between the DNA of yeast, for example, and that of human beings. Because human cells can do many of the things that yeast can do, we share similarities in the DNA sequences that code for the enzymes and proteins that do the same jobs in both types of cells. Some of the sequences, for example those that code for the proteins involved in chromosome structure, are almost identical.

What if human and chimp DNA were 96% homologous? What would that mean? Would it mean that humans could have 'evolved'from a common ancestor with chimps? Not at all. DNA carries its information in the sequence of four chemical compounds known as nucleotides, abbreviated C, G, A, T. Groups of three at a time of these chemical 'letters' are 'read' by complex translation machinery in the cell to determine the sequence of amino acids, of which there are 20 different types, to be incorporated into proteins. The human DNA has 3 billion nucleotides. The amount of information in these 3 billion base pairs in the DNA of every human cell has been compared to that in 1,000 books of 500 pages each.[6] So, if humans were 'only' 4% different, this still amounts to 120 million base pairs, equivalent to about 40 large books of information. This is an impossible barrier for mutations (random changes) to cross, even given the several million years widely claimed as the time available for this to happen.

Does a high degree of similarity mean that two DNA sequences have the same meaning or function? No, not necessarily. Compare the

5. Molecular homology studies could be quite useful to creationists in determining what were the original created 'kinds' and what has happened since to generate new species within each kind. For example, the varieties/species of finch on the Galápagos Islands obviously derived from an original small number that made it to the islands. Recombination of the genes in the original migrants and natural selection could account for the varieties of finch on the islands today—just as all the breeds of dogs in the world today were artificially bred from the original wild dog kind not long ago. The molecular homology studies have been most consistent when applied within what are probably biblical kinds. However, the results contradict the major predictions of evolution regarding the relationships between the major groups such as phyla and classes (see ref. 6 regarding the latter).

6. Denton, M., Evolution: Theory in Crisis, Burnett Books, 1985.

following sentences:

• There are many scientists today who question the evolutionary paradigm and its atheistic philosophical implications.

• There are **NOT** many scientists today who question the evolutionary paradigm and its atheistic philosophical implications.

These sentences have 97% homology and yet have almost opposite meanings! There is a strong analogy here to the way in which large DNA sequences can be turned on or off by relatively small control sequences. Indeed, large differences between humans and chimps are being discovered in the gene control sequences.[7]

There are also almost no similarities in the 'hot spots' where chromosomes rearrange pieces of DNA during sexual reproduction. The Y-chromosomes are also extremely different, with the human one being much larger.

There is no way that mutations could bridge the gap between chimps and humans. Chimps are just animals. We are made in the image of God (no chimps will be reading this or discussing it with one another).

Similarities between embryos

Most people have heard of the idea that the human embryo, during its early development in the womb, goes through various evolutionary stages, such as having gill slits like a fish, a tail like a monkey, etc. Abortion clinics have used the idea to soothe the consciences of clients, saying, 'We're only taking a fish from your body.'

This concept was pretentiously called the 'biogenetic law', which the German evolutionist Ernst Haeckel popularized in the late 1860s. It is also known as 'embryonic recapitulation' or 'ontogeny recapitulates phylogeny', meaning that during an organism's early development it retraces its evolutionary history. So, a human embryo supposedly passes through a fish stage, an amphibian stage, a reptile stage, and so on.

Within months of the popular publication of Haeckel's work in 1868, L. Rütimeyer, professor of zoology and comparative anatomy at the University of Basel, showed it to be fraudulent. William His Sr, professor of anatomy at the University of Leipzig, and a famous comparative embryologist, corroborated Rütimeyer's criticisms.[8] These scientists

---

7. Keightley, P. D. et al., Evidence for widespread degradation of gene control regions in hominid genomes. PLoS Biol. 3, e42, 2005. Comment from Nature Reviews Genetics 6(3):163, March 2005.

8. Rusch, W.H. Sr, 1969. Ontogeny recapitulates phylogeny. *CRSQ* **6**(1):27–34.

showed that Haeckel fraudulently modified his drawings of embryos to make them look more alike. Haeckel even printed the same woodcut several times, to make the embryos look absolutely identical, and then claimed they were embryos of different species! Despite this exposure, Haeckel's woodcuts appeared in textbooks for many years.[9]

Has the 'biogenetic law' any merit? In 1965, evolutionist George Gaylord Simpson said, 'It is now firmly established that ontogeny does not repeat phylogeny.'[10] Prof. Keith Thompson (biology, Yale) said,[11]

'Surely the biogenetic law is as dead as a doornail. It was finally exorcized from biology textbooks in the fifties. As a topic of serious theoretical inquiry, it was extinct in the twenties.'

However, even textbooks in the 1990s were still using Haeckel's fraudulent drawings, including a textbook used in introductory biology courses in many universities, which said,[12]

'In many cases the evolutionary history of an organism can be seen to unfold during its development, with the embryo exhibiting characteristics of the embryos of its ancestors. For example, early in their development, human embryos possess gill slits like a fish ... .'

Despite the fraudulent basis of the idea and its debunking by many high-profile scientists, the idea persists.

Scientists who should have known better have promoted the myth of embryonic recapitulation in the 1990s. For example, science popularizer, the late Carl Sagan, in a popular article titled 'Is it possible to be pro-life and pro-choice?',[13] described the development of the human embryo as follows:

'By the third week ... it looks a little like a segmented worm. ... By the end of the fourth week, ... something like the gill-arches of a fish or an amphibian have become conspicuous ... It looks something like a newt or a tadpole. ... By the sixth week ... reptilian face ... By the end of the seventh week ... the face is mammalian, but somewhat pig-like. ... By the end of the eighth week, the face resembles a primate, but is still not quite human.'

---

9. Grigg, R., 1996, Ernst Haeckel: evangelist for evolution and apostle of deceit. *Creation* **18**(2):33–36.
10. Simpson and Beck, 1965. *An Introduction to Biology*, p. 241.
11. Thompson, K., 1988. Ontogeny and phylogeny recapitulated. *American Scientist* **76**:273.
12. Raven, P.H. and Johnson, G.B., 1992. *Biology (3rd edition)*, Mosby–Year Book, St. Louis, p. 396.
13. *Parade Magazine*, 22 April, 1990.

Replica human embryos at various stages of development

This is straight from Haeckel. A human embryo never looks reptilian or pig-like. A human embryo is always a human embryo, from the moment of conception; it is never anything else, contrary to what Sagan implies! It does not **become** human sometime after eight weeks. This is just what the Bible says—the unborn baby is a tiny human child (Gen. 25:21–22, Psalm 139:13–16, Jer. 1:5, Luke 1:41–44), so abortion takes an innocent human life.

Gill slits—something fishy?

The university textbook referred to above[12] claims that 'human embryos possess gill slits like a fish', although it has been known for many decades that human embryos *never* have 'gill slits'. There are markings on a human embryo which superficially look like the 'gill slits' on a fish embryo. These 'pharyngeal clefts', as they are more properly called,

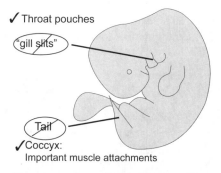

✓ Throat pouches

"gill slits"

Tail

✓ Coccyx: Important muscle attachments

Wrong terms are used to label human embryos, indoctrinating students in evolutionary belief.

which delineate 'throat pouches', never have any breathing function, and are never 'slits' or openings. They develop into the thymus gland, parathyroid glands and middle ear canals—none of which has anything to do with breathing, under water or above water!

Specialist embryology textbooks acknowledge that human embryos do not have gill slits. For example, Langman said,[14]

'Since the human embryo never has gills—branchia—the term pharyngeal arches and clefts has been adopted in this book.'

However, most evolutionists still use the term 'gill slits', especially in public presentations and when teaching students. The term prevails in school and university textbooks.

---

14. Langman, J., 1975. *Medical Embryology* (3rd edition), p. 262.

More revelations about Haeckel's fraud!

While the popularizers of evolution, when pressed, will admit that human embryos do not have gill slits and that Haeckel's drawings were to some extent fraudulent, they still believe that similarities between embryos are evidence for evolution (common ancestry). But this confidence rests, consciously or unconsciously, on the woodcuts published by Haeckel and reproduced, in whole or in part, in many textbooks since.[15] These drawings are widely believed to bear some resemblance to reality. But apparently no one had bothered to check.

Now it comes to light that Haeckel's fraud was far worse than anyone realized. An embryologist, Dr Michael Richardson, with the co-operation of biologists around the world, collected and photographed the types of embryos Haeckel supposedly drew.[16] Dr Richardson found that Haeckel's drawings bore little resemblance to the embryos.[17] Haeckel's drawings could only have come from his imagination, which was harnessed to produce 'evidence' to promote the acceptance of evolution.

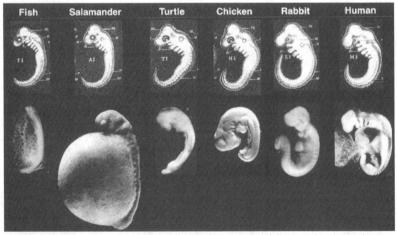

Haeckel's fraudulent drawings (top row) and photographs of the actual embryos (bottom row). After Richardson et al.[16] Used with permission.

15. For example, Gilbert, S., 1997. *Developmental Biology* (5th edition), Sinauer Associates, Ma, pp. 254, 900. Gilbert wrongly credits the drawings to 'Romanes, 1901'.
16. Richardson, M., *et al.,* 1997. There is no highly conserved stage in the vertebrates: implications for current theories of evolution and development. *Anatomy and Embryology* **196**(2):91–106, 1997, © Springer-Verlag GmbH & Co., Heidelburg.
17. Grigg, R., 1998. Fraud rediscovered. *Creation* **20**(2):49–51.

Haeckel's drawings should no longer be used to support the evolutionists' claim that embryos are similar and that this supports evolution.

Are some similarities in early embryos inevitable?

To construct anything, you begin with something without shape, or with a basic form and then build upon that. An illustration from pottery may help. A potter starts with a lump of clay. For a goblet or a slender vase, the potter would shape it initially into a cylinder. At this stage both the goblet and the vase look similar—they have the same basic plan. Further work results in the goblet and vase looking more and more different. The analogy with embryos breaks down in that the potter could change his mind and make *either* a vase or goblet at the completion of the basic plan. A fish embryo, however, could never become a human embryo (or *vice versa*) because a fish embryo has the coded instructions only for making a fish.

Some principles known as *von Baer's Laws* express this concept in regard to embryo development. Namely, the general features of a large group of animals appear earlier in the embryo than the specialized features. Less general characters are developed from the more general, and so forth, until finally the most specialized appear. Each embryo of a given species, instead of passing through the stages of other animals, departs more and more from them as it develops.

Von Baer's laws indicate that the younger the embryonic stage, the more closely organisms tend to resemble each other because they share the more generalized features, which appear first. Development can be likened to the radial spokes on a wheel. The spokes start at the hub and diverge outward, getting further and further apart.

Anomalies point to creation!

There are interesting exceptions to von Baer's laws. If we compare vertebrate embryos at the pharyngula stage (i.e. the stage showing the pharyngeal clefts), they look somewhat similar, but at *earlier* stages they are quite different! Ballard said,[18]

'... from very different eggs the embryos of vertebrates pass through cleavage stages of very different appearance, and then through a

---

18. Ballard, W.W., 1976. Problems of gastrulation: real and verbal. *Bioscience* **26**(1):36–39.

period of morphogenetic movements showing patterns of migration and temporary structures unique to each class. All then arrive at a pharyngula stage, which is remarkably uniform throughout the subphylum, consisting of similar organ rudiments similarly arranged (though in some respects deformed in respect to habitat and food supply).'

After 'converging' together, the embryos then diverge away from each other in the classic von Baer pattern. How can this be explained through evolution? ReMine[19] argues that it points to an intelligent designer who designed living things. God made things similar to show that there is *one* creator (similarity at the pharyngula stage), but with a pattern of similarity that could not result from common ancestry (the earlier stages of embryo development differ). The differences at the earlier stages give no support to a naturalistic explanation for similarities at the later pharyngeal stage being due to common descent.

Likewise, with the mode of development of amphibian and mammal foot bones in the embryo. They can end up looking very similar, but the amphibian's toes develop by growth from buds outwards, whereas the mammal's toes develop from a plate where the material between the toes dissolves. Thus the similarities we see in amphibians and mammals are due to common design, not common ancestry.

Sir Gavin de Beer, embryologist and past Director of the British Museum of Natural History, addressed the problem of the lack of a genetic or embryological basis for homology more than 30 years ago in a monograph titled *Homology, an Unsolved Problem* (1971, Oxford Biology Reader, Oxford University Press). Although De Beer believed in evolution, he showed that similarity is often only apparent and is not consistent with common ancestry.

Patterns of embryo development point to creation, not evolution! We are indeed *'fearfully and wonderfully made'* (Psalm 139:14).[20]

19. ReMine, W.J., 1993. *The Biotic Message: Evolution versus Message Theory,* St Paul Science, St Paul, Minn., USA, p. 370.
20. For more information on embryos: Parker, G., 1994, *Creation: Facts of Life,* Master Books, Green Forest, AR; Vetter, J., 1991, Hands and feet—uniquely human, right from the start! *Creation* 13(1):16–17; Glover, W. and Ham, K., 1992. A surgeon looks at creation. *Creation* 14(3):46–49.

Useless organs?

Evolutionists often argue that such things as flightless birds' small wings, pigs' toes, male nipples, legless lizards, the rabbit's digestive system, the human appendix, and hip bones and teeth in whales are useless and have no function. They claim these features are 'leftovers of evolution' and evidence for evolution.

The 'vestigial' organ argument for evolution is an old chestnut, but it is not valid.

First, it is impossible to prove that an organ is useless. The function may simply be unknown and its use may be discovered in future. This has happened with more than 100 formerly alleged useless vestigial organs in humans that are now known to be essential.

Second, even if the alleged vestigial organ were no longer needed, it would prove 'devolution' not evolution. The creation model allows for deterioration of a perfect creation since the Fall. However, the particles-to-people evolution model needs to find examples of *nascent* organs, i.e. those which are *increasing* in complexity.

Wings on birds that do not fly?

There are at least two possibilities as to why flightless birds such as ostriches and emus have wings:

1. The wings are indeed 'useless' and derived from birds that once could fly. This is possible in the creationist model. Loss of features is relatively easy by natural processes, whereas acquisition of new characters, requiring significant specific new DNA information, is impossible. Loss of wings most probably occurred in a beetle species that colonized a windy island. Again, this is *loss* of genetic information, so it is not evidence for microbe-to-man evolution, which requires masses of new genetic information.[21]

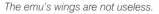

The emu's wings are not useless.

Photo by Amanda Greenslade

---

21. Wieland, C., 1997. Beetle bloopers: even a defect can be an advantage sometimes. *Creation* **19**(3):30.

2. The wings have a function. Some possible functions, depending on the species of flightless bird, are: balance while running, cooling in hot weather, warmth in cold weather, protection of the rib-cage in falls, mating rituals, scaring predators (emus will run at perceived enemies of their chicks, mouth open and wings flapping), sheltering of chicks, etc. If the wings are useless, why are the muscles functional, allowing these birds to move their wings?

Pigs with two toes that do not reach the ground?

Does this mean that the shorter toes have no function? Not at all. Pigs spend a lot of time in water and muddy conditions for cooling purposes. The extra toes probably make it easier to walk in mud (a bit like the rider wheels on some long trucks that only touch the road when the truck is heavily loaded). Perhaps the muscles attached to the extra toes give strength to the 'ankle' of the pig.

Why do males have nipples?

Males have nipples because of the common plan followed during early embryo development. Embryos start out producing features common to male and female—again an example of 'design economy'. Nipples are a part of this design economy. However, as Bergman and Howe[22] point out, the claim that they are useless is debatable.

What is the evolutionist's explanation for male nipples? Did males evolve (devolve) from females? Or did ancestral males suckle the young? No evolutionist would propose this. Male nipples are neither evidence for evolution nor evidence against creation.

Why do rabbits have digestive systems that function 'so poorly that they must eat their own feces'?

This is an incredible proposition. One of the most successful species on Earth would have to be the rabbit! The rabbit's mode of existence is obviously very efficient (what about the saying 'to breed like rabbits'?). Just because eating feces may be abhorrent to humans, it does not mean it is inefficient for the rabbit! Rabbits have a special pouch called the

---

22. Bergman J. and Howe, G., 1990. *'Vestigial Organs' are Fully Functional,* Creation Research Society Monograph No. **4**, Creation Research Society Books, Terre Haute, Indiana.

Sceptics have claimed that rabbits are poorly designed, yet they are one of the most successful animals, in terms of reproduction.

caecum, containing bacteria, at the beginning of the large intestine. These bacteria aid digestion, just as bacteria in the rumen of cattle and sheep aid digestion. Indeed, rabbits 'chew the cud' in a manner that parallels sheep and cattle.

The rabbit produces two types of fecal pellet, a hard one and a special soft one coming from the caecum. It is only the latter that is eaten to enrich the diet with the nutrients produced by the bacteria in the caecum. In other words, this ability of rabbits is a design feature; it is not something they have learned to do because they have 'digestive systems that function so poorly'. It is part of the variety of design, which speaks of creation, not evolution.

Sceptics have claimed the Bible is in error in saying that the rabbit 'chews the cud' (Lev. 11:6). The Hebrew literally reads, 'raises up what has been swallowed'. The rabbit does re-eat what has been swallowed—its partly digested fecal pellets. The sceptics are wrong.

Legless lizards

It is quite likely that legless lizards could have arisen through loss of genetic information from an original created kind, and the structures are consistent with this. 'Loss' of a structure is of no comfort to evolutionists, as they have to find a mechanism for creating new structures, not losing them. Loss of information cannot explain how evolution 'from ameba to man' could occur. Genesis 3:14 suggests that snakes may have once had legs.[23]

Adaptation and natural selection are biological facts; ameba-to-man evolution is not. Natural selection can only work on the genetic information present in a population of organisms—it cannot create new information. For example, since no known reptiles have genes for feathers, no amount of selection will produce a feathered reptile.

23. Brown, C., 1989. The origin of the snake (letter). *Creation Research Society Quarterly* **26**:54. Brown suggests that monitor lizards may have been the precursors of snakes.

Mutations in genes can only modify or eliminate existing structures, not create new ones. If in a certain environment a lizard survives better with smaller legs, or no legs, then varieties with this trait will be selected for. This might more accurately be called **devolution**, not **evolution**.

Rapid minor changes in limb length can occur in lizards, as demonstrated on Bahamian islands by Losos *et al.*[24] The changes occurred much faster than evolutionists thought they could. Such changes do not involve new genetic information and so give no support to microbe-to-man evolution. They do illustrate how quickly animals could have adapted to different environments after the Flood.

The human appendix

It is now known that the human appendix contains lymphatic tissue and helps control bacteria entering the intestines. It functions in a similar way to the tonsils at the upper end of the alimentary canal, which are known to fight throat infections. Tonsils also were once thought to be useless organs.[25,26]

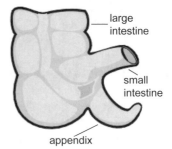

large intestine

small intestine

appendix

The human appendix helps protect the small intestine from microbes in the large intestine.

Hip bones in whales

Some evolutionists claim that these bones show that whales evolved from land animals. However, Bergman and Howe[22] point out that they are different in male and female whales. They are not useless at all, but help with reproduction (copulation).[27]

Teeth in embryonic baleen whales

Evolutionists claim that these teeth show that baleen whales evolved from toothed whales. However they have not provided an adequate

---

24. Losos, J.B., Warheit, K.I. and Schoener, T.W., 1997. Adaptive differentiation following experimental island colonization in anolis lizards. *Nature* **387**:70–73. See comment by Case, T.J., *Nature* **387**:15–16, and *Creation* **19**(4):9.
25. Ham, K. and Wieland, C., 1997. Your appendix … it's there for a reason. *Creation* **20**(1):41–43.
26. Glover, J.W., 1988. The human vermiform appendix—a general surgeon's reflections, *Journal of Creation* **3**:31–38.
27. See Wieland, C., 1998. The strange tale of the leg on a whale. *Creation* **20**(3):10–13.

mechanism for scrapping one perfectly good system (teeth) and replacing it with a very different system (baleen or whalebone). Also, the teeth in the embryo function as guides for the correct formation of the massive jaws.

As Scadding, an evolutionist, said, '...vestigial organs provide no evidence for evolutionary theory.'[28]

Ape-men?

Is there really evidence that man descended from the apes? Many people believe that the ancestry of mankind has been mapped faithfully and nearly completely. They have heard about 'missing links', and regard them as scientific proof of man's evolution. However, no ancestor for man has ever been convincingly documented. The 'missing links' are still missing. Here is a summary of facts relating to some of the best known fossils.[29,30]

Defunct ape-men

These are ones claimed at various times as intermediates between apes and humans but now rejected by evolutionists themselves.

- *Homo sapiens neanderthalensis* (Neandertal man)—150 years ago Neandertal reconstructions were stooped, very much like an 'ape-man'. Many now admit that the stooped posture was due to disease (such as rickets) and that Neandertals were human, fully able to speak, artistic and religious.[31]
- *Ramapithecus*—once widely regarded as the ancestor of humans, it has now been recognized as an extinct type of orangutan (an ape).
- *Eoanthropus* (Piltdown man)—a hoax based on a human skull cap and an orangutan's jaw. It was widely publicized as the missing link for 40 years, and it was not even a competent forgery.
- *Hesperopithecus* (Nebraska man)—based on a single tooth of a type of pig now living only in Paraguay.

---

28. Scadding, S.R., 1981. Do vestigial organs provide evidence for evolution? *Evolutionary Theory* **5**:173–176.
29. For details, see Lubenow, M., 1994, *Bones of Contention: A Creationist Assessment of the Human Fossils,* Baker Books, Grand Rapids, Michigan.
30. For a documentary DVD on so-called 'ape-men', see *The Image of God,* Keziah Films.
31. Lubenow, M.L., 1998, Recovery of Neandertal mtDNA: an evaluation. *Journal of Creation* **12**(1):87–97.

- ***Pithecanthropus*** (Java man)—now regarded as human and called *Homo erectus* (see below).
- ***Australopithecus africanus***—this was at one time promoted as the missing link. It is very ape-like and evolutionists no longer consider it to be transitional.
- ***Sinanthropus*** (Peking man)—has now been reclassified as *Homo erectus,* of the human kind (see below).

Currently fashionable 'ape-men'

These 'ape-men' adorn the evolutionary trees today that supposedly trace how *Homo sapiens* evolved from a chimp-like creature.
- ***Australopithecus***—various species of these have been proclaimed at times as human ancestors. One remains: *Australopithecus afarensis*, popularly known by the fossil 'Lucy'. However, detailed studies of the inner ear, skulls and bones indicate that 'Lucy' and her like are not part-human transitions. For example, they may have walked differently to most apes, but not in the human manner. Zihlman pointed out that *Australopithecus* is very similar to the pygmy chimpanzee, or bonobo.[32]
- ***Homo habilis***—there is a growing consensus among most palaeoanthropologists that this is a 'junk' category. It actually includes bits and pieces of various other types—such as *Australopithecus* and *Homo erectus*. It is therefore an 'invalid taxon'. Such a creature never existed. This was formerly claimed as *the* 'clear link' between apes and humans.

Homo erectus, *a variant of the human kind, was once promoted as 'the missing link'.*

- ***Homo erectus***—many remains of this type have been found around the world. This classification now includes Java man *(Pithecanthropus)* and Peking man *(Sinanthropus),* which were once promoted as 'missing links'. Their skulls have prominent brow ridges,

---

32. Zihlman, A., 1992, The promiscuous primate. *Nature* **359**:786

similar to Neandertals; their bodies were just like those of people today, only more robust. The brain size is within the range of people today and studies of the inner ear have shown that *Homo erectus* walked just like us. Both morphology and associated archaeological/cultural findings in association suggest that *Homo erectus* was fully human. Some evolutionists now agree that *erectus* is fully human and should be included in *Homo sapiens*.[33]

There is no clear fossil evidence that man evolved from apes. The whole chain of missing links is still missing because they simply never existed. The Bible clearly states, *'then the* LORD *God formed man of the dust of the ground, and breathed into his nostrils the breath of life; and man became a living soul.'* (Gen. 2:7). Considering the history of defunct 'ape-men', all new claims should be treated sceptically.

Other transitional fossils

If the evolutionary story about the origin of living things were true there should be millions of fossils showing the transitions from one kind of organism to another. After all, they say there have been hundreds of millions of years of mutations and natural selection, and the rock layers recorded this 'natural history' as fossils. Yet there are precious few, and even evolutionists cannot agree on their significance. Claimed evidence of fossils linking different kinds of organisms does not stand scrutiny.[34]

The lack of transitional fossils even drove evolutionists to propose a new mode of evolution in the late 1970s so they could go on believing in evolution without the need to find transitional fossils. This idea—*punctuated equilibrium*—basically says that the evolutionary changes occurred so quickly, geologically speaking, that no fossils were preserved to show them.[35]

---

33. For example, Milford Wolpoff—see Ref. 29, pp. 134–143.
34. Gish, D.T., 1995. *Evolution: The Fossils Still Say No!* Institute for Creation Research, El Cajon, CA, 391 pp.
35. Batten, D., 1994. Punctuated equilibrium: come of age? *Journal of Creation* 8(2):131–137.

Conclusion

The supposed evidence for evolution does not withstand critical examination.[36] The evidence is better understood in the context of God creating different basic kinds of organisms. These were capable of adapting to different environments by sorting the original created genetic information (reshuffled by sexual reproduction), via natural selection. Some variation has been generated by mutations, but these are degenerate changes involving loss of genetic information, or at best horizontal changes where information is not lost or gained.

The probability of natural processes generating new genetic information is so low that evolution could not possibly account for the origin of the vast amounts of complex coded information in living things.[37] Creation is the explanation consistent with the evidence.

36. For further reading on the supposed evidence for evolution: Wieland, C., 1994, *Stones and Bones, Creation Ministries International*, Queensland, Australia; Parker, G., 1994, *Creation: Facts of Life*, Master Books, Green Forest, AR; and Sarfati, J., 1999, *Refuting Evolution*, Master Books, Green Forest, AR. For in depth reading see Ref. 19.
37. Spetner, L.M., 1998. *Not by Chance*, Judaica Press, New York.

Chapter 8

Who was Cain's wife?

- It's now not lawful to marry your sister. So if Adam and Eve were the only two people God created, how could their son Cain find a wife?
- What about the land of Nod?
- How is this important to the Gospel?

'**W**HO was Cain's wife?' (in one form or another) is one of *the* most commonly asked questions, by believers and unbelievers alike.

Sometimes the person asking is genuinely seeking an answer, puzzled about the issue. At other times, the question is asked triumphantly, even smugly, as if to imply, 'There can't be an answer; it's an impossible conundrum.' And indeed, on the surface it looks like an insoluble 'catch-22' for the Bible-believer.

Three of Adam and Eve's children are mentioned by name: Cain, Abel and Seth. Cain kills Abel, and then it refers to his wife. So where did she come from?

The Bible makes it plain that Adam and Eve were the only two people that God created in the beginning. Adam is called 'the first man' (1 Corinthians 15:45,47), and Eve 'the mother of all the living' (Genesis 3:20).

To start a whole population off from only one couple means that in the early generations, there would have to be all sorts of close intermarriage, and at least one instance of brother-sister intermarriage.

If Cain himself did not marry his sister, but rather a niece, that means that at least one of Cain's brothers must have married a sister, anyway.

However, here it seems that the Bible-believer is faced with a dilemma.

1. The (apparent) biological problem

In the rare instances of known brother-sister intermarriage, there is a very strong likelihood that there will be various defects and deformities in the offspring. This is a biological fact.

2. The (apparent) moral problem

Doesn't God Himself prohibit brother-sister intermarriage? Yes, God's Law, handed to the Israelites via Moses, makes it clear that close relatives may not intermarry. In fact, even marrying a half-sister was strictly forbidden in the laws detailed in Leviticus. The law codes of many countries reflect similar prohibitions.

The 'other people' escape hatch—does it work?

Some have tried to solve the problem by claiming that there must have been other people present at the time, i.e. that God originally created more than the one man and woman. However, this causes even bigger problems. First, as already alluded to, it undermines the plain reading of several different parts of the Bible that make it clear that Adam and Eve were the first man and woman, respectively. And most Bible sceptics are quick to point this out.

Also, Paul makes it clear in the New Testament that all people alive on Earth today are Adam's descendants. He says, 'From one man he [God] made every nation of men…' (Acts 17:26). And Genesis 2:20 (where Adam names the animals) indicates that there was no other member of Adam's kind present—no living creature on Earth at that time was suitable to be a mate for him.

More importantly, the suggestion that some humans did not descend from Adam and Eve undermines the logic of the Gospel presented in the New Testament. It is clear that a precondition for salvation is to be a physical descendant of Adam. Jesus Christ is called the 'last Adam' (1 Corinthians 15:45). The Lord Jesus is stated to be our 'kinsman-redeemer' (the definite sense of the word used in Isaiah 59:20, 'the Redeemer shall come to Zion'—this uses the same Hebrew word גואל (gôēl) as used to describe Boaz in relation to Ruth (Ruth 4:14)). This is so because He, God the Son, took on human nature as well as being divine, becoming the perfect God-man.

This was God's solution to the problem of sin. After the disobedience of the first Adam brought in the Curse of death and bloodshed, the obedient last Adam shed His blood in death, overcoming death through His Resurrection. That is the whole point of Paul's message in 1 Corinthians 15:21–22. As a result, those who receive, by faith, His gracious gift of forgiveness of sin are no longer subject to eternal condemnation, but have everlasting life.

So this means that for anyone to be saved, they must first be a physical descendant of Adam, or else the Redeemer could not be their 'kinsman'.[1] The book of Hebrews also explains how Jesus took upon Himself the nature of a man to save mankind, but not angels (Hebrews 2:11–18). We can be saved because the last Adam entered our human line— descended from the first Adam, as we all are. The repeated Adam-Christ linkage is clear. That may be why it was important for Eve herself, in order to qualify for salvation, to also be a physical descendant of Adam ('bone of my bone, flesh of my flesh'—woman made from man's rib). If she had been created in a totally separate fashion—from raw materials, as Adam was—she would not have been a 'descendant' of the 'first Adam'.

The same principle also explains why long-age beliefs are so injurious to people such as the Australian Aborigines. If they have really been in Australia for 40,000 years (according to carbon-14 dating that is so uncritically accepted by so many—see Chapter 4), then how could they come from Adam, who lived about 6,000 years ago according to the Bible. This means they could not be related to Christ, so how can they be saved?

This 'Gospel link' is an important reason why this issue of Cain's wife is so important to the Christian. The other main reason is that it is such a widely-used point with which the reliability (and hence the authority) of the Bible is challenged and attacked.

Proposing that there were people around that could serve as spouses for Cain and his siblings opens the door for all manner of bizarre (even racist) ideas. It suggests that some people were/are 'human' enough to intermarry with others, but not 'human' enough to be saved by the Lord Jesus.[2]

All in all, it is biblically unacceptable to try to escape the 'Cain's wife' conundrum by proposing this idea of 'other created people'.

---

1. Being descended from Adam is the reason we need salvation anyway, as we have inherited his fallen nature.
2. Grigg, R., 1999. Darwin's quisling, *Creation* **22**(1):50–51.

So we are back to the seeming dilemma. The Bible says Cain had a wife—how could that be? Perhaps it's no wonder that sceptics trying to find reasons not to believe the Bible, and/or to dissuade others from doing so, have attacked this part of Genesis repeatedly. They are confident that there is no rational solution. One of the most well-known was the agnostic antitheist Clarence Darrow, lawyer for the evolution side at the famous Scopes trial. He cross-examined the anti-evolutionist William Jennings Bryan on the witness stand at that trial. Darrow successfully humiliated his opponent when Bryan was unable to give an answer concerning Cain's wife.[3] And thanks to biased reporting of the event from anti-Christian H.L. Mencken, this ignorance was imputed to all who believed in the truth of Genesis.

In the popular movie *Contact* (based on a book by the atheist evolutionist Carl Sagan), the atheist heroine (played by Jodie Foster) says that she lost her childhood faith because her pastor was unable to answer when asked, 'Where did Cain get his wife?' The message that this movie preached to millions was clear: 'There is no answer; Christianity is not rationally defensible.'

If Hollywood thought that Christians were able to easily answer this question, it would be very unlikely to put dialogue like this into a major movie, for fear of a major public loss of face.

The sad thing is that many, perhaps the majority of believers down through the years, have not been able to answer this. They often avoid the question, in fact, saying that it is 'unimportant'. But the message that onlookers get from such evasiveness is clear: 'They don't want to answer because they have no answer.' Another reason for this inability to answer may well be that we are not used to thinking within a consistent biblical worldview; one in which everything fits together. Mostly, we become used to thinking in terms of 'spiritual' things being quite separate from the facts, such as science, history, and so on.

However, the Bible's salvation message is firmly rooted in history. If it is wrong about the early history of this world, how can it be trusted with our spiritual destiny at stake? Jesus said in John 3:12: 'If I have told you of earthly things and you don't believe, how will you believe when I tell you of heavenly things?' Jesus always spoke of the characters

---

3. Trial transcript: *The World's Most Famous Court Trial, the Tennessee Evolution Case.* 1990. Bryan College (reprinted original edition), p. 302. Summary, including this incident at: <www.bryan.edu/802.html>

in Genesis as real and literal people, and the events as straightforward history.[4]

A supporter of Creation Ministries told us that an acquaintance of his, aged in his 90s, was dying. He had for years resisted all witnessing, including that of our supporter, his friend. When that supporter pleaded with him to accept Christ before he passed into eternity and it was too late, the dying elderly man stated that he could not, because he could not believe the Bible. And the reason was that no Christian he asked could answer his question on Cain's wife, which is why he had years ago given up. He had stopped even asking the question.

A few years ago, at a country fair[5] in Goondiwindi, Australia, a CMI representative was displaying a large model of Noah's Ark. As folk milled around, fascinated by the huge size of the vessel relative to the model animals, a brash woman approached, pushing her way through the crowd. With a smug expression, she said, in a broad rural Queensland accent, 'I betcha can't answer my question. I've been asking Christians the same question for years, folks, and no-one can give me an answer, even though I tell 'em I'll give 'em a thousand dollars if they can answer it. So there you are', she said gloatingly to the Ark displayer in front of everyone, 'You can have a thousand dollars if you can answer my question.'

'What is your question, then?' said the man representing our ministry. Hands on hips, the woman said, with a triumphant smirk, 'All right, then … where did Cain get his wife, eh?' When she received the answer (which we will see is rational, coherent, and both biblically and scientifically sound) she seemed shell-shocked. She walked around as if in a daze, saying repeatedly to herself, 'They answered my question … They answered my question …' (She may have been even more shocked when told she could keep her thousand dollars!)

The point of all this lead-up to giving the answer is to show that the failure to come to grips with this challenge has been widespread, and has serious consequences. Believers are commanded to be ready to give an answer to defend our faith (1 Peter 3:15).[6]

So, what is the answer?

---

4. See Batten, D. and Sarfati, J., 2006. *15 Reasons to Take Genesis as History*, Creation Ministries International, Brisbane, Australia.
5. Called a 'show' in that part of the world.
6. See also Sarfati, J., 1998. Loving God with all your mind: logic and creation, *Journal of Creation* 12(2):142–151, <creation.com/logic>.

First, the biological issue

It is not true to say that marrying a relative will inevitably cause deformities—we all marry relatives. We are all related to varying degrees, because we have all descended from the same original parents. (If your husband or wife is not a relative, you have a problem, as it would mean you're not married to a human being!)

The biological problems (and the moral and legal prohibitions) which we are considering here have to do with marrying *close* relatives. So let's look at why there are defects and deformities in the offspring of *close* intermarriages. Where do the defects come from?

To understand this, we need some basic facts of genetics. The hereditary information that is passed on from generation to generation is encoded on stretches of DNA that include the well-known 'genes'.[7] As that information is copied repeatedly, it is copied chemical letter by letter. During this, copying mistakes can arise. These are called *mutations*. Mutations are responsible for thousands of inherited diseases, like cystic fibrosis, hemophilia, progeria, sickle cell anemia and phenylketonuria. These are passed on through the generations, because once such a mistake or 'copying error' has arisen, that error is copied, too. (When making a copy of a computer program or word processing file that has a defect, one ends up copying the defect, too.)

If there are successive generations of copying, as in biological heredity, then that mistake is not only passed on, but sooner or later another mistake will arise, which is then added to the original mistake. And so on. If we had a population whose genetic information contained only one mistake, then sooner or later there will be a population containing two mistakes. And then three, and so on. Future defects will tend to be added to the existing ones. This problem of the increasing genetic (or mutational) *burden* or *load* is a well-known phenomenon.[8]

In other words, over time such mistakes accumulate. The number of these defects in the population tends to progressively and relentlessly

---

7. See Sarfati, J., DNA: marvellous messages or mostly mess? *Creation* **25**(2):26–31, 2003; <creation.com/message>.

8. The rare evolutionist who faces up to the obvious difficulty that, if we had been around for a very long time, we would be carrying an impossible load of mutations, often tries to evade this difficulty by relying on selection to eliminate the harmful mutations. But most mutations are only harmful (and thus exposed to selection) if inherited from both parents— see shortly in main text. So even if only at a low frequency, they would overwhelmingly tend to remain in the population, thus adding to the already existing burden. This is why such accumulation of mutations is an ever-increasing problem for any population. Geneticist Dr John Sanford has described this problem for evolution and its long ages in *Genetic Entropy and the Mystery of the Genome,* Elim Publishing, NY, USA, 2005.

increase. This is why each one of us carries *hundreds* of such genetic mistakes. They have been inherited from the accumulation of copying mistakes occurring as our ancestors had children.

So why don't we show all these hundreds of mistakes as defects or deformities? The main reason is that genes come in pairs.[9] For a gene involved in a particular trait (the ability to make insulin, for example[10])

MUTATION INHERITANCE

————————— = Normal gene   〜〜〜〜 = Defective gene

—————————   —————————

This person has normal instructions for this characteristic inherited from both parents—he/she will not express any defect for this particular characteristic.

〜〜〜〜   —————————

This person has a defective gene from one parent. However, the gene from the other parent carries the normal instructions for this characteristic, functioning like a 'backup copy'. So this person will normally not show any defect for this characteristic.[11] This person is a 'carrier' for the defect, without showing it. We all 'carry' many such mistakes, which we don't show.

〜〜〜〜   〜〜〜〜

This person has inherited the defective gene from both parents. He/she does not now have any normal instructions for this characteristic, so the characteristic itself will be defective/deformed.[12] We are all related, but the closer your relatedness with the person you marry, the greater the chance you have some of the *same* mistakes. This makes it more probable that a child of such a marriage will inherit the same mistake (mutation) from both parents, thus giving rise to the expression of overt deformities and defects.

---

9. Not all mutations cause overt defects; many are neutral because they occur in a non-critical part of the instructions. We are referring here to those with functional significance.
10. This is the important hormone that controls blood sugar levels.
11. Some defective (mutated) genes are harmful even if the person only has one of them. This is much rarer, and such genes are more likely to be eliminated by natural selection (the person dies before reproducing).
12 The genetic system is incredibly complex, and this will inevitably be an oversimplification, though not misleading in its essence.

you inherit one gene from your mother and one from your father. So it is as if you have a 'backup copy' of normal instructions if one should be defective. Say you have inherited a defective copy of a particular gene, giving, for example, the instructions to make 'feature F' (whatever that might be—something affecting the way your ears are constructed, for instance). The point is that the normal gene inherited from the other parent still carries the normal instructions to make F—so your F (e.g., ears) will generally be OK. But what happens if you inherit the same defective gene from both parents? Now you have no instructions to make normal F—so your F will now be defective (see Mutation Inheritance box on previous page).

This explains why, when two people marry today, their children rarely show mutational defects. The point is that even though each parent carries hundreds of mistakes, and passes many on,[13] the mistakes carried by each parent are not usually the same sets of mistakes. Because a husband and wife usually have parents with quite different genetic backgrounds, they will have significantly different sets of mistakes. So any defective gene inherited from one parent will normally be 'covered up' or 'compensated for' by the normal gene, carrying the normal instructions, passed on from the other parent.

Hemochromatosis, sickle-cell anemia, cystic fibrosis, hereditary diabetes, and 1000+ other genetic diseases.

Mutations have accumulated since the Fall, causing many human diseases.

Sometimes, in this fallen world, even when husband and wife are not closely related, it will just so happen that two of the same mistakes will pair together in the genes for one characteristic—i.e. the same mistake will be inherited from each parent, a tragic, but relatively rare situation.

But brother and sister have the same parents, i.e. the sources from which they obtain their mistakes are the same. So there is a rather

---

13. We have about 25,000 gene pairs with one gene (allele) of each pair coming from each parent. So we each copy, and pass on, only half of our genetic information to each child, though it is a 'different half' each time (identical twins result from a natural cloning process at the first cell division of the new embryo). With half from each parent, the child then has a full complement.

high chance that the offspring of a brother-sister union will inherit at least one pair of genes in which the same mistake is present from each parent.[14] This is why there is such a high chance of deformities and other defects showing up if brother and sister procreate.

People who are closely related, but less so than brother and sister (such as half-brothers and half-sisters), will have a lesser, but still substantial, chance of their offspring having such deformities. The closer the relatedness, the bigger the risk. So it makes biological sense for there to be legal and moral prohibitions against even half-siblings intermarrying.

The punch line

So how is this relevant to Cain's wife? Simple. Since going forward in time means that a population will have more and more mistakes, going backwards in time means that there are fewer and fewer such mistakes. Ultimately, one could extrapolate that back to a situation in which there were *no* defects. This makes sense in a biblical framework of understanding, since the first man and woman, created in a perfect world before it was corrupted by sin, would not have had *any* defective genes. Remember, God pronounced His creation 'very good' (Genesis 1:31). After the Fall (Genesis 3), such copying mistakes could now arise. But it would take time—many generations, involving hundreds of years—for the mistakes to accumulate (add up) to a level at which it would be a significant risk for brother to marry sister.

In other words, Cain, or any of his brothers, could have married his sister (or niece, or any other close relative) without any *biological* problem. Even though only Cain, Abel and Seth are mentioned by name, the Bible says clearly (in Genesis 5:4) that Adam and Eve had 'other sons and daughters'. And we have already seen that such intermarriage *must* have occurred, since there were only two people in the beginning.

Remember that all this is referring to lawful, monogamous marriages before God. We will cover the moral issues shortly.

---

14. Although there is only a one in four chance with any *particular* gene locus, with hundreds of possible mutations around there is a high chance that at least one will be inherited from both parents.

Biblical support

Starting the human race off with two people, as God chose to do, means logically that there *must* have been intermarriage between close relatives originally, in order for humanity to multiply and fill the earth (Genesis 1:28).[15]

But there is separate biblical support of another kind. Abraham, who lived some hundreds of years after the Flood (which was some 1700 years after creation) was still able to marry his half-sister, Sarah—and there is no hint of any biological defects in the offspring.

So why didn't God condemn Abraham and his wife? Hadn't they broken the law against half-siblings marrying each other? Not at all. That law was only proclaimed hundreds of years after Abraham lived—at the time of Moses. It's helpful to remember that things are right or wrong not on the basis of our opinion, but based upon what the Creator determines. And how do we know what His requirements are? Through His revealed standards of moral absolutes to mankind, through His written Word, the Bible.

God changing His mind?

This sometimes causes people to ask if that makes God inconsistent—isn't He changing His standards? Imagine a shepherd looking after his flock on an open meadow. There are no wild animals around, and the only danger to the sheep is at one end of the meadow, where there are some cliffs from which they could fall down. So the shepherd builds a fence, but only around the cliffs. That fence represents a law, a 'Thou shalt not'. There is no need to fence the rest of the meadow.

Some time later, wolves move into the district. Now there is a new danger to the sheep; if they stray beyond the sight of the shepherd, they risk being killed and eaten. So a new set of rules is called for, a new 'Thou shalt not', and the shepherd now puts a fence around the entire meadow.

The shepherd's standards have not changed; his loving care for the flock is the same as always. But times have changed, and a new law is called for in order to express that loving care.

In the same way, having permitted intermarriage between close relatives in order to commence humanity from one man (and one woman

---

15. Remember that the word 'replenish' in this verse in the King James Version, in the English of that day, simply meant 'fill'—just as the Hebrew word does. See Chapter 3 (on the Gap Theory).

who also came from that one man), a point was reached where God clearly chose to institute a new law which was, like in the case of the sheep, a benefit to them, for their own protection. This might have been particularly important in the case of the children of Israel (to whom the Mosaic Law was given). They were a genetically 'isolated' population; they were told to avoid intermarriage outside their own group (unless the person converted to worshipping the true God of Israel). So there was an increased likelihood of close relatives marrying—which is why the prohibition was necessary. Out-marriage would otherwise tend to 'dilute and delay' the effects of the accumulating mutations. Preserving the Nation of Israel was vital, because from them would come the promised Messiah, the 'seed of the woman' (Genesis 3:15).

But what about the land of Nod?

Some understandably bring up the fact that after Cain slew Abel, there are indicators of many other people around. Referring to Cain's exile, the Bible says that 'the Lord put a mark on Cain so that no one who found him would kill him.' (Gen 4:15) And it says that he went to the 'land of Nod' and built a 'city'. Often people read the passage as saying that he found a wife from among the inhabitants of Nod. However, the Scripture does not actually say that, it says (after mentioning that he went to live in that land) that he 'knew' his wife (in the sense of sexual relations). For all we know, the land of Nod may have been totally empty before Cain moved there—and he may have moved there with his wife, rather than meeting her there.

Furthermore, the Hebrew word (עיר ir) translated as 'city' does not have the meaning that we might think with our modern understanding that entails many tens of thousands of people. The Hebrew word applied to a walled town or even something as small as a protected encampment.

But in any case, these are moot points, since it can be shown that there was plenty of time for a substantial population to have built up on Earth before Cain killed Abel—well over a hundred years. Cain was the first child born to Adam and Eve, and he appears to have been conceived shortly after the Fall, which was itself likely to have occurred only a few days or possibly weeks after the Creation. (Eve did not fall pregnant before the Fall, even though she and Adam were presumably healthy individuals in a perfect world and had been commanded to be fruitful and multiply.)

Seth appears to have been a replacement for Abel (Genesis 4:25), and

Adam was 130 years old when Seth was born. So this means that by the time Cain killed Abel and went into exile, nearly 130 years had likely passed. (Given Cain's age, even in those days of 900-year lifespans, it is highly likely that he had already been married for a long time prior to his migration to Nod.) If we assume that the first generation of Adam and Eve's children could have had their own children 25 to 30 years after creation, there would be time for another 3–4 additional generations, with the numbers increasing exponentially each time.

This population build-up would have been the result of intermarriage between Adam and Eve's children—as mentioned earlier, Genesis 5:4 tells us they had sons and daughters other than those named in the text. We do not know how many sons and daughters they had, but the more it was, the more quickly the numbers would build up in later generations. A footnote to Whiston's translation of *The Works of Josephus*, a Jewish historian, says that 'the number of Adam's children, as says the old tradition, was thirty-three sons and twenty-three daughters.'[16] Whatever their exact number, it is obvious that there could have been a substantial population, perhaps even dispersed among many different settlements, within those 130 or so years. The 'city' Cain built may have been one more to add to the several that already existed.

Some state that for Cain to be fearful of retribution (Genesis 4:14) there must have been other people around. And of course there would have been, as explained above. However, it is interesting to ponder who would have any interest in avenging the death of Abel and thus posing a threat to Cain, unless it were Abel's relatives. So the fact that all people at that time would have been relatively closely related to Abel (and Cain, and each other) may possibly make even more sense of the text.

Summary and conclusion

- The Bible without any doubt teaches that God chose to start humanity off from only two people. This means that in the first few generations, marriage had to be between extremely closely related people, including at least one brother-sister union. The Bible says that Adam and Eve had daughters as well. Cain could have married his sister, or niece.

---

16   Josephus, Flavius, (translated by William Whiston, A.M.) 1981. *The Complete Works of Josephus*, Kregel Publications, Grand Rapids, Michigan, p. 27.

- The biological problems caused by such unions today come from a progressive accumulation of genetic defects since the Fall. An originally perfect population would not have had any such problem.
- The Bible teaches that even Abraham, living a long time after creation, was still able to marry his half-sister, Sarah, without any hint of biological problems in the offspring (Isaac). In doing so he was not breaking God's law. The law of Moses forbidding intermarriage between close relatives was not given until centuries after Abraham.

Chapter 9

Were the 'sons of God' and/or the *nephilim* extraterrestrials?[1]

- Has Earth been visited by extra-terrestrials?
- Could life exist 'out there'?
- What about UFOs and government cover-ups?

For decades, speculation about extra-terrestrial life has been boosted by tales of flying saucers and encounters with aliens. Some have even claimed that the 'sons of God' and/or the *nephilim* of Genesis 6:4 were aliens (see later).

Secular humanists, like Carl Sagan, have passionately believed that intelligent life has evolved 'out there' in addition to on Earth. Belief in the evolution of life on Earth has clearly encouraged the belief that life could/would have evolved elsewhere as well, considering the size of the universe. This has certainly encouraged belief in 'ET'.

---

1. Parts of this chapter are based on an article by Dr Werner Gitt, published in *Creation* **19**(4):46–48, 1997. See also Grigg, R., 2000. Did life come from outer space? Creation **22**(4):40–43. For detailed treatment of this topic, see Bates, G., 2004, *Alien Intrusion: UFOs and the Evolution Connection*, <www.alienintrusion.com>.

Photo by NASA

The meteorite that was falsely claimed to show that life was once on Mars.

In 1996 this was fuelled from another source. NASA researchers claimed to have found evidence for simple life forms in a meteorite, allegedly from Mars, found in Antarctica. Since then, this 'proof' of life in the 'Mars rock' has very much lost favour among the scientific community.[2,3] The supposed 'nanofossils' were probably no more than magnetite whiskers plus artefacts of the experimental process.[4] Despite this, the 2 kg rock ignited a new surge of 'Mars fever'. In the next 20 years, the Americans, Europeans, Japanese and Russians plan around 20 projects to explore our neighbouring planet, which is some 78 million kilometres away at its closest approach to us.

Meanwhile, belief in extra-terrestrial intelligence continues to grow with an almost religious fervour.

The UFO wave

Harvard University psychiatry professor John E. Mack attracted worldwide attention with his best-selling book, *Abduction: Human Encounters with Aliens.*

There was also the sensational film of an alleged autopsy on an alien from a crash in New Mexico close to the U.S. Air Force Base at Roswell. The blurry footage was the main attraction at the 1995 UFO World Congress in Düsseldorf, Germany. It has since been shown to be a crude forgery. Then of course, there was the blockbuster 'alien invasion' film *Independence Day,* which grossed more in its opening week than any previous film. Such science-fiction stories, most of which contain 'alien' themes, are the most popular entertainment genre in the world today. Popular polls show that up to four out of five people

2. Sarfati, J.D., 1996. Life on Mars? *Creation* **19**(1):18–20; Sarfati, J.D., 1996. Life from Mars? *Journal of Creation* **10**(3):293–296. <creation.com/mars>
3. Holmes, Bob, 1996. Death knell for Martian life. *New Scientist* **152**(2061/2):4.
4. See Anon., 1998. Another blow to Mars 'life' claim. *Creation* **20**(2):8.

believe in alien life and that aliens may be even monitoring human activities.[5] So, what should Christians think about UFO accounts?

What does the Bible say?

(a) Scripture does not mention 'ET' visits

The Bible, the revealed written Word of God, teaches that life is only possible through a process of creation. Even if there were other galaxies with planets very similar to Earth, life could only be there if the Creator had fashioned it. If God had done that, and if these beings were going to visit us one day, then He would surely not have left us unenlightened about this. Alien beings with such power and technology would be superior to mankind in many ways. This would usurp God's dominion mandate given to man to 'subdue the earth' (Gen. 1:28).

God *has* given us rather specific details of the future—for example, the return of Jesus, and some details about the end of the world. The universe will, at some future point, be rolled up like a scroll (Isa. 34:4; Rev. 6:14). If God had created living beings elsewhere, this would automatically destroy their dwelling place as well. Adam's sin caused all of creation to be affected by the Curse—otherwise God need not create a 'new heavens and Earth'. So why would a race of beings, not of Adam's (sinful) seed, have their part of creation affected by the Curse, and then be part of the restoration brought about by Christ, the last Adam? This would not make any sense.[6] Jesus is not going to be crucified and raised again many times over on other planets. Scripture says He 'died once for all' (Rom. 6:10).

Some have claimed that the *nephilim,* or the 'sons of God', both mentioned in Genesis 6:2–4, were aliens. This is a wild extension of a common view that the 'sons of God' who married the 'daughters of men' were fallen angels.

'Sons of God' (Hebrew: *bene elohim)* is clearly used of angels in Job 38:7. The Septuagint (LXX[7]) here translates 'sons of God' as 'angels of God'. A straight-forward reading of Genesis 6:4 implies that evil

---

5. Out there—*Readers Digest* exclusive poll, July 2005.
6. Furthermore, Jesus dying for alien beings makes no sense, since Jesus took on *human* nature, and remains the God-man forever as our Saviour. If He were to atone for Vulcans, say, He would need to become a Vulcan. The whole purpose of creation is focused on the race on Earth, of which some will be Christ's 'bride' throughout eternity. Christ will not have multiple 'brides'.
7. A translation in Greek, commissioned by Ptolemy in the 3rd Century BC.
8. Morris, H.M., 1976. *The Genesis Record,* Baker Book House, Grand Rapids, MI, p. 169.

angels actually cohabited with women. The resultant offspring were called the *Nephilim*, which literally means 'fallen ones'. Although this is a troubling passage that challenges our views of the spiritual dimension and the physicality of angels, the strongest argument for this view comes from the simplest understanding of the text itself. There is also New Testament support for this view (Jude 6—7; 2 Pet. 2:4–5; 1 Pet. 3:18–20).

Some suggest that evil angels on Earth could have used the bodies of ungodly men, by demonic possession, to achieve their evil purpose of producing an evil generation of people (Gen. 6:12). [8] But this has little textual support.

Interestingly, the word *nephilim* is only used in Gen. 6:4 and in Num. 13:33. The latter refers to the descendants of Anak, who were big people, but still people. However, it is likely that the mention of the nephilim in this latter passage, whether referring to the descendants of Anak, or the pre-Flood group of nephilim, was a lie by the spies to dissuade the Hebrews from entering the Promised Land. God punished the spies for bringing back an untruthful report (Num. 14:11, 36–37).

Although 'sons of God' is used exclusively of angels in the Old Testament, in Hosea 1:10 *'the sons of the living God'*, specifically refers to the children of Israel. The Bible scholar, H.C. Leupold, suggested that the 'sons of God' were descendants of Seth, the godly line who are detailed in Genesis 4:25–5:32. Leupold wrote, 'But who were these "sons of God"? Without a shadow of a doubt, the Sethites …'.[9] In this view, the descendants of Seth became wayward and married the 'daughters of men' indiscriminately, basing their choice only on appearance, without concern for godliness, and the *nephilim* were their offspring. However, others have argued against this view suggesting that the text would have specifically said 'sons of Seth' and 'daughters of Cain'. Also, it is claimed that the Sethites could not have been a godly group in toto because family heritage does not guarantee piety or righteousness anyway (witness the kings of Israel, for example).

Rulers in ancient Egypt and Mesopotamia often proclaimed themselves as 'sons of God' to enhance their power and prestige. So, another view is that the 'sons of God' were power-hungry rulers and despots, who, in their hunger for power and influence, took many wives in polygamy. They, and their offspring, through tyranny, became 'mighty

---

9. Leupold, H.C., 1942. *Exposition of Genesis, Vol. 1,* Wartburg Press, Ann Arbor, MI, p. 250.
10. See <creation.com/space_life>.

men' (Nimrod was described as such a 'mighty one', Gen. 10:8).

Whatever the correct view, there is no need to resort to fanciful suggestions involving aliens to understand this passage of Scripture.

(b) The purpose of the stars

The Bible tells us in several places why the stars were made, not only in the well-known Psalm 19 but especially in the Creation account. In Genesis 1:14 we read: *'And God said, Let there be lights in the expanse of the heavens to divide between the day and the night. And let them be for* signs, *and for seasons, and for days and years.'* Thus God made the stars for mankind on Earth, not for another alien race 'out there'. Add to this the sequence of creation (Earth on Day 1, and only on Day 4 the stars), and it is easy to see the thrust of the biblical testimony, that the purpose of the Creation is uniquely centred on this Earth.

Science

1. Never a single contact with an 'extra-terrestrial'

In 1900, the French Academy of Science offered a prize of 100,000 francs for the first person to make contact with an alien civilization—so long as the alien was not from Mars, because the Academy was convinced that Martian civilization was an established fact! Since then, not a trace of 'little green men', or indeed any life, has been found on any of the planets that our probes have explored, including Mars. Despite this, a great number of astronomers

'Is it true that not one of your experiments has shown signs of intelligence?'

think that since life supposedly evolved here on Earth it must have evolved near one of the many stars out there. Around the world, SETI (Search for Extra Terrestrial Intelligence) researchers have scanned the sky, looking in vain for signals from intelligent beings. Despite all the listening, on many millions of frequencies over many years, nothing indicating intelligent alien life has ever been heard.

2. Conditions must be 'just right'

Life on any planet can only survive provided a great number of very stringent requirements are met. For example, the planet must be at the right distance from its sun, so as to be neither too hot nor too cold. In particular, it must be in a very narrow temperature range so that liquid water exists. Even if planets around other stars are confirmed, it is extremely improbable that any of them would fulfil all the requirements needed for life. Just having liquid water is completely insufficient, despite the excitement created when such was possibly detected on the surface of Jupiter's moon, Europa.

The improbability of life elsewhere refutes the idea that life may have inadvertently drifted to Earth, or may have been deliberately sent here by aliens ('panspermia' and 'directed panspermia').[10]

3. Life cannot form spontaneously anyway

Without intelligent, creative input, lifeless chemicals cannot form themselves into living things.[11] The idea that they can is the theory of spontaneous generation, disproved by the great creationist founder of microbiology, Louis Pasteur. Without unfounded evolutionary speculation, UFOlogy would not have its present grip on the public imagination.

4. Vast distances

Even if we assumed life existed somewhere else in the universe, a visit by extra-terrestrials to Earth, such as is claimed in UFO reports, seems completely impracticable, if not impossible. The distances (and therefore the likely travel times) are unimaginably vast.

The *closest* star to Earth, Proxima Centauri (α-Centauri C) is 40.7 million million kilometres (c. 25 million million miles) away. The Apollo flights took three days to get to the moon. At the same speed, it would take 870,000 years to get to this nearest star. Of course, one could accelerate (particularly unmanned) probes to a greater speed.

At the incredible speed of one-tenth of the speed of light, the trip, *one way*, would still take 43 years. One would need enormous amounts

---

11. Some creationist critiques of evolutionary origin of life theories are: Aw, S.E., 1996. The origin of life: a critique of current scientific models. *Journal of Creation* **10**(3):300–314; Sarfati, J.D., 1997. Self-replicating enzymes. *Journal of Creation* **11**(1):4–6; Thaxton, C.B., Bradley, W.L. and Olsen, R.L., 1984. *The Mystery of Life's Origin*, Philosophical Library Inc., New York. See articles on the origin of life, <creation.com/origin>

12. This means there is a small chance of hitting one in each linear kilometre travelled, but over such vast distances, a hit is almost certain. The Appendix (p. 149) gives calculations of the damaging effects of dust at such high speeds.

of energy for such an acceleration. Even a very small, 10 kg, craft would need energy equivalent to all that generated in four days by the world's largest hydroelectric power station (see Appendix, p. 149).

Furthermore, in every cubic kilometre of space, there are an estimated 100,000 dust particles (made up of silicates and ice) weighing only a tenth of a gram. At such a velocity, colliding with even one of these tiny objects could destroy a spaceship.[12]

So what about UFOs?

How, then, should one understand the UFO phenomena and all the associated hype? The German magazine *Focus* recently stated, '90% of UFO reports turn out to be humbug, but there is a residual 10% which are not easy to dismiss.'[13] The article quoted sociologist Gerald Eberlein as saying:

'Research has shown that people who are not affiliated with any church, but who claim that they are religious, are particularly susceptible to the possible existence of extra-terrestrials. For them, UFOlogy is a substitute religion.'[14]

However, credible witnesses sometimes recount tales of seeing strange objects that even resemble metallic craft. Many of the world's leading UFO researchers concur that a small percentage of these objects seem to perform supernatural feats that defy the laws of physics, such as changing shape and merging into one another at incredible speeds.

The Bible goes somewhat deeper in this matter, identifying a supplementary cause and effect:

'... *the one whose coming is in accord with the activity of Satan, with all power and signs and false wonders, and with all the deception of wickedness for those who perish, because they did not receive the love of the truth so as to be saved. For this reason God will send upon them a deluding influence so that they will believe what is false, ...'* (2 Thess. 2:9–11).

The Bible gives a description of reality concerning all living things. The living God reveals himself as the Triune One—Father, Son and Holy

---

13. Erdling, Hallo, 1995. Ufologie. *Focus* **45**:254.
14. Ref. 13, p. 252.
15. The devil and his evil angels are fallen created beings. Satan's kingdom will exist only as long as God permits.
16. William Alnor, cult expert and award-winning journalist, studied the UFO phenomenon

Spirit. In Heaven there are the angels, powerful created beings who also serve mankind on Earth.

There is another kingdom—that of the devil and the demons.[15] Ephesians 2:2 talks about the 'prince of the power of the air', whose reign is on Earth, and who masquerades as 'an angel of light' (2 Cor. 11:14)

The devil has his own repertoire of deception in the form of various occult practices and a multitude of religious rites. It could be that behind those unexplainable UFO reports there is the work of the arch-deceiver.[16]   UFO reports, by definition, remain nebulous and not identifiable. People who do not know Christ are easily fascinated by all sorts of phenomena that are difficult to explain. For Christians, there is Jesus' warning in Matthew 24:4 to *'Take care that no man deceive you.'* What is the best antidote to deception? Paul exhorts us, in 2 Timothy 2:15, to *'study'* the Scripture, so we might *'accurately handle the word of truth'*.

Secret bases? ... government cover-ups? ...

Many UFO enthusiasts spread the 'urban myth' of secret U.S. Government experiments on aliens, etc.—an idea reinforced by movies such as *Independence Day*. However, does a cover up make sense when, under the inspiration of atheists like the late Carl Sagan, the U.S. government has spent millions of taxpayers' dollars listening 'out there' for signs of intelligent ET life? Many other evolutionary humanists, like Sagan, passionately believe that intelligent life has evolved 'out there' in addition to on Earth, and would pounce on any hard evidence for this idea. Consider the media frenzy about the 'life in Mars rock' fiasco. To imagine that a much more exciting discovery could be kept secret for decades defies credibility.

---

for many years. His book, *UFOs in the New Age* (Baker Book House), 1992, documents his investigations that lead to the conclusion that some UFO phenomena have an occult source. Gary Bates came to a similar conclusion (see in Ref. 1).

Appendix: feasibility of inter-stellar travel

The following calculations are given for the benefit of the more technically-minded.

1. For a spacecraft to acquire a speed of 1/10th the speed of light (c/10), the kinetic energy needed is given accurately enough by the non-relativistic formula of $\frac{1}{2}mv^2$. For a very small unmanned spacecraft of 10 kg, this is $\frac{1}{2} \times 10$ kg $\times (3 \times 10^7$ m/s$)^2 = 4.5 \times 10^{15}$ J. The largest hydroelectric power station in the world, Itaipu, jointly run by Brazil and Paraguay, has a huge output of 14 gigawatts. It would take the total energy generated by the 20 turbines in 3.7 days to accelerate a 10 kg spacecraft to a speed of c/10, assuming perfect efficiency. For a manned spacecraft weighing several tonnes, the energy requirements would greatly exceed the world's daily electricity consumption. For the city-sized spacecraft in *Independence Day,* the energy requirements would be staggering. And when the spacecraft slowed again, it would need to use up almost this amount of energy in braking. If the spacecraft had to accelerate to c/10, slow down and speed up many times, the energy needed would be many times greater. It would probably be impossible for enough fuel to be carried without some sort of antimatter drive. If perfect annihilation—complete conversion of matter to energy ($E = mc^2$)—were possible, 1 tonne of antimatter could annihilate 1 tonne of ordinary matter to produce: 2000 kg $\times (3 \times 10^8$ m/s$)^2$, or 1.8×10^{20} J. And this is the absolute maximum amount of energy that could be produced from a given mass of fuel. A real spacecraft could be nowhere near this efficient.

2. The kinetic energy of a speck of dust with a mass of just 0.1 gram impacting at c/10, calculated from the spacecraft's reference frame, is $\frac{1}{2}mv^2$, or $\frac{1}{2} \times 10^{-4}$ kg $\times (3 \times 10^7$ m/s$)^2 = 4.5 \times 10^{10}$ J.

   The combustion energy of TNT is 4520 kJ/kg, or 4.52×10^9 J/tonne. So 4.5×10^{10} J is equivalent to 9.95 tonnes of TNT. Therefore the impact energy of a 0.1 g object hitting a spacecraft travelling at c/10 would be the equivalent to an explosion of about 10 tonnes of TNT.

Chapter 10

Was the Flood global?

- Does it matter?
- Does the Bible say that Noah's Flood covered
  the whole Earth?
- Is there any evidence outside the Bible for such a Flood?

MANY Christians today claim that the Flood of Noah's time was only a *local* flood. They claim it was confined to somewhere around the Mesopotamian region and never really covered the whole Earth. The discovery of a layer of mud by archaeologists in the Middle East and more recently the finding of evidence for a local flood in the Black Sea have both been claimed as evidence for a (local) biblical flood.

People generally want a local flood because they have accepted the widely believed evolutionary history of the Earth, which interprets the fossils under our feet as the history of the sequential appearance of life over eons of time.

Scientists once understood the fossils (which are buried in water-carried sediments of mud and sand) to be mostly the result of the great Flood. Those who now accept the evolutionary billions of years of gradual accumulation of fossils have, in their way of thinking, explained away the evidence for the Flood—hence their belief in a local flood, or none at all. If they would think from a biblical perspective, they would see the abundant evidence for the Flood. As someone quipped, 'I wouldn't have seen it if I hadn't believed it.'

Those who accept the eons of time with its fossil accumulation also, perhaps unwittingly, rob the Fall of its serious consequences. They put the fossils, which testify of disease, suffering and death before mankind appeared; before Adam and Eve sinned and brought death and suffering into the world. In doing this they also undermine the meaning of the death and resurrection of Christ. Such a scenario also robs God's description of His finished creation as 'very good' of all meaning (see Chapter 2).

Some preachers will say they believe in a 'universal' or 'world-wide' flood, but really they do not believe that the Flood covered the whole Earth. They side-step the clear teaching of the Bible, while giving the appearance of believing it, by cleverly redefining words. They mean 'universal' and 'world-wide' only in terms of an imagined limited extent of human habitation at the time. They imagine that people lived only (say) in a valley in Mesopotamia and so the flood could kill all the people without being global in extent.

Biblical evidence for the global Flood

The local flood idea is totally inconsistent with the Bible, as the following points demonstrate:

The need for the Ark

If the Flood were local, why did Noah have to build an Ark? He could have walked to the other side of the mountains and escaped. Travelling just 20 km per day, Noah and his family could have travelled

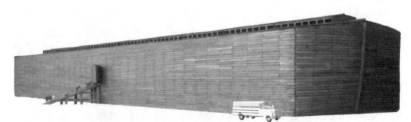

The size of the Ark makes sense only if the Flood were global.

over 3,000 km in six months. God could have simply warned Noah to flee, as He did for Lot in Sodom.

The size of the Ark

If the Flood were local, why was the Ark big enough to hold all the different kinds of land vertebrate animals in the world? If only Mesopotamian animals were aboard, or only domestic animals, the Ark could have been much smaller.[1]

The need for animals to be on the Ark

If the Flood were local, why did God send the animals to the Ark to escape death? There would have been other animals to reproduce those kinds even if they had all died in the local area. Or He could have sent them to a non-flooded region.

The need for birds to be on the Ark

If the Flood were local, why would *birds* have been sent on board? These could simply have winged across to far-distant higher ground. Birds can fly several hundred kilometres in one day.

The judgment was universal

If the Flood were local, people who did not happen to be living in the vicinity would not have been affected by it. They would have escaped God's judgment on sin. It boggles the mind to believe that, after all those centuries since creation, no one had migrated to other parts—or that people living on the periphery of such a local flood would not have moved to the adjoining high ground rather than be drowned. Jesus stated that the Flood killed everyone not on the Ark (Matt. 24:37–39).

Of course those who want to believe in a local flood generally say that the world is old and that people were here for many tens of thousands of years before the Flood. If this were the case, it is inconceivable that all the people could have fitted in a localized valley in Mesopotamia, for example, or that they had not migrated further afield as the population grew.

---

1.   See Chapter 13, p. 181.

The Flood was a type of the judgment to come

In 2 Peter 3, the coming universal judgment by fire is likened to the judgment by water of Noah's Flood: the world that then existed was deluged with water and perished. But by the same word the heavens and earth that now exist are stored up for fire, being kept until the day of judgment and destruction of the ungodly (verses 6,7).

The waters were above the mountains

If the Flood were local, how could the waters rise to 15 cubits (8 metres) *above* the mountains (Gen. 7:20)? Water seeks its own level. It could not rise to cover the local mountains while leaving the rest of the world untouched.[2]

The duration of the Flood

Noah and company were on the Ark for one year and 10 days (Gen. 7:11, 8:14)—surely an excessive amount of time for any local flood? It was more than seven months before the tops of any mountains became visible. How could they drift around in a local flood for that long without seeing any mountains?

God's promise broken?

If the Flood were local, God would have repeatedly broken His promise never to send such a Flood again. There have been huge 'local' floods

Flood water entering the roads of Chennai, India. If Noah's Flood was only local, what would God's promise not to send a flood again, mean?

---

2. Mt Everest has marine fossils at its peak. There is enough water in the oceans so that if all the surface features of the Earth were evened out, including the ocean basins, water would cover the Earth to a depth of 2.7 km. This is not enough to cover mountains the height of Everest now, but it shows that the pre-Flood mountains could have been quite high and still been covered. See Chapter 11 for more details about how this could have occurred.

in recent times: in Bangladesh, for example, where 80% of that country has been inundated, or Europe in 2002.

All people are descendants of Noah and his family

The genealogies of Adam (Gen. 4:17–26, 5:1–31) and Noah (Gen. 10:1–32) are exclusive—they tell us that all the pre-Flood people came from Adam and all the post-Flood people came from Noah. The descendants of Noah were all living together at Babel and refusing to 'fill the earth', as they had been commanded (Gen. 9:1). So God confused their one language into many and scattered them (Gen. 11:1–9).

There is striking evidence that all peoples on Earth have come from Noah, found in the Flood stories from many cultures around the world—North and South America, South Sea Islands, Australia, Papua New Guinea, Japan, China, India, the Middle East, Europe and Africa. Hundreds of such stories have been gathered.[3] The stories closest to the area of dispersion from Babel are nearest in detail to the biblical account—for example, the Gilgamesh epic.

The Hebrew terminology of Genesis 6–9[4]

- *'The earth'* (Heb. *erets*) is used 46 times in the Flood account in Genesis 6–9, as well as in Genesis 1. The explicit link to the big picture of creation, especially in Genesis 6:6–7, clearly implies a universal Flood. Furthermore, the judgment of God is pronounced not just on *all flesh*, but on *the earth:*
  *And God said to Noah, The end of all flesh has come before me, for the earth is filled with violence through them. And, behold, I will destroy them **with the earth**.* (Gen. 6:13)
- *'Upon the face of all the earth'* (Gen. 7:3, 8:9) clearly connects with the same phrase in the creation account where Adam and Eve are given the plants on Earth to eat (Gen. 1:29). Clearly, in God's decree the mandate is universal—the whole Earth is their domain. God uses the phrase in Genesis also of the dispersal of people at the Tower of Babel (Gen. 11:8, 9)—again, the context is the whole land surface of the globe. The exact phrase is used nowhere else in Genesis.

3. Frazer, J.G. 1918. *Folk-lore in the Old Testament: studies in comparative religion, Vol. 1,* Macmillan, London, pp. 105–361.
4. Davidson, R.M., 1995. Biblical evidence for the universality of the Genesis Flood. *Origins* **22**(2):58–73.

- *'Face of the ground'*, used five times in the Flood account, also connects back to the universal context of creation (Gen. 2:6), again emphasizing the universality of the Flood.
- *'All flesh'* (Heb. *kol-basar*) is used 12 times in the Flood account and nowhere else in Genesis. God said He would destroy *'all flesh'*, apart from those on the Ark (Gen. 6:13,17),[5] and He did (Gen. 7:21–22). In the context of the Flood, 'all flesh' clearly includes all nostril-breathing land animals as well as mankind—see Genesis 7:21–23. 'All flesh' could not have been confined to a Mesopotamian valley.
- *'Every living thing'* (Heb. *kol chai*) is again used in the Flood account (Gen. 6:19, 8:1,17) and in the creation account (Gen. 1:28). In the creation account the phrase is used in the context of Adam and Eve's dominion over the animals. God said (Gen. 7:4) that He would destroy *'every living thing'* He had made and this happened—**only** Noah and those with him on the Ark survived (Gen. 7:23).
- *'Under the whole heaven'* (Gen. 7:19) is used six times outside of the Flood account in the Old Testament, and always with a universal meaning (Deut. 2:25, 4:19, Job 28:24, 37:3, 41:11, Daniel 9:12). For example, *'Whatever is under the whole heaven is mine'* said the LORD (Job 41:11).
- *'All the fountains of the great deep'*. The fountains of the great deep are mentioned only in the Flood account (Gen. 7:11, 8:2) and Proverbs 8:28. *'The deep'* (Heb. *tehom*) relates back to creation (Gen. 1:2) where it refers to the one ocean covering the whole world before the land was formed. And it was not just *'the fountains of the great deep'* but *'**all** the fountains of the great deep'* which broke open.
- A special Hebrew word was reserved for the Flood or Deluge: *Mabbul*. In every one of the 13 occasions this word is used, it refers to Noah's Flood. Its one use outside of Genesis, Psalm 29:10, refers to the universal sovereignty of God in presiding over the Deluge. The New Testament also has a special word reserved for the Flood, *cataclysmos,* from which we derive our English word 'cataclysm'.

The decrees in Genesis 9 parallel those in Genesis 1

In Genesis 9:1 God gives man the exact same commission as in Genesis 1:28—*'Be fruitful and multiply and fill the earth'*. He also gives man

---

5. Some translations wrongly render 'all flesh' in Gen. 6:13 as 'all people' (e.g. NIV, whereas KJV and NASB are correct). This is clearly not the meaning of 'all flesh', as revealed by its use in Genesis 7:21 (where the NIV renders 'all flesh' correctly as 'every living thing').

dominion over *'every beast of the earth'* (Gen. 9:2, cf. 1:28) and man is instructed as to what he can and cannot eat (Gen. 9:4–5), which parallels Genesis 1:29–30. These decrees in Genesis 1 are universal in extent, and clearly they are also here, after the Flood. If Adam and his descendants were to rule the whole Earth, so were Noah and his descendants. If 'earth' in Genesis 9:1 is the whole Earth, as all would agree it is, then surely it is also the whole Earth in the context of the Flood in Genesis 8:13!

The New Testament speaks of the Flood as global[4]

New Testament passages which speak of the Flood use universal language: *'the flood came and took them **all** away'* (Jesus, Matt. 24:39); *'the flood came and destroyed them **all***' (Jesus, in Luke 17:27); *'did not spare the ancient **world** [Greek:* kosmos*], but preserved Noah, a preacher of righteousness, and seven others, bringing in the flood upon the **world** of the ungodly'* (2 Peter 2:5); *'a **few**, that is eight people, were saved through the water'* (1 Peter 3:20); Noah *'condemned the **world**'* through his faith in God (Heb. 11:7); *'the **world** that then was, being flooded by water, perished'* (2 Pet 3:6). All these statements presuppose a global Flood, not some localized event.

Answers to objections to a global Flood

Objection 1: 'All' does not always mean 'all'[6]

Some have argued that since 'all' does not always mean 'each and every' (e.g. Mark 1:5) the use of 'all' in the Flood account does not necessarily mean the Flood was universal. That is, they claim that this use of 'all' allows for a local flood.

However, the meaning of a word is decided by the context. From the context of 'all' in Luke 2:1, for example, we can see that 'all the world' meant all the Roman Empire. So, it is the context that tells us that 'all' here does not mean every bit of the whole land surface of the globe.

However, to determine the meaning of 'all' in Genesis 6–9, we must consider the context, not just transfer the inferred meaning from somewhere else.

The word 'all' (Heb. *kol*) is used 72 times in the 85 verses of Genesis

6.   For a full treatment, see Kruger, M., 1996. Genesis 6–9: Does 'all' always mean all? *Journal of Creation* **10**(2):214–218.

6–9, 21% of all the times it is used in all 50 chapters of Genesis.

In Genesis 7:19 we read that *'all* (Heb. *kol*) *the high mountains under all* (Heb. *kol*) *the heavens were covered'*. Note the double use of 'all'. In Hebrew this gives emphasis so as to eliminate any possibility of ambiguity.[7] This could be accurately translated as 'all the high mountains under the *entire* heavens', to reflect the emphasis in the Hebrew. Leupold, in his authoritative commentary on Genesis, said of this, '… the text disposes of the question of the universality of the Flood'.[7]

Objection 2: The post-Flood geography is the same as the pre-Flood

Because the Tigris and Euphrates rivers were mentioned in the description of the Garden of Eden, and we have the Tigris and Euphrates rivers now, some have argued that the Flood could not have altered the topography of the world, and therefore it must have been local.[8]

However, there are major differences in the topography described for the Garden of Eden and the world now. There was one river flowing from Eden which separated into four rivers (Gen. 2:10–14), two of which were called the Tigris and the Euphrates. So the rivers had a common source before the Flood, which is very different from today. The other two rivers were the Pishon and the Gihon. The Pishon is not mentioned post-Flood and Gihon is used of the locality of a spring near Jerusalem in the times of Kings David, Solomon and Hezekiah.[9]

The post-Flood world is not the same as the pre-Flood world. Someone may ask, 'Then why do we have a Tigris and Euphrates today?' Answer: the same reason there is a Liverpool and Newcastle in Australia; and London, Oxford and Cambridge in North America, although they were originally place names in England. Features in the post-Flood world were given names familiar to those which survived the Flood.

7. Leupold, H.C., 1942. *Exposition of Genesis,* Baker Book House, Grand Rapids, MI, USA, vol. 1, pp. 301–302.

8. For example, Young, D.A., 1977. *Creation and the Flood: an alternative to Flood geology and theistic evolution,* Baker Book House, Grand Rapids, MI, USA, p. 210. Sadly, Dr Young has drifted more and more towards full-blown theistic evolution since he wrote this book, wherein he compromised the Bible by advocating 'progressive creationist' views.

9. The Gihon spring of 1 Kings 1:33, 38, 45 and 2 Chron. 32:30; 33:14 clearly has nothing to do with the Tigris-Euphrates river system of today, or the four-way split river system described in Eden.

Fossil 'graveyards' around the world, where the bones of many animals were washed together, buried and fossilized, are evidence for a watery cataclysm like the Flood.

Objection 3: There is no evidence for such a Flood in the geologic record

What evidence would one expect from a global watery cataclysm that drowned the animals, birds and people not on the Ark? All around the world, in rock layer after rock layer, we find billions of dead things that have been buried in water-carried mud and sand. Their state of preservation frequently tells of rapid burial and fossilization, just like one would expect in such a flood.

There is abundant evidence that many of the rock strata were laid down quickly, one after the other, without significant time breaks between them. Preservation of animal tracks, ripple marks and even raindrop marks, testifies to rapid covering of these features to enable their preservation. Polystrate fossils (ones which traverse many strata) speak of very quick deposition of the strata. The scarcity of erosion, soil formation, animal burrows and roots between layers also shows they must have been deposited in quick succession. The radical deformation of thick layers of sediment without evidence of cracking or melting also shows how all the layers must have been still soft when they were bent. Dykes (walls) and pipes (cylinders) of sandstone which connect with

Photo by Joachim Scheven

Preservation of ripple marks (left) requires rapid burial, as in the Flood (lower Triassic rock, England). Folding of sedimentary rock without cracking or heating (right), such as at Eastern Beach, Auckland, New Zealand, suggests the folding occurred before the sand and mud had time to turn into stone, consistent with rapid deposition during the Flood (note people for scale).

the same material many layers beneath show that the layers beneath must have been still soft, and contained much water. That the sandstone could be squeezed up through cracks above to form the 'clastic' dykes and pipes, again shows rapid deposition of many strata.

The world-wide distribution of many geological features and rock types is also consistent with a global Flood. The Morrison Formation is a layer of sedimentary rock that extends from Texas to Canada, clearly showing the fallacy of the still-popular belief that 'the present is the key to the past'—there are no processes occurring on Earth today that are laying down such large areas of sedimentary layers. In reality, God's revelation about the past is the key to understanding the present.

The limited geographic extent of unconformities (clear breaks in the sequence of deposition with different tilting of layers, etc.) is also consistent with the reality of the global Flood. And there are many other evidences for the Flood.[10,11]

The problem is not the evidence but the mind-set of those looking at the evidence. One geologist testified how he never saw any evidence for the Flood—until, as a Christian, he was convinced from the Bible that the Flood must have been a global cataclysm. Now he sees the evidence everywhere. The Bible talks about people being corrupted in their thinking after turning their backs on God (Romans 1:18ff.) and of people being so spiritually blind that they cannot see the obvious (Acts 28:25–27).

Conclusion

A universal **world-wide, globe-covering** Flood is clearly taught by the Bible. The only reasons for thinking the Flood was otherwise come from outside the Bible. When we use the framework provided by the Bible we find that the physical evidence from the rocks and fossils beautifully fits what the Bible says.[12]

Furthermore, the realization of the reality of God's judgment by the Flood in the past should warn us of the reality of the judgment to come—a judgment by fire—and stimulate us to be ready for that judgment (2 Peter 3:3–13). Those who are not 'in Christ' will suffer the wrath of God (John 3:36).

---

10. Morris, J.D. 1994. *The Young Earth,* Master Books, Colorado Springs.
11. Austin, S. (Ed.), 1994. *Grand Canyon: Monument to Catastrophe,* Institute for Creation Research, Santee, CA, USA.
12. See Chapters 11–15 for other questions about the Flood and Noah's Ark.

Chapter 11

What about continental drift?

- Have the continents really moved apart?
- How could this relate to the Bible's account of history?
- Could it have had something to do with the Flood?

BEFORE the 1960s, most geologists were adamant that the continents were stationary. A handful promoted the notion that the continents had moved (continental drift), but they were accused by the majority of indulging in pseudo-scientific fantasy. Today, that opinion has reversed—plate tectonics, incorporating continental drift, is the ruling theory. (Interestingly, it was a creationist, Antonio Snider, who in 1859 first proposed horizontal movement of continents catastrophically during the Genesis Flood.[1] The statements in Genesis 1:9,10 about the gathering together of the seas in one place, which implies there was one landmass, influenced his thinking.)

Geologists put forward several lines of evidence that the continents were once joined together and have moved apart, including:

1.   Snider–Pellegrini, A., 1858/9, *Le Création et ses Mystères Devoilés*, Franck and Dentu, Paris.

- The fit of the continents (taking into account the continental shelves).
- Correlation of fossil types across ocean basins.
- A zebra-striped pattern of magnetic reversals parallel to mid-ocean floor rifts, in the volcanic rock formed along the rifts, implying sea-floor spreading along the rifts.
- Seismic observations interpreted as slabs of former ocean floor now located inside the Earth.

The current theory that incorporates sea-floor spreading and continental drift is known as 'plate tectonics'.[2]

Plate tectonics

The general principles of plate tectonic theory may be stated as follows.[3] The Earth's surface consists of a mosaic of rigid plates, each moving relative to adjacent plates. Deformation occurs at the edges of the plates by three types of horizontal motion: extension (or rifting, moving apart), transform faulting (horizontal slipping along a fault line), and compression, mostly by subduction (one plate plunging beneath another).

1. Extension occurs as the sea floor pulls apart at rifts, or splits.
2. Transform faulting occurs where one plate slips horizontally past another (e.g., the San Andreas Fault of California).
3. Compressional deformation occurs when one plate subducts beneath another, e.g., the Pacific Plate beneath Japan and the Cocos Plate beneath Central America, or when two continental plates collide to produce a mountain range, e.g., the Indian-Australian Plate colliding with the Eurasian Plate to form the Himalayan Mountains. Volcanoes often occur in regions of subduction.

Sea-floor spreading

One argument advanced for plate tectonics is sea-floor spreading. In the ocean basins, along mid-ocean ridges (e.g., the Mid-Atlantic Ridge and East Pacific Rise), observations are interpreted to indicate that plates

2. Some geologists are still sceptical of various aspects of plate tectonics.
3. Nevins, S.E. [Austin, S.A.], 1978. Continental drift, plate tectonics, and the Bible. In: *Up with Creation!* D.R. Gish, and D.H. Rohrer (eds.), Creation-Life Publishers, San Diego, pp. 173–180. See also *Longman Illustrated Dictionary of Geology,* Longman Group, Essex, UK, 1982, pp. 137–172.

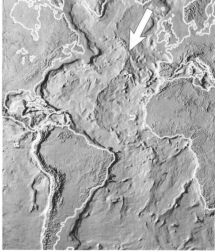

Mountain High Maps® <www.digiwis.com>

The mid-Atlantic Ridge (indicated by arrow), clearly visible on this topographic map.

are diverging, with molten material from the mantle[4] rising up in the gap between the plates and cooling to form new crust under the ocean. The youngest crust is at the ridge axis, with progressively older rocks away from the axis. World-wide, it is estimated that currently about 20 cubic kilometres of molten magma rises each year to create new oceanic crust.[5]

At the time of cooling, some of the rocks' minerals acquire magnetism from the Earth's magnetic field, recording the field's direction at the time. Evidence indicates that the Earth's magnetic field has reversed many times in the past. So, during the cooling, some of the oceanic crust was magnetized in a reverse direction. If sea-floor spreading is continuous, the ocean floor should possess a smooth magnetic 'tape-recording' of reversals.

Indeed, the zebra stripe pattern of linear 'magnetic anomalies' parallel to the mid-ocean ridge crest has been recorded in many areas.[6]

Problems for 'slow-and-gradual' plate tectonics

While the zebra-stripe pattern has been confirmed, drilling through the basalt adjacent to the ridges has shown that the neat pattern recorded by dragging a magnetometer above the ridge is not present when the rock is actually sampled. The magnetic polarity changes in patches down the holes, with no consistent pattern with depth.[7] This would

---

4. The zone within the Earth that extends from below the crust down to the core—i.e. to a depth of about 2,900 km.
5. Cann, J., 1998. Subtle minds and mid-ocean ridges. *Nature* **393**:625, 627.
6. Cox, A. (ed.), 1973. *Plate Tectonics and Geomagnetic Reversals,* W.H. Freeman and Co., San Francisco, pp. 138–220.
7. Hall, J.M. and Robinson, P.T., 1979. Deep crustal drilling in the North Atlantic Ocean. *Science* **204**:573–586.

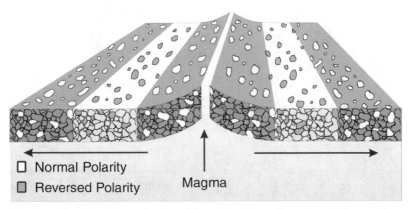

The magnetic pattern in the volcanic rock formed on the sea-floor at the mid-ocean ridges suggests very rapid processes, not millions of years. The patchwork patterns of polarity are evidence for rapid formation of the rock.

be expected with rapid formation of the basalt, combined with rapid field reversals, not the slow-and-gradual formation with slow reversals assumed by uniformitarians.

Physicist Dr Russell Humphreys predicted that evidence for rapid field reversals would be found in lava flows thin enough to cool in a few weeks.[8] He suggested that such rapid reversals could have happened during Noah's Flood. Such evidence for rapid reversals was later found by the respected researchers, Coe and Prévot.[9,10] Their later work[11] confirmed these findings and showed that the magnetic reversals were 'astonishingly rapid'.

A biblical view

Evidence indicates that the continents have moved apart in the past, but can today's supposed drift rates of 2–15 cm per year be extrapolated far back into the past? Is the present really the key to the past, as uniformitarians earnestly proclaim? Such extrapolation would mean

8. Humphreys, D.R. 1986. Reversals of the earth's magnetic field during the Genesis Flood. *Proc. First ICC,* Pittsburgh, PA **2**:113–126.

9. Coe, R.S. and Prévot, M., 1989. Evidence suggesting extremely rapid field variation during a geomagnetic reversal. *Earth and Planetary Science Letters* **92**:292–298.

10. For details, see Snelling, A.A., 1991. 'Fossil' magnetism reveals rapid reversals of the earth's magnetic field. *Creation* **13**(3):46–50.

11. Coe, R.S., Prévot, M. and Camps, P., 1995. New evidence for extraordinary rapid change of the geomagnetic field during a reversal. *Nature* **374**:687–692. For comment see Snelling, A.A., 1995. The 'Principle of Least Astonishment'! *Journal of Creation* **9**(2):138–139.

that an ocean basin or mountain range would take about 100 million years to form.

The Bible does not speak directly about continental drift and plate tectonics, but if the continents were once together, as Genesis 1:9–10 suggests, and are now apart, how does that fit into a biblical view of geology with a time line of only thousands of years?[12]

Dr John Baumgardner, working at the Los Alamos National Laboratory (USA), has used supercomputers to model processes in the Earth's mantle to show that tectonic plate movement could have occurred very rapidly, and 'spontaneously'.[13–17] This concept is known as *catastrophic plate tectonics*. At the time of writing, Baumgardner, a creationist scientist, is acknowledged as having developed the world's best 3-D super-computer model of plate tectonics.[16]

Catastrophic plate tectonics

The model proposed by Baumgardner begins with a pre-Flood super-continent (*'Let the waters ... be gathered together into one place'*, Genesis 1:9) and dense ocean floor rocks. The process starts with the cold and dense ocean floor beginning to sink into the softer, less dense mantle beneath. The friction from this movement generates heat, especially around the edges, which softens the adjacent mantle material, making it less resistant to the sinking of the ocean floor.[17] The edges sink faster, dragging the rest of the ocean floor along, in conveyor-belt fashion. Faster movement creates more friction and heat in the

12. Some have suggested that the continents (with their loads of Flood-deposited, fossil-bearing strata) separated to their present position, for example, at the time of the Tower of Babel, because Genesis 10:25 says *'the earth was divided'* in the days of Peleg. However, the Hebrew translated 'the earth' can as easily refer to the people (nations) divided because of Babel. Also, the short time involved would lead to enormous difficulties in accounting for the heat energy to be dissipated, not to mention the destruction at the Earth's surface that would result from rapid continent-wide motion. This would be a global catastrophe as devastating as the Noachian Flood itself.

13. Baumgardner, J.R., 1986. Numerical simulation of the large-scale tectonic changes accompanying the Flood. *Proc. First ICC* **2**:17–30.

14. Baumgardner, J.R., 1990. 3-D finite element simulation of the global tectonic changes accompanying Noah's Flood. *Proc. Second ICC* **2**:35–45.

15. Baumgardner, J.R., 1994. Computer modeling of the large-scale tectonics associated with the Genesis Flood. *Proc. Third ICC*, pp. 49–62.

16. Beard, J., 1993. How a supercontinent went to pieces. *New Scientist* **137**:19, Jan. 16.

17. Baumgardner, J.R., 1994. Runaway subduction as the driving mechanism for the Genesis Flood. *Proc. Third ICC*, Pittsburgh, pp. 63–75.

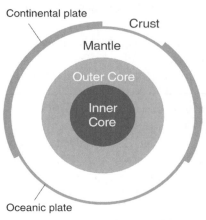

Continental plate

Crust

Mantle

Outer Core

Inner Core

Oceanic plate

Earth's current structure (not to scale).

surrounding mantle, reducing its resistance further and so the ocean floor moves even faster, and so on. At its peak, this thermal runaway instability would have allowed for sub-duction at rates of metres-per-second. This key concept is called runaway subduction.

The sinking ocean floor would displace mantle material, starting large-scale movement throughout the entire mantle. However, as the ocean-floor sank and rapidly subducted adjacent to the pre-Flood super-continent's margins, elsewhere the Earth's crust would be under such tensional stress that it would be torn apart (rifted), breaking up both the pre-Flood super-continent and the ocean floor.

Thus, crustal spreading zones would rapidly extend along cracks in the ocean floor for some 10,000 km where the splitting was occurring. Hot mantle material displaced by the subducting slabs would well up, rising to the surface along these spreading zones. On the ocean floor, this hot mantle material would vaporize copious amounts of ocean water, producing a linear geyser of superheated steam along the whole length of the spreading centres (perhaps the *'fountains of the great deep'*? Gen. 7:11; 8:2). This steam would disperse, condensing in the atmosphere to fall as intense global rain (*'and the flood-gates of heaven were opened'*? Gen. 7:11). This could account for the rain persisting for 40 days and 40 nights (Gen. 7:12).

Baumgardner's catastrophic plate tectonics global Flood model for Earth history[18] is able to explain more geological data than the conventional plate tectonics model with its many millions of years. For example, rapid subduction of the pre-Flood ocean floor into the mantle results in new ocean floor that is dramatically hotter, especially in its upper 100 km, not just at spreading ridges, but everywhere. Being hotter, the new ocean floor is of lower density and therefore rises 1,000 to

18. Austin, S.A., Baumgardner, J.R., Humphreys, D.R., Snelling, A.A., Vardiman, L. and Wise, K.P., 1994. Catastrophic plate tectonics: a global Flood model of earth history. *Proc. Third ICC*, Pittsburgh, pp. 609–621.

2,000 metres higher than before and implies a dramatic rise in global sea level.

This higher sea level floods the continental surfaces and makes possible the deposition of large areas of sedimentary deposits on top of the normally high-standing continents. The Grand Canyon provides a spectacular window into the amazing layer-cake character of these sediment deposits that in many cases continue uninterrupted for more than 1,000 km.[19] Uniformitarian ('slow and gradual') plate tectonics simply cannot account for such thick continental sediment sequences of such vast horizontal extent.

Moreover, the rapid subduction of the cooler pre-Flood ocean floor into the mantle would have resulted in increased circulation of viscous fluid (note: plastic, not molten) rock within the mantle. This mantle-flow (i.e. 'stirring' within the mantle) suddenly altered the temperatures at the core-mantle boundary, as the mantle near the core would now be significantly cooler than the adjacent core, and thus convection and heat loss from the core would be greatly accelerated. The model suggests that under these conditions of accelerated convection in the core, rapid geomagnetic reversals would have occurred. These in turn would be expressed on the Earth's surface and recorded in the so-called magnetic stripes.[20] However, these would be erratic and locally patchy, laterally and at depth, just as the data indicate,[7] even according to the uniformitarian scientists cited earlier.

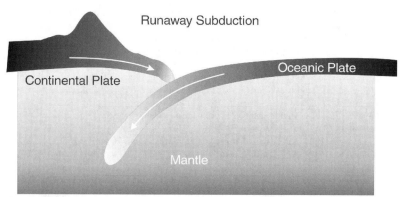

The movement of Earth's crustal plates during 'runaway subduction'.

19. Austin, S.A. (ed.), 1994. *Grand Canyon: Monument to Catastrophe,* Institute for Creation Research, Santee, California.
20. Humphreys, D.R., 1988. Has the earth's magnetic field ever flipped? *Creation Research Society Quarterly* **25**(3):130–137.

This model provides a mechanism that explains how the plates could move relatively quickly (in a matter of months) over the mantle and subduct. And it predicts that little or no movement would be measurable between plates today, because the movement would have come almost to a standstill when the entire pre-Flood ocean floor was subducted. From this we would also expect the trenches adjacent to subduction zones today to be filled with undisturbed late-Flood and post-Flood sediments, just as we observe.

Aspects of Baumgardner's mantle modelling have been independently duplicated and thus verified by others.[21-23] Furthermore, Baumgardner's modelling predicts that because this thermal runaway subduction of cold ocean floor crustal slabs occurred relatively recently, during the Flood (about 5,000 or so years ago), then those slabs would not have had sufficient time since to be fully assimilated into the surrounding mantle. So evidence of the slabs above the mantle-core boundary (to which they sank) should still be found today. Indeed, evidence for such unassimilated relatively cold slabs has been found in seismic studies.[24-26]

The model also provides a mechanism for retreat of the Flood waters. Psalm 104:6–7 describes the abating of the waters which had stood above the mountains. Verse 8 most naturally translates as, *'The mountains rose up; the valleys sank down'*,[27] implying that vertical earth movements

21. Weinstein, S.A., 1993. Catastrophic overturn of the earth's mantle driven by multiple phase changes and internal heat generation. *Geophysical Research Letters* **20**:101–104.
22. Tackley, P.J., Stevenson, D.J., Glatzmaier, G.A. and Schubert, G., 1993. Effects of an endothermic phase transition at 670 km depth on spherical mantle convection. *Nature* **361**: 699–704.
23. Moresi, L. and Solomatov, V., 1998. Mantle convection with a brittle lithosphere: thoughts on the global tectonic styles of the earth and Venus. *Geophysical Journal International* **133**:669–682.
24. Grand, S.P., 1994. Mantle shear structure beneath the Americas and surrounding oceans. *Journal of Geophysical Research* **99**:11591–11621.
25. Vidale, J.E., 1994. A snapshot of whole mantle flow. *Nature* **370**:16–17.
26. Vogel, S., 1995. Anti-matters. *Earth: The Science of Our Planet*, August 1995, pp. 43–49.
27. Many English translations, following the KJV, have *'the waters'* in verse 6 the subject of the verbs *'go up'* and *'go down'* in verse 8. According to linguist Dr Charles Taylor, the more natural and literal reading is to have the *'mountains'* in verse 8 going up and the *'valleys'* (verse 8) going down. The Septuagint (LXX), a Greek translation done about 250 BC, Luther's German translation, which predates the KJV, and French and Italian translations all agree. English translations that convey this meaning include the ASV, RSV and NASB. See Taylor, C.V., 1998. Did the mountains really rise according to Psalm 104:8? *Journal of Creation* **12**(3):312–313.

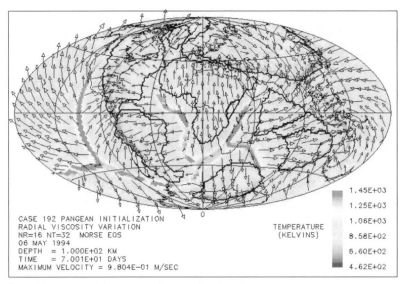

CASE 192 PANGEAN INITIALIZATION
RADIAL VISCOSITY VARIATION
NR=16 NT=32 MORSE EOS
06 MAY 1994
DEPTH = 1.000E+02 KM
TIME = 7.001E+01 DAYS
MAXIMUM VELOCITY = 9.804E-01 M/SEC

TEMPERATURE
(KELVINS)

1.45E+03
1.25E+03
1.06E+03
8.58E+02
6.60E+02
4.62E+02

One of Baumgardner's computer images showing plate movement.

were the dominant tectonic forces operating at the close of the Flood, in contrast to the horizontal forces dominant during the spreading phase.

Plate collisions would have pushed up mountains, while cooling of the new ocean floor would have increased its density, causing it to sink and thus deepen the new ocean basins to receive the retreating Flood waters. It may be significant, therefore, that the *'mountains of Ararat'* (Genesis 8:4), the resting place of the Ark after the 150th day of the Flood, are in a tectonically active region at what is believed to be the junction of three crustal plates.[28]

If a centimetre or two per year of inferred movement today is extrapolated back into the past as uniformitarians do, then their conventional plate tectonics model has limited explanatory power. For example, even at a rate of 10 cm/yr, it is questionable whether the forces of the collision between the Indian-Australian and Eurasian Plates could have been sufficient to push up the Himalayas. On the other hand, catastrophic plate tectonics in the context of the Flood can explain how the plates overcame the viscous drag of the Earth's mantle for a short time due to the enormous catastrophic forces at work, followed by a rapid slowing down to present rates.

28. Dewey, J.F., Pitman, W.C., Ryan, W.B.F. and Bonnin, J., 1973. Plate tectonics and the evolution of the Alpine System. *Geological Society of America Bulletin* **84**:3137–3180.

Continental separation solves apparent geological enigmas. For instance, it explains the amazing similarities of sedimentary layers in the north-eastern United States to those in Britain. It also explains the absence of those same layers in the intervening North Atlantic ocean basin, as well as the similarities in the geology of parts of Australia with South Africa, India, and Antarctica.

Conclusion

Early scepticism about plate tectonics has largely evaporated because the framework has such great explanatory power. The catastrophic plate tectonics model for the Flood not only includes these explanatory elements, but also accounts for widespread evidences of massive flooding and catastrophic geological processes on the continents. Future refinement of the model may also help to explain the order and distribution of fossils observed in the fossil record in the context of the Genesis Flood (see Chapter 15).

The Bible is silent about plate tectonics. Many creationists believe the concept is helpful in explaining Earth's history. Some are still cautious. The idea is quite new, and radical, and much work has yet to be done to flesh out the details. There may even be major modifications to the theory that increase its explanatory power, or future discoveries could cause the model to be abandoned. Such is the nature of scientific progress. Scientific models come and go, *'But the word of the Lord endures forever'* (1 Peter 1:25).

Chapter 12

Noah's Flood—what about all that water?

- Where did all the water come from for the Flood?
- Was there a water vapour canopy?
- How was Mt Everest covered with water?
- Where did the water go after the Flood?
- How could this have happened?

IN telling us about the globe-covering Flood in the days of Noah, the Bible gives us information about where the waters came from and where they went. The sources of the water are given in Genesis 7:11 as *'the fountains of the great deep'* and the *'windows of heaven'*.

The fountains of the great deep

The *'fountains of the great deep'* are mentioned before the *'windows of heaven'*, indicating either relative importance or the order of events.

What are the *'fountains of the great deep'*? This phrase is used only in Genesis 7:11. *'Fountains of the deep'* is used in Genesis 8:2, where it clearly refers to the same thing, and Proverbs 8:28, where the precise meaning is not clear. *'The great deep'* is used three other times: Isaiah 51:10, where it clearly refers to the ocean, Amos 7:4, where God's fire of judgment is said to dry up the great deep, probably the oceans, and Psalm 36:6 where it is used metaphorically of the depth of God's justice/ judgment. *'The deep'* is used more often, and usually refers to the oceans (e.g. Gen. 1:2, Job 38:30, 41:32, Psalm 42:7, 104:6, Isa. 51:10, 63:13, Eze. 26:19, Jon. 2:3), but sometimes to subterranean sources of water (Eze. 31:4,15). The Hebrew word (*mayan*) translated 'fountains' means 'fountain, spring, well' (Strong's Concordance).

So, the *'fountains of the great deep'* are probably oceanic or possibly subterranean sources of water. In the context of the Flood account, it could mean both.

If the fountains of the great deep were the major source of the waters, then they must have been a huge source of water. Some have suggested that when God made the dry land appear from under the waters on the third day of creation, some of the water that covered the Earth became trapped underneath and within the dry land.[1]

Genesis 7:11 says that on the day the Flood began, there was a 'breaking up' of the fountains, which implies a release of the water, possibly through large fissures in the ground or in the sea floor. The waters that had been held back burst forth with catastrophic consequences.

There are many volcanic rocks interspersed between the fossil layers in the rock record—layers that were obviously deposited during Noah's Flood. So it is quite plausible that these fountains of the great deep involved a series of volcanic eruptions with prodigious amounts of water bursting up through the ground. It is interesting that up to 70% or more of what comes out of volcanoes today is water, often in the form of steam.

In their catastrophic plate tectonics model for the Flood (see Chapter 11), Austin *et al.*[2] have proposed that at the onset of the Flood, the ocean floor rapidly lifted up to 2,000 metres (6,500 feet) due to an increase in

---

1. Evidence is mounting that there is still a huge amount of water stored deep in the earth in the crystal lattices of minerals, which is possible because of the immense pressure. See Bergeron, L., 1997. Deep waters. *New Scientist* **155**(2097):22–26: 'You have oceans and oceans of water stored in the transition zone. It's sopping wet.'

2. Austin, S.A., Baumgardner, J.R., Humphreys, D.R., Snelling, A.A., Vardiman, L. and Wise, K.P., 1994. Catastrophic plate tectonics: A global Flood model of Earth history. *Proc. Third ICC*, pp. 609–621.

A lot of volcanic activity would be expected with such a cataclysm as the Flood.

temperature as horizontal movement of the tectonic plates accelerated. This would spill the seawater onto the land and cause massive flooding—perhaps what is aptly described as the breaking up of the *'fountains of the great deep'*.

The windows of heaven

The other source of the waters for Noah's Flood was *'the windows of heaven'*. Genesis 7:12 says that it rained for 40 days and 40 nights continuously.

Genesis 2:5 tells us that there was no rain before man was created. Some have suggested that there was no rainfall anywhere on the Earth until the time of the Flood. However, the Bible does not actually say this, so we should not be dogmatic.[3]

Some have argued that God's use of the rainbow as the sign of His covenant with Noah (Gen. 9:12–17) suggests that there were no rainbows, and therefore no clouds or rain, before the Flood. However, if rainbows (and clouds) existed before the Flood, this would not be the only time God used an existing thing as a special 'new' sign of a covenant (e.g., bread and wine in the Lord's Supper).

---

3. Some have claimed that because the people scoffed at Noah's warnings of a coming flood, they must not have seen rain. But people today have seen lots of rain and floods, and many still scoff at the global Flood. Gen. 2:5 says there was no rain *yet* upon the earth, but whether or not it rained after that in the pre-Flood world is not stated.

It is difficult to envisage a pre-Flood water cycle without clouds and rain, as the sun's heat, even in that era, must have evaporated large volumes of surface waters which would have to have eventually condensed back into liquid water. And droplets of liquid water form clouds from which we get rain.

The Bible uses 'windows of heaven' twice in reference to the Flood (Gen. 7:11, 8:2). The term is used four times elsewhere in the Old Testament: in 2 Kings 7:2,19, Isaiah 24:18 and Malachi 3:10. In all cases, it refers to God intervening in an extraordinary way to pour out blessings or judgment on his people. 'Windows of heaven' is not a term applied to ordinary events. Clearly, in Genesis the expression suggests the extraordinary nature of the rainfall attending the Flood. The rain was extraordinary; like nothing anyone had seen before.

What about 'the waters above'?

We are told in Genesis 1:6–8 that on the second day of creation God divided the waters that were on the Earth from the waters that He placed above the Earth when He made a *'firmament'* (Hebrew, *raqiya,* meaning 'expanse') between those waters.[4] Many have concluded that this *'expanse'* was the atmosphere, because God placed the birds in the expanse,

---

4. In trying to disparage the Bible, some sceptics claim that *raqiya* describes a solid dome and that the ancient Hebrews believed in a flat Earth with a slotted dome over it. Such ideas are not in the Bible or in the Hebrew understanding of *raqiya*. See Holding, J.P., 1999. Is the *raqiya'* ('firmament') a solid dome? Equivocal language in the cosmology of Genesis 1 and the Old Testament: a response to Paul H. Seely. *Journal of Creation* **13**(2):44–51.

suggesting that the expanse includes the atmosphere where the birds fly. This would put these waters above the atmosphere.

However, Gen. 1:20, speaking of the creation of the birds, says (literally) *'let birds fly above the ground **across the face of** the expanse of the heavens.'*[5] This at least allows that 'the expanse' may include the space beyond the atmosphere.

Dr Russell Humphreys[6] has argued that since Genesis 1:17 tells us that God put the sun, moon and stars also *'in the expanse of the heaven'* then the expanse must at least include interstellar space, and thus the waters above the expanse of Genesis 1:7 would be beyond the stars at the edge of the universe.[7]

However, prepositions (in, under, above, etc.) are somewhat flexible in Hebrew, as well as English. A submarine can be spoken of as both **under** the sea and **in** the sea. Likewise, the waters could be **above** the expanse and **in** the expanse, so we should perhaps be careful not to draw too much from these expressions.

So what were these *'waters above'*? Some have said that they are simply the clouds. Others thought of them as a 'water vapour canopy', implying a blanket of water vapour surrounding the Earth.

A water vapour canopy?

Dr Joseph Dillow did much research into the idea of a blanket of water vapour surrounding the Earth before the Flood.[8] In a modification of the canopy theory, Dr Larry Vardiman[9] suggested that much of the *'waters above'* could have been stored in small ice particles distributed in equatorial rings around the Earth similar to those around Venus.

The Genesis 7:11 reference to the windows of heaven being opened has been interpreted as the collapse of such a water vapour canopy, which somehow became unstable and fell as rain. Volcanic eruptions associated with the breaking up of the fountains of the great deep could

---

5. Leupold, H.C., 1942. *Exposition of Genesis,* Vol. 1, Baker Book House, Grand Rapids, Michigan, p. 78.
6. Humphreys, D.R., 1994. A biblical basis for creationist cosmology. *Proc. Third ICC,* Pittsburgh, PA, pp. 255–266).
7. This could help explain the background microwave radiation seen in the Universe. See Chapter 5 and Humphreys, Ref. 6.
8. Dillow, J.C., 1981. *The Waters Above,* Moody Press, Chicago.
9. Vardiman, L., 1986. The sky has fallen. *Proc. First ICC* 1:113–119.

have thrown dust into the water vapour canopy, causing the water vapour to nucleate on the dust particles and make rain.

Dillow, Vardiman and others have suggested that the vapour canopy caused a greenhouse effect before the Flood with a pleasant subtropical-to-temperate climate all around the globe, even at the poles where today there is ice. This would have caused the growth of lush vegetation on the land all around the globe. The discovery of coal seams in Antarctica containing vegetation that is not now found growing at the poles, but which obviously grew under warmer conditions, was taken as support for these ideas.[10]

A vapour canopy would also affect the global wind systems. Also, the mountains were almost certainly not as high before the Flood as they are today (see later). In today's world, the major winds and high mountain ranges are a very important part of the water cycle that brings rain to the continents. Before the Flood, however, these factors would have caused the weather systems to be different.

Those interested in studying this further should consult Dillow's and Vardiman's works.

A major problem with the canopy theory

Vardiman[11] recognized a major difficulty with the canopy theory. The best canopy model still gives an intolerably high temperature at the surface of the Earth.

Rush and Vardiman have attempted a solution,[12] but found that they had to drastically reduce the amount of water vapour in the canopy from a rain equivalent of 12 m (40 ft) to only 0.5 m (20 in.). Further modelling suggested that a maximum of 2 m of water could be held in such a canopy, even if all relevant factors were adjusted to the best possible values to maximize the amount of water stored.[13] Such a reduced canopy would not significantly contribute to the 40 days and nights of rain at the beginning of the Flood.

---

10. Movement of tectonic plates could also explain the polar occurrence of such warm-climate plant remains (see Chapter 11, p. 161).
11. Vardiman, Ref. 9, pp. 116,119.
12. Rush, D.E. and Vardiman, L., 1990. Pre-Flood vapor canopy radiative temperature profiles. *Proc. Second ICC*, Pittsburgh, PA **2**:231–245.
13. Vardiman, L. and Bousselot, K., 1998. Sensitivity studies on vapor canopy temperature profiles. *Proc. Fourth ICC*, pp. 607–618.

Many creationist scientists are now either abandoning the water vapour canopy model[14] or no longer see any need for such a concept, particularly if other reasonable mechanisms could have supplied the rain.[15] For example, in the catastrophic plate tectonics model for the Flood (see Chapter 11),[16] volcanic activity associated with the breaking up of the pre-Flood ocean floor would have created a linear geyser (like a wall) of superheated steam from the ocean, causing intense global rain.

Nevertheless, whatever the source or mechanism, the scriptural statement about the windows of heaven opening is an apt description of global torrential rain.

> **A vapour canopy holding more than two metres (7 feet) of rain would cause the Earth's surface to be intolerably hot, so a vapour canopy could not have been a significant source of the Flood waters.**

Where did the waters go?

The whole Earth was covered with the Flood waters (see Chapter 10, *Was the Flood global?*), and the world that then existed was destroyed by the very waters out of which the land had originally emerged at God's command (Gen. 1:9, 2 Peter 3:5–6). But where did those waters go after the Flood?

There are a number of Scripture passages that identify the Flood waters with the present-day seas (Amos 9:6 and Job 38:8–11, note 'waves'). If the waters are still here, why are the highest mountains not still covered with water, as they were in Noah's day? Psalm 104 suggests an answer. After the waters covered the mountains (verse 6), God rebuked them and they fled (verse 7); the mountains rose, the valleys sank down (verse 8) and God set a boundary so that they will never again cover the Earth (verse 9).[17] They are the same waters!

---

14. Psalm 148:4 seems to speak against the canopy theory. Written after the Flood, this refers to '*waters above the heavens*' still existing, so this cannot mean a vapour canopy that collapsed at the Flood. Calvin, Leupold and Keil and Delitzsch all wrote of '*the waters above*' as merely being the clouds.

15. Of course we may never arrive at a correct understanding of exactly how the Flood occurred, but that does not change the fact that it did occur.

16. Austin *et al.,* Ref. 2.

17. The most natural translation of Psalm 104:8a is '*The mountains rose up; the valleys sank down*'. See Chapter 11, footnote 27, p. 168.

Isaiah gives this same statement that the waters of Noah would never again cover the Earth (Isa. 54:9). Clearly, what the Bible is telling us is that God altered the Earth's topography. New continental land-masses bearing new mountain chains of folded rock strata were uplifted from below the globe-encircling waters that had eroded and levelled the pre-Flood topography, while large deep ocean basins were formed to receive and accommodate the Flood waters that then drained off the emerging continents.

That is why the oceans are so deep, and why there are folded mountain ranges. Indeed, if the entire Earth's surface were levelled by smoothing out the topography of not only the land surface but also the rock surface on the ocean floor, the waters of the ocean would cover the Earth's surface to a depth of 3 kilometres (1.8 miles). We need to remember that about 70% of the Earth's surface is still covered by water. Quite clearly, then, the waters of Noah's Flood are in today's ocean basins.

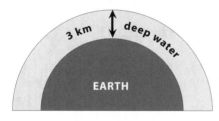

Without mountains or sea basins, water would cover the whole Earth to a depth of 3 km, or 1.8 miles (not to scale).

A mechanism?

The catastrophic plate tectonics model (Chapter 11) gives a mechanism for the deepening of the oceans and the rising of mountains at the end of the Flood.

As the new ocean floors cooled, they would have become denser and sunk, allowing water to flow off the continents. Movement of the water off the continents and into the oceans would have weighed down the ocean floor and lightened the continents, resulting in the further sinking of the ocean floor, as well as upward movement of the continents.[18] The deepening of the ocean basins and the rising of the continents would have resulted in more water running off the land.

---

18. The geological principle involved is *isostasy*, where the plates are 'floating' on the mantle. The ocean basins are composed of denser rock than the continents, so the ocean basins sit lower in the mantle than the less dense continents with their mountains.

Even the high mountains of today have fossils of sea creatures near their peaks.

The collision of the tectonic plates would have pushed up mountain ranges also, especially towards the end of the Flood.

Could the water have covered Mount Everest?

Mt Everest is almost 9 km (5½ miles) high. How, then, could the Flood have covered *'all the high hills under the whole heaven'*?

The Bible refers only to 'high hills', and the mountains today were formed only towards the end of, and **after**, the Flood by collision of the tectonic plates and the associated upthrusting. In support of this, the layers that form the uppermost parts of Mt Everest are themselves composed of fossil-bearing, water-deposited layers. [19]

This uplift of the new continental land-masses from under the Flood waters would have meant that, as the mountains rose and the valleys sank, the waters would have rapidly drained off the newly emerging land surfaces. The collapse of natural dams holding back the floodwaters on the land would also have caused catastrophic flooding. Such rapid movement of large volumes of water would have caused extensive erosion and shaped the basic features of today's Earth surface.

Thus it is not hard to envisage the rapid carving of the landscape features that we see on the Earth today, including places such as the

19. Gansser, A., *Geology of the Himalayas*, Wiley Intersciences, London, 1964, p. 289.

Grand Canyon of the USA. The present shape of Uluru (Ayers Rock), a sandstone monolith in central Australia, is the result of erosion, following tilting and uplift, of previously horizontal beds of water-laid sand. The feldspar-rich sand that makes up Uluru must have been deposited very quickly and recently. Long-distance transport of the sand would have caused the grains to be rounded and sorted, whereas they are jagged and unsorted. If they had sat accumulating slowly in a lake bed drying in the sun over eons of time, which is the story told in the geological display at the park centre, the feldspar would have weathered into clay. Likewise, if Uluru had sat in the once-humid area of central Australia for millions of years, it would have weathered to clay.[20] Similarly, the nearby Kata Tjuta (The Olgas) are composed of an unsorted mixture of large boulders, sand and mud, indicating that the material must have been transported and deposited very rapidly.

Receding floodwaters eroded the land, creating river valleys. This explains why rivers are often so much smaller than the valleys they flow in today—they did not carve the valleys. The water flow that carved out the river valleys must have been far greater than the volume of water we see flowing in the rivers today. This is consistent with voluminous Flood waters draining off the emerging land surfaces at the close of Noah's Flood, and flowing into the rapidly sinking, newly prepared, deep ocean basins.

Our understanding of how the Flood could have occurred is continually developing. Ideas come and go, but the fact of the Flood remains. Genesis clearly testifies to it, Jesus and the Apostles confirmed it, and there is abundant global geological evidence for a global watery cataclysm.

Photo by Carol Drew

Kata Tjuta in central Australia is composed of material which must have been deposited very quickly by water.

---

20. Snelling, A.A., 1998. Uluru and Kata Tjuta: Testimony to the Flood. *Creation* **20**(2):36–40.

Chapter 13

How did the animals fit on Noah's Ark?

- What animals did Noah take onto the Ark?
- Where did they store all the food?
- How could the Ark be big enough?
- What about all the animal wastes?

MANY sceptics assert that the Bible must be wrong, because they claim that the Ark could not possibly have carried all the different types of animals. This has persuaded some Christians to deny the Genesis Flood, or believe that it was only a local flood involving comparatively few animals.

Usually such doubters have not thought it through. On the other hand, the classic creationist book *The Genesis Flood* contained a detailed analysis as far back as 1961.[1] A more comprehensive and updated

---

1. Whitcomb, J.C. and Morris, H.M., 1961. *The Genesis Flood*, Presbyterian and Reformed Publishing Co., Phillipsburg, NJ, USA.

technical study of this and many other related questions is John Woodmorappe's book *Noah's Ark: a Feasibility Study*.[2] This chapter is based on material in these books plus some independent calculations. There are two questions to ask:

- How many types of animals did Noah need to take?
- Was the Ark's volume large enough to carry all the necessary types?

How many types of animals did Noah need to take?

Relevant passages are:

And you shall bring into the ark two of every kind of every living thing of all flesh, to keep them alive with you. They shall be male and female. Two of every kind shall come to you to keep them alive; of birds after their kind, and of beasts after their kind, of every creeping thing of the earth after its kind. (Gen. 6:19–20)

You shall take with you every clean animal by sevens, the male and female. And take two of the animals that are not clean, the male and female. Also take of the birds of the air by sevens, the male and the female, to keep seed alive upon the face of all the earth. (Gen. 7:2–3)

In the original Hebrew, the word variously translated as 'beast' or 'cattle' in these passages is the same: *behemah*, and it refers to land vertebrate animals in general. The word for 'creeping things' is *remes*, which has a

Image by Steve Cardno

---

2. Woodmorappe, J., 1997. *Noah's Ark: A Feasibility Study.* Institute for Creation Research, El Cajon, CA, USA. Woodmorappe has devoted seven years to this scholarly, systematic answer to virtually all the anti-Ark arguments, alleged difficulties with the biblical account, and other relevant questions. Nothing else like this has been written before—a powerful vindication of the Genesis Ark account.

God brought to Noah all kinds of air-breathing land animals to be saved from the Flood.

number of different meanings in Scripture, but here it probably refers to reptiles.[3] Noah did not need to take sea creatures[4] because they would not necessarily be threatened with extinction by a flood. However, turbulent water carrying sediment would cause massive carnage, as seen in the fossil record, and many oceanic species probably did become extinct because of the Flood. If God in His wisdom decided not to preserve some ocean creatures, this was none of Noah's business.

Noah did not need to take plants either—many could have survived as seeds, and others could have survived on floating mats of tangled vegetation, as seen today after severe storms. Many insects and other invertebrates were small enough to have survived on these mats as well. According to Genesis 7:22, the Flood wiped out all land animals that breathed *through nostrils* except those on the Ark. Insects do not breathe through nostrils but through tiny pores ('tracheae') in their exterior skeleton ('shell').

Clean animals: God instructed Noah to take 'seven pairs of all clean animals, the male and its mate, and a pair of the animals that are not clean, the male and its mate' (Gen. 7:2). The term 'clean animal' is not defined in Scripture until the Mosaic Law. But since Moses was also the writer / compiler of Genesis, and following the principle that 'Scripture interprets Scripture', the Mosaic Law definitions can be applied to Noah's situation. Actually, Leviticus 11 and Deuteronomy 14 list very few 'clean' land animals. So the vast majority of animals were not classed as clean, and

3. Jones, A.J., 1973. How many animals on the Ark? *Creation Research Society Quarterly* **10**(2):16–18.
4. It is high time that certain atheistic sceptics showed some intellectual integrity and actually read the Bible. Then they would stop making ridiculous comments about whales flopping up gangplanks, and fish-tanks on the Ark.

would have been represented by only a pair.

What is a 'kind'?

God created a number of different types of animals with much capacity for variation within limits.[5] The descendants of each of these different kinds, apart from humans, would today mostly be represented by a larger grouping than what is called a *species*. In many cases, those species descended from a particular original kind would be grouped today within what modern taxonomists (biologists who classify living things) call a *genus* (plural *genera*).

Zebras, donkeys and horses—probably one biblical kind.

One common definition of a species is a group of organisms which can interbreed, producing fertile offspring, and do not mate with other species. However, most of the so-called species within a particular genus or family have not been tested to see what they can or cannot mate with. Obviously the extinct ones cannot be tested. In fact, not only are there known crosses between so-called species, but there are many instances of mating between genera, so the 'kind' may in some cases be as high as the family. Identifying the 'kind' with the genus is also consistent with Scripture, which spoke of kinds in a way that the Israelites could easily recognize without the need for tests of reproductive isolation.

For example, horses, zebras and donkeys are probably descended from an equine (horse-like) kind, since they can interbreed, although the offspring are largely sterile. Dogs, wolves, coyotes and jackals are probably from a common canine (dog-like) kind. All different types of domestic cattle (which are clean animals) are descended from the aurochs,[6] so there were probably at most seven (or possibly 14) domestic

---

5. One common fallacy brought up by evolutionists is that variation within a kind somehow proves particles-to-people evolution. Examples cited, such as antibiotic resistance in bacteria, are indeed examples of *natural selection*. But this is *not* evolution. Evolution requires the creation of *new* genetic information, which is not possible by natural processes, such as mutations and natural selection. See Chapter 1, pp. 9–10, 13–15.
6. Wieland, C., 1992. Re-creating the extinct aurochs? *Creation* **14**(2):25–28.

cattle aboard. The aurochs itself may have been descended from a cattle kind that also gave rise to bison and water buffaloes. We know that tigers and lions can produce hybrids called tigons and ligers, so it is likely that they are descended from the same original kind.

Woodmorappe tallied up about 8,000 genera, including extinct genera. Thus about 16,000 individual animals had to be aboard. With extinct genera, there is a tendency among some paleontologists to give each of their new finds a new genus name. But this is arbitrary, so the number of extinct genera is probably highly overstated.

Consider the sauropods, which were the largest dinosaurs—the huge plant-eaters like *Brachiosaurus*, *Diplodocus*, *Apatosaurus*, etc. There are 87 sauropod genera commonly cited, but only 12 are 'firmly established' and another 12 are considered 'fairly well established'.[7]

Dinosaurs?

One commonly raised problem is 'How could Noah fit all those huge dinosaurs on the Ark?' First, of the 668 supposed dinosaur genera, only 106 weighed more than ten tonnes when fully grown. Second, the Bible does not say that the animals had to be fully-grown. The largest animals were probably represented by 'teenage' or even younger specimens. It may seem surprising, but the median size of all animals on the Ark would most likely have been that of a small rat, according to Woodmorappe's up-to-date tabulations, while only about 11 percent would have been much larger than a sheep. See also Chapter 19, pp. 230 ff.

The eggs of even the largest dinosaurs were no bigger than a football, so all young dinosaurs were quite small.

Germs?

Another problem often raised by atheists and theistic evolutionists is 'How did disease germs survive the Flood?' This is a leading question— it presumes that germs were as specialized and infectious as they are

7.   McIntosh, J.S., 1992. Sauropoda. In: Wieshampel, D.B. *et al.*, *The Dinosauria*, University of California Press, Berkeley, CA, p. 345.

now, so all the Ark's inhabitants must have suffered from every disease on Earth today. But germs were probably more robust in the past, and may have only fairly recently lost the ability to survive in different hosts or independently of a host. In fact, even now many germs can survive in insect vectors or corpses, or in the dried or frozen state, or be carried by a host without causing disease. Furthermore, degeneration of hosts could allow microbes to cause disease where in the past the microbes may have lived in the host's gut, for example, without causing disease. Such loss of resistance would be consistent with the general degeneration of life since the Fall.[8]

Was the Ark large enough to carry all the necessary types?

The Ark measured 300x50x30 cubits (Gen. 6:15), which is about 137x23x13.7 metres or 450x75x45 feet, so its volume was 43,200 m^3 (cubic metres) or 1.52 million cubic feet. To put this in perspective, this is the equivalent volume of 522 standard railroad stock cars, each of which can hold 240 sheep.

If the animals were kept in cages with an average size (some would be much bigger, others smaller) of 50x50x30 centimetres (20x20x12 inches), that is 75,000 cm^3 (cubic centimetres) or 4,800 cubic inches, the 16,000 animals would only occupy 1,200 m^3 (42,000 cubic feet) or 14.4 stock cars. Even if a million insect species had to be on board as well, it would not be a problem, because they require little space. If each pair was kept in cages of 10 cm (four inches) per side, or 1,000 cm^3, all the insect species would occupy a total volume of only 1,000 m^3, or another 12 cars. This would leave room for five trains of 99 cars each for food, Noah's family and 'range' for the animals, and air space. However, insects are not included in the meaning of *behemah* or *remes,* so Noah probably did not have to take them on board as passengers anyway.

Tabulating the total volume is fair enough, since this shows that there would be plenty of room on the Ark for the animals with ample left over for food, space to move, etc. It would be possible to stack cages, with food

---

8. Wieland, C., 1994. Diseases on the Ark. *Journal of Creation* 8(1):16–18. Viruses often become much more infectious by random mutations causing changes in their protein coats. This makes it harder for the antibodies to recognize them, but there is no increase in information content, so no real evolution.

on top or nearby (to minimize the amount of food carrying the humans had to do), to fill up more of the Ark space, while still allowing plenty of gaps for air circulation. We are discussing an emergency situation, not necessarily luxury accommodation. Although there is plenty of room for exercise, sceptics have overstated animals' needs for exercise anyway.

Even if we don't allow stacking one cage on top of another to save floor space, there still would be no problem. Woodmorappe shows from standard recommended floor space requirements for animals that all the animals together would have needed less than half the available floor space of the Ark's three decks. This arrangement allows for the maximum amount of food and water storage on top of the cages close to the animals.

Food requirements

The Ark would probably have carried compressed and dried foodstuffs, and a lot of concentrated food. Perhaps Noah fed the cattle mainly on grain, plus some hay for fibre. Woodmorappe calculated that the volume of foodstuffs would have been only about 15% of the Ark's total volume. Drinking water would have taken up less than 10 % of the volume. This volume would be reduced further if rainwater were collected and piped into troughs.

Excretory requirements

How did Noah's family dispose of the waste of thousands of animals every day? The amount of labour could be minimized in many ways. Possibly they had sloped floors and/or slatted cages, where the manure could fall away from the animals and be flushed away (plenty of water around!) or destroyed by vermi-composting (composting by worms) which would also have provided earthworms as a food source for animals. Very deep bedding can sometimes last for

Simple sloped floors under cages with slatted floors would make them self-cleaning (from Woodmorappe,[2] used with permission).

a year without needing a change. Absorbent material (e.g. sawdust, softwood shavings and especially peat moss) would have reduced the moisture content and hence the odour.

Hibernation

The space, feeding and excretory requirements were adequate even if the animals had normal day/night sleeping cycles. But hibernation is a possibility that would reduce these requirements even more. It is true that the Bible does not mention it, but it does not rule it out either. Some creationists suggest that God created, or enhanced, the hibernation instinct for the animals on the Ark, but we should not be dogmatic either way.

Some sceptics argue that food taken on board rules out hibernation, but this is not so. Hibernating animals do not sleep all winter, despite popular portrayals, so they would still need food occasionally.

Conclusion

We have shown here that the Bible can be trusted on testable matters like Noah's Ark. Many Christians believe that the Bible can only be trusted on matters of faith and morals, not scientific matters. But we should consider what Jesus Christ Himself told Nicodemus:

> *If I have told you earthly things and you do not believe, how shall you believe if I tell you heavenly things?* (John 3:12)

Similarly, if the Bible can be wrong on testable matters such as geography, history and science, why should it be trusted on matters like the nature of God and life after death, which are not open to empirical testing? Hence Christians should *'be ready always to give an answer to everyone who asks you a reason of the hope in you'* (1 Peter 3:15), when sceptics claim that the Bible conflicts with known 'scientific facts'.

Seeing that the Bible can be trusted on testable matters, nonbelievers disregard its warnings concerning future judgment at their own peril.

Chapter 14

How did freshwater and saltwater fish survive the Flood?

- How did saltwater fish survive dilution of the seawater with freshwater, or how did freshwater types survive in saltwater?
- And how did plants survive?

IF the whole Earth were covered by water in the Flood, then there would have been a mixing of fresh and salt waters. Many of today's fish species are specialized and do not survive in water of radically different saltiness to their usual habitat. So how did they survive the Flood?

Note that the Bible tells us that only land-dwelling, air-breathing animals and birds were on the Ark (Gen. 7:14, 15, 21–23).

We do not know how salty the sea was before the Flood. The Flood was initiated by the breaking up of the *'fountains of the great deep'* (Gen. 7:11). Whatever the 'fountains of the great deep' were (see Chapter 9), the Flood must have been associated with massive earth movements, because of the weight of the water alone, which would have resulted in great volcanic activity.

Volcanoes emit huge amounts of steam, and underwater lava creates hot water/steam, which dissolves minerals, adding salt to the water.

Furthermore, erosion accompanying the movement of water off the continents after the Flood would have added salt to the oceans. In other words, we would expect the pre-Flood ocean waters to be less salty than they were after the Flood.

Eels, like many sea creatures, can move between salt and fresh water.

The problem for fish coping with saltiness is this: fish in fresh water tend to absorb water, because the saltiness of their body fluids draws in the water (by osmosis). Fish in saltwater tend to lose water from their bodies because the surrounding water is saltier than their body fluids.

Saltwater/freshwater adaptation in fish today

Many of today's marine organisms, especially estuarine and tidepool species, are able to survive large changes in salinity. For example, starfish will tolerate as low as 16–18% of the normal concentration of sea salt indefinitely. Barnacles can withstand exposure to less than one-tenth the usual salt concentration of sea-water.

There are migratory species of fish that travel between salt and fresh water. For example, salmon, striped bass and Atlantic sturgeon spawn in freshwater and mature in saltwater. Eels reproduce in saltwater and grow to maturity in freshwater streams and lakes. So, many of today's species of fish are able to adjust to both freshwater and saltwater.

There is also evidence of post-Flood specialization within a kind of fish. For example, the Atlantic sturgeon is a migratory salt/freshwater species but the Siberian sturgeon (a different species of the same kind) lives only in freshwater.

Many families[1] of fish contain both fresh and saltwater species. These include the families of toadfish, garpike, bowfin, sturgeon, herring/anchovy, salmon/trout/pike, catfish, clingfish, stickleback, scorpionfish, and flatfish. Indeed, most of the families alive today have both fresh and saltwater representatives. This suggests that the ability to tolerate

---

1. 'Family' is one of the main levels of classification for fish. In fish there is plenty of evidence for hybridization within families—the trout/salmon family, for example—suggesting that families may represent the biblical 'kind' in fish.

large changes in salinity was present in most fish at the time of the Flood. Specialization, through natural selection, may have resulted in the loss of this ability in many species since then (see Chapter 1, pp. 9–10).

Hybrids of wild trout (freshwater) and farmed salmon (migratory species) have been discovered in Scotland,[2] suggesting that the differences between freshwater and marine types may be quite minor. Indeed, the differences in physiology seem to be largely differences in degree rather than kind.

The kidneys of freshwater species excrete excess water (the urine has low salt concentration) and those of marine species excrete excess salt (the urine has high salt concentration). Saltwater sharks have high concentrations of urea in the blood to retain water in the saltwater environment whereas freshwater sharks have low concentrations of urea to avoid accumulating water. When sawfish move from saltwater to freshwater they increase their urine output twenty fold, and their blood urea concentration decreases to less than one-third.

Major public aquariums use the ability of fish to adapt to water of different salinity from their normal habitat to exhibit freshwater and saltwater species together. The fish can adapt if the salinity is changed slowly enough.

So, many fish species today have the capacity to adapt to both fresh and salt water within their own lifetimes.

Aquatic air-breathing mammals such as whales and dolphins would have been better placed than many fish to survive the Flood, not being dependent on clean water to obtain their oxygen.

Many marine creatures would have been killed in the Flood because of the turbidity of the water, changes in temperature, etc. The fossil record testifies to the massive destruction of marine life, with marine creatures accounting for 95% of the fossil record.[3] Some,

Image by Marcus Österberg <sxc.hu>

Freshwater trout can hybridize with (saltwater) salmon.

2. Charron, B., 1995. Escape to sterility for designer fish. *New Scientist* **146**(1979):22.

3. There is a huge number of marine fossils. If they really formed in the manner claimed by evolutionists (over hundreds of millions of years), then transitional fossils showing gradual change from one kind to another should be most evident here. But they are conspicuous by their absence. Furthermore, fossils of such things as jellyfish, starfish and clams are found near the bottom of the fossil record of multi-cellular organisms, and yet they are still around today, fundamentally unchanged.

such as trilobites and ichthyosaurs, probably became extinct at that time. This is consistent with the Bible account of the Flood beginning with the breaking up of the 'fountains of the great deep' (i.e. beginning in the sea; 'the great deep' means the oceans).

There is also a possibility that stable fresh and saltwater layers developed and persisted in some parts of the ocean. Freshwater can sit on top of saltwater for extended periods of time. Turbulence may have been sufficiently low at high latitudes for such layering to persist and allow the survival of both freshwater and saltwater species in those areas.

Survival of plants

Many terrestrial seeds can survive long periods of soaking in various concentrations of saltwater.[4] Indeed, saltwater impedes the germination of some species so that the seed lasts better in saltwater than freshwater. Other plants could have survived in floating vegetation masses, or on pumice from the volcanic activity. Pieces of many plants are capable of asexual sprouting.

Many plants could have survived as planned food stores on the Ark, or accidental inclusions in such food stores. Many seeds have devices for attaching themselves to animals, and some could have survived the Flood by this means. Others could have survived in the stomachs of the bloated, floating carcasses of dead herbivores.

The olive leaf brought back to Noah by the dove (Gen. 8:11) shows that plants were regenerating well before Noah and company left the Ark.

Conclusion

There are many simple, plausible explanations for how fresh and saltwater fish and plants could have survived the Flood. There is no reason to doubt the reality of the Flood as described in the Bible.

Recommended reading: John Woodmorappe, 1996, *Noah's Ark: A feasibility study,* Institute for Creation Research, Santee, CA, USA.

---

4. Howe, G.F., 1968. Seed germination, sea water, and plant survival in the Great Flood. *Creation Research Quarterly* 5:105–112. Ironically, Charles Darwin similarly proved that seeds could survive months of soaking in seawater.

Chapter 15

Where are all the human fossils?

- Why are human fossils not found with trilobites, for example?
- If humans and dinosaurs lived at the same time, why aren't their fossils found together?
- How could the Flood produce the order in the fossil record?

THE Bible teaches (Genesis 1) that man was here from Day Six of the creation week—created the same day as land animals (which includes dinosaurs) and one day after the sea creatures and the birds.

Evolutionists claim that the order in the fossil record (e.g. trilobites deep down and humans near the top) is due to a succession of life forms on Earth, which occurred over many hundreds of millions of years. In this view, the rock strata represent huge periods of time.

On the other hand, creationists believe that most of the fossils were formed during the year-long global Flood recorded in Genesis Chapters 6–9 (see Chapter 10, *Was the Flood Global?*). Thus creationists believe that the order in the fossil record is due to the order of burial during the Flood, and the local catastrophes that followed. So, sceptics ask, why are human fossils not found with dinosaur fossils, for example?

Do the rock strata represent eons of time?

There is a wealth of evidence that the rock strata do not represent vast periods of time. For example, the huge Coconino sandstone formation in the Grand Canyon is about 100 m thick and extends to some 250,000 km² in area. The large-scale cross-bedding shows that it was all laid down in deep, fast-flowing water in a matter of days. Other rock layers in the Grand Canyon indicate that they were rapidly deposited also, and without substantial time-breaks between the laying down of each unit.[1] Indeed, the whole Grand Canyon sequence is bent at the Kaibab Upwarp, in some spots quite radically, and without cracking. This indicates that the strata, which supposedly represent some 300 million years of evolutionary time, were all still soft when the bending occurred.[1,2] This is consistent with the layers being deposited and bent quickly, during the Genesis Flood.

Photo by Andrew Snelling

There could have been no significant time between the deposition of these two geological formations, or there would have been erosion at the join between them (arrow). The join, or contact, is between the Coconino Sandstone (top) and the Hermit Shale (bottom), beside the Grandview Trail, Grand Canyon. The time gap is supposed to be 10 million years or more.

1. Austin, S.A., 1994. *Grand Canyon: Monument to Catastrophe,* Institute for Creation Research, San Diego, CA.
2. Morris, J., 1994. *The Young Earth,* Creation-Life Publishers Inc., Colorado Springs, CO, USA.

Some other evidences for the non-existence of the eons of time and for the rapid deposition of the layers are:

- polystrate fossils—tree trunks, for example, running through strata supposedly representing many millions of years (these are common in coal) show that the strata must have been deposited in quick succession, otherwise the tops of the trunks would have rotted away;
- delicate surface features preserved on underlying rock units—such as ripple marks and footprints—indicate that there was no long time gap before the next unit was deposited;
- lack of fossilized soil layers in the rock strata, indicating no long time gaps;
- lack of erosion features in the rock layers or between the rock units (any significant time break would result in channels being formed in the exposed strata from the action of water or wind);
- limited extent of unconformities. Although unconformities (clear breaks in deposition) indicate time breaks, such unconformities are localized, with no break evident in rocks of the same strata elsewhere, thus indicating that any time break was localized and brief;
- clastic dykes and pipes—where a sand/water mixture has squeezed up through overlying layers. Although the underlying sand is supposed to be millions of years older than the overlying layers, it obviously did not have time to harden.
- and much else.[2,3]

Uluṟu (Ayers Rock), in central Australia, is also supposed to have formed slowly over hundreds of millions of years, but the structure of the rock shows that it must have formed very quickly and recently (see pp. 169–170).[4]

The existence of many 'living fossils' also challenges the supposed hundreds of millions of years of 'Earth history'. For example, starfish, jellyfish, brachiopods, clams and snails, which are known as fossils dated by evolutionists as 530 million years old, look like those living today. Dr Joachim Scheven, a German scientist, has a museum with over 500 examples of such 'living fossils'. Furthermore, some of these fossils are missing from intervening strata that supposedly represent many millions of years of evolutionary time, again indicating that there were no time gaps.

3. *Raging Waters,* video produced by Keziah Videos, 1998.
4. Snelling, A., 1998. Uluṟu and Kata Tjuṯa. *Creation* **20**(2):36–40.

Evidence that dinosaurs and humans co-existed

Much evidence suggests that people and dinosaurs lived together, not separated by 65 million years or more, as evolutionists believe:

- Many historical accounts of living animals, which were known as 'dragons', are good descriptions of what we call dinosaurs—such as *Triceratops, Stegosaurus, Tyrannosaurus* and *Ankylosaurus*. The video, *The Great Dinosaur Mystery* documents some of these.[5] The account in Job 40 of *behemoth* sounds like one of the big dinosaurs, such as *Apatosaurus* or *Brachiosaurus*.

- Unmineralized ('unfossilized') dinosaur bones.[6] How could these bones, some of which even have blood cells in them, be 65 million years or more old? It stretches the imagination to believe they are even many thousands of years old.

- Rocks bearing dinosaur fossils often contain very little plant material—e.g., in the Morrison formation in North America. This is another indication that the strata do not represent eras of life on Earth. If the strata represent an age of dinosaurs, what did they eat? A large *Apatosaurus* would need over three tonnes of vegetation per day, yet there is no indication of significant vegetation in many of these dinosaur-bearing strata. In other words, we see buried dinosaurs, not buried ecosystems or an 'Age of Dinosaurs'.

Out-of-sequence fossils

Many fossils and artefacts have been found 'out of place'.[7] That is, they are in strata that the evolutionist says represent a period of time when, for example, that organism did not live, or human artefacts could not have been made. There are plenty of examples; some published in respectable journals before the evolutionary paradigm became locked in. Such examples do not get published in modern standard evolutionary journals, possibly because it is inconceivable that such could exist in

---

5. Eden Films / Films for Christ. See also Chapter 19.
6. Wieland, C., 1999. Dinosaur bones: just how old are they really? *Creation* **21**(1):54–55), and references therein.
7. For example: Howe, G.F., Williams, E.L., Matzko, G.T. and Lammerts, W.E., 1988. Creation Research Society studies on Precambrian pollen, Part III: A pollen analysis of Hakatai Shale and other Grand Canyon rocks, *Creation Research Society Quarterly* **24**(4):173–182.

the evolutionary world-view. In another context, Nobel Prize winner Sir Fred Hoyle said,

'Science today is locked into paradigms. Every avenue is blocked by beliefs that are wrong, and if you try to get anything published by a journal today, you will run up against a paradigm, and the editors will turn it down.'[8]

Forbidden Archeology, by Cremo and Thompson, lists some out-of-place human artefacts.[9] They wrote the book from a westernized Hindu perspective to show that humans were present from antiquity, as required for the eons of multi-cycles of reincarnation of Hindu belief. (True Hindus are not concerned about such rationalizing, believing the physical world to be illusory.[10]) Cremo and Thompson are not worried about the millions of years, just whether humans were there. They are 'fellow-travellers' with creationists only in the sense that we also believe that people were here almost all along, except we do not accept the billions of years. Cremo and Thompson have done a thorough job, with the final work being 914 pages long.

Human fossils have been found, hundreds of them, but generally in deposits which most creationists would think were post-Flood (e.g. buried in caves during the post-Flood Ice Age—see Chapter 16). However, in at least one case, human bones have been found in 'older' strata.[11] Unfortunately, the lack of detailed documentation associated with their removal makes it impossible to say with certainty that they were not the result of subsequent intrusive burial, although nothing we know of suggests they were.

In regard to whether things found together necessarily lived and died together, paleontologists can inspect fossils for damage due to 'reworking' for clues that the organisms did not necessarily live or die together. However, the 'reworked' or 'stratigraphic leak' (where something 'young' is found in 'old' rock) explanation is almost invariably invoked for 'out-of-place' fossils.

---

8. Horgan, J., 1995. Profile: Fred Hoyle. *Scientific American* **272**(3):24–25.
9. Cremo, M.A. and Thompson, R.L., 1993, *Forbidden Archeology.* Bhaktivedanta Institute, San Diego, CA, pp. 797–814.
10. One reason why science flourished only in Bible-believing nations.
11. Two human skeletons in a copper mine in Moab, Utah, in the (Cretaceous) Dakota Sandstone, which is supposed to be 'dinosaur age'. C.L. Burdick, 1973, Discovery of human skeletons in Cretaceous formation (Moab, Utah). *Creation Research Society Quarterly* **10**(2):109–10.

What about the general pattern?

Although the rock strata do not represent a series of epochs of Earth history, as is widely believed, they still follow a general pattern. For example, relatively immobile and bottom-dwelling sea creatures tend to be found in the lower strata that contain complex organisms, and the mobile land vertebrates tend to be found in the top layers. Consider the following factors:

Vertebrate fossils are exceedingly rare compared with invertebrate (without a backbone) sea creatures. The vast proportion of the fossil record is invertebrate sea creatures, and plant material in the form of coal and oil. Vertebrate fossils are relatively rare and human fossils are even rarer.[2]

If there were, say, 10 million people at the time of the Flood[12] and all their bodies were preserved and uniformly distributed throughout the 700 million cubic kilometres of fossil-bearing sedimentary rock layers, only one would be found in every 70 cubic kilometres of rock. Thus you would be unlikely to find even one human fossil.

A global Flood beginning with the breaking up of the fountains of the great deep would tend to bury bottom-dwelling sea creatures first— many of these are immobile, or

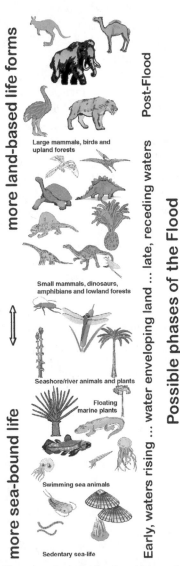

more land-based life forms

Large mammals, birds and upland forests

Small mammals, dinosaurs, amphibians and lowland forests

Seashore/river animals and plants

Floating marine plants

Swimming sea animals

Sedentary sea-life

more sea-bound life

Post-Flood

late, receding waters

water enveloping land ...

Early, waters rising ...

Possible phases of the Flood

There is order in the fossils, which would be expected from a global Flood.

12. Woodmorappe, J., 1983. A diluviological treatise on the stratigraphic separation of fossils. *Creation Research Society Quarterly* **20**(3):133–185.

relatively so. They are also abundant and generally robust (for example, shellfish).[13] As the waters rose to envelop the land, land creatures would be buried last.[14] Also, water plants would tend to be buried before land-based swamp plants, which in turn would be buried before upland plants.

On the other hand, land animals, such as mammals and birds, being mobile (especially birds), could escape to higher ground and be the last to succumb. People would cling to rafts, logs etc. until the very end and then tend to bloat and float and be scavenged by fish, with the bones breaking down rather quickly, rather than being preserved. This would make human fossils from the Flood exceedingly rare.

Further, the more mobile, intelligent animals would tend to survive the Flood longest and be buried last, so their remains would be vulnerable to erosion by the receding floodwaters at the end of the Flood and in the aftermath of the Flood. Hence their remains would tend to be destroyed. The intelligence factor could partly account for the apparent separation of dinosaurs and mammals such as cattle, for example.[15]

Another factor is the sorting action of water. A coal seam at Yallourn in Victoria, Australia, has a 0.5 m thick layer of 50% pollen. The only way such a layer of pollen could be obtained is through the sorting action of water in a massive watery catastrophe that gathered the plant material from a large area and deposited it in a basin in the Yallourn area.

'Cope's Rule' describes the tendency of fossils (e.g. shellfish) to get bigger as you trace them upward through the geological strata. But why should evolution make things generally bigger? Indeed, living forms of fossils tend to be smaller than their fossil ancestors. A better explanation may be the sorting action of water.[16]

See geologist Woodmorappe's paper for an in-depth treatment of the fossil record of cephalopods (such as octopuses and squid) and how it concurs with Creation and the Flood.[17]

These are some factors that could account for the patterns seen in the fossil record, including the general absence of human fossils in Flood

---

13. However, the preservation of impressions of soft creatures such as jellyfish also occurs, and this testifies to the rapidity of burial.
14. The Bible suggests the Flood began in the 'great deep' (the sea). See p. 161.
15. Most creationists would regard large mammal fossil deposits, such as in the John Day County of Oregon, USA, as post-Flood.
16. Although bigger rocks tend to be sorted to the bottom, larger shellfish, for example, are overall less dense than smaller ones and could be deposited after smaller ones in a sorting situation.
17. Woodmorappe, J., 1978, The cephalopods in the creation and the universal Deluge. *Creation Research Society Quarterly* **15**(2):94–112.

deposits. Most of the fossil record does not represent a history of life on Earth, but the order of burial during the Flood. We would expect a pattern with a global Flood, but not an entirely consistent pattern, and this is what we find in the geological strata.

There are problems in reconstructing any historical event, but especially one that has no modern analogue. And such is the Flood.[18] So we have problems imagining the precise sequence of events by which the Flood eroded and deposited material, creating fossils. It may well be that some enterprising creationist scientists will come up with a model of the Flood that will fully account for the fossil and rock sequences.

Of interest in this regard is the TAB (**T**ectonically **A**ssociated **B**iological) provinces model of Woodmorappe.[12] Dr Tasman Walker has suggested a model of the Flood that also seems to explain much of the data.[19] The catastrophic plate tectonics model of Drs Austin, Baumgardner and colleagues also looks interesting in explaining much of the fossil distribution (see Chapter 11). Other models are being developed which may also be helpful in explaining the evidence.[20]

One can be confident that the evolutionary view of Earth history is wrong and the record in the rocks and fossils, including the distribution of human fossils, makes much more sense in the light of the Bible's account of Creation, the Fall and the Flood.

When God pronounced judgment on the world, He said, *'I will destroy [blot out] man whom I have created from the face of the earth'* (Gen. 6:7). Perhaps the lack of pre-Flood human fossils is part of the fulfilment of this judgment?

---

18. Secular geologists wrongly assume that all Earth's history was shaped by the same processes we see happening **today**—this is the doctrine of *uniformitarianism,* which has directed geology for the last 200 years. As there is no global flood happening today, such thinking prevents most of today's geologists from seeing any evidence for the Flood—they try to explain the evidence seen in the present by the processes seen operating only in the present. The Bible has a prophecy, in 2 Peter 3:3–7, regarding this wrong approach to geology that denies miraculous creation and the Deluge.

19. Walker, T., 1994. A biblical geologic model. *Proc. Third ICC,* pp. 581–92.

20. Oard, Michael, personal communication.

Chapter 16

What about the Ice Age?

- How many ice ages were there?
- Where does an ice age fit into the biblical account?
- How much of the Earth was covered by ice?
- How long did it last?
- What about the frozen mammoths?
- How were people affected?

THE only clear evidence we have is for one Ice Age. We still see its remnants in such things as glaciers and the U-shaped valleys they carved. This Ice Age is said by evolutionists to have started about two million years ago and ended about 11,000 years ago. It was punctuated by relatively warm 'interglacial periods, which lasted about 10% of the time. Most creationists, on the other hand, believe the Ice Age began soon after the Flood and continued for less than a thousand years. Indeed, as we shall see later, the biblical Flood provides a good basis for understanding how the *one* Ice Age developed. However, evolutionists have great difficulty accounting for any ice age.[1] In their understanding there would have been multiple ice ages, every 20–30 million years or so.

---

1. Anon., 1997. Great science mysteries. *U.S. News and World Report,* Aug. 18.

Charcoal by Robert Smith.

Arctic fox

Earlier ice ages?

Using their principle that 'the present is the key to the past'[2] evolutionists claim that there is evidence for earlier ice ages. However, supposed similarities between the rocks in those geological systems and the special features produced in **the** Ice Age are not consistent.[3-5]

Today, glaciers grind up the rock they travel over, creating deposits of fine and coarse material mixed together. This unsorted material is known as *till,* or *tillite* when it becomes bound together to form a rock unit. The grinding action of rocks embedded in the glacier also scores parallel grooves in the bedrock the glacier slides over—these grooves are called *striations.* When some melting occurs in summer, the glacier releases rock 'flour' which is washed into glacial lakes and settles to form fine and coarse alternating layers known as *varves.* Sometimes a piece of ice will break off the glacier or ice sheet and float into such a

2. The Apostle Peter prophesied that in the latter days scoffers would claim that *'all things continue as they were from the beginning'* (2 Peter 3:3–7).
3. Oard, M.J., 1997. *Ancient Ice Ages or Gigantic Submarine Landslides?* Creation Research Society Books, Chino Valley, Arizona.
4. Molén, M., 1990. Diamictites: ice-ages or gravity flows? *Proc. Second ICC* **2**:177–190.
5. Oard, M.J., 1990. *An Ice Age Caused by the Genesis Flood*, Technical Monograph, Institute for Creation Research, El Cajon, CA, pp. 135–149.

glacial lake, dropping embedded boulders as it melts. These 'dropstones' fall into the fine sediments (varves) on the lake floor, so that stones are sometimes found in the varves.

Geologists have claimed that these features have been found in ancient rock layers, proving that there had been **previous** ice ages over geologic time. Many lines of evidence now indicate that the observations have been misinterpreted:[3]

- The 'tillites' of lower rock layers are small in area, commonly thick, and probably all of marine origin, whereas those of modern glaciers are relatively large in area, thin and continental.

- There are limestones and dolomites frequently associated with these 'tillites'—carbonates which form today in warm water, not cold.

- The largest boulders in the ancient 'tillites' are much smaller than the larger boulders being deposited by glacial action today.

- Underwater mass flows can produce tillite-like deposits, as well as striated bedrock and striated stones in the 'tillite'. Such mass flows would be expected during Noah's Flood.

- Turbidity currents can deposit varve-like laminated sediments very quickly.[6] These sediments are more accurately called rhythmites. A varve is defined as a rhythmite deposited in one year. Lambert and Hsu have presented evidence from a Swiss lake that such varve-like rhythmites form rapidly by catastrophic, turbid water underflows.[7] At one location, five couplets of these varve-like rhythmites formed during a single year. At Mount St Helens in the USA, an 8 m (25 ft) thick stratified deposit consisting of many thin varve-like laminae was formed in less than one day (June 12, 1980).[8] Flow tank experiments have shown how laminations can form rapidly when two different grain sizes are carried together in flowing water.[9]

- The so-called 'dropstones' could not have been dropped into the ancient 'varvites'[10] because such a method of placement would result in tell-tale disturbance of the laminations, which is rarely observed.

6. A turbidity current is a dense mass of sediment-laden water travelling rapidly and violently down a slope underwater.

7. Lambert, A. and Hsu, K.J., 1979. Non-annual cycles of varve-like sedimentation in Walensee, Switzerland. *Sedimentology* 26:453–461.

8. Austin, S.A., 1986. Mount St Helens and catastrophism. *Proc. First ICC*, Pittsburgh, PA 1:3–9.

9. Julien, P.Y., Lan, Y.Q. and Raslan, Y., 1998. Experimental mechanics of sand stratification. *Journal of Creation* 12(2):218–221.

10. 'Varves' of rhythmites which have become rock, or lithified.

The evidence suggests they were placed **with** the enclosing sediments by turbidity currents or other mass flows—again consistent with what would be expected during a global Flood. In other words the 'varvites' did not come from cyclical, annual, glacial lake deposition.

The extent of the ice

The effects of **the** Ice Age are still with us, particularly the giant ice sheets of Antarctica and Greenland, the alpine glaciers, and the glacial landforms and sediments. Because these effects are seen on the current land surface, it is clear that the Ice Age occurred after the Flood.

During the Ice Age, great ice sheets developed over Greenland and North America (as far south as the northern United States) and in northern Europe from Scandinavia to Germany and England (see diagram).

In the North American Rockies, the European Alps, the South American Andes and other mountain chains, permanent ice caps rested on the summits, and extensive valley glaciers descended down almost to the plains below.

Another ice sheet covered most of Antarctica. Ice caps developed on the mountains of New Zealand, Tasmania, and the highest parts of southeastern mainland Australia. Some glaciers still remain in the high Southern Alps of New Zealand, and in the Andes Mountains, but glacial landforms are all that are left in New South Wales' Snowy Mountains, and in Tasmania, as a reminder of the action of the ice.

Nearly all textbooks used to claim that the Ice Age involved at least four advances and retreats of the ice, with relatively warm periods (called

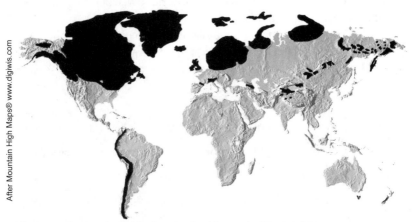

After Mountain High Maps® www.digiwis.com

The approximate extent of the ice sheets at the peak of the Ice Age.

inter-glacials) in between. Based on the quest to find a cyclical pattern of ice ages, the number of ice ages during the past two million years of geological time has jumped to more than 20. However, the dense clay soils, old river terraces, and other phenomena, interpreted as evidence for multiple ice ages, can be more readily understood as resulting from advance and retreat phases of a *single* ice age after the Flood.[11]

The Ice Age and human habitation

It is important to realize that the ice never covered more than a third of the Earth's land surface, even at its greatest extent. At the same time as there was glaciation in the upper latitudes, there was probably a period of higher rainfall in the lower latitudes. Such higher rainfall towards the equator would have assured an abundant water supply even in present-day desert areas such as the Sahara, the Gobi, and Arabia. Indeed, archaeological excavations have yielded abundant evidences of lush vegetation, human occupation and complex irrigation economies in these now desolate regions.

There is also evidence that human societies lived near the edge of the ice sheet in Western Europe throughout the Ice Age—the Neandertal peoples, for instance. Many anthropologists now recognize that their somewhat brutish appearance was at least partly due to disease (rickets, arthritis) caused by the dark, cold and damp climate of the region at that time. Their resulting lack of exposure to sunlight, which stimulates vitamin D synthesis necessary for normal bone development, and poor diet, would have caused rickets.[12]

Apart from highly questionable dating methods (see Chapter 4), there is no reason why Neandertals could not have lived at the same time as the advanced civilizations of Egypt, Babylonia, and others that were developing unhindered in the lower latitudes. The Ice Age can be better understood as lasting 700 years or so rather than two million years.

The biblical Flood: the trigger for the Ice Age

To develop an ice age, where ice accumulates on the land, the oceans need to be warm at mid- and high latitude, and the land masses need to

---

11. Oard, Ref. 5, pp. 149–166.
12. Ivanhoe, F., 1970. Was Virchow right about Neandertal? *Nature* **227**:577–579.

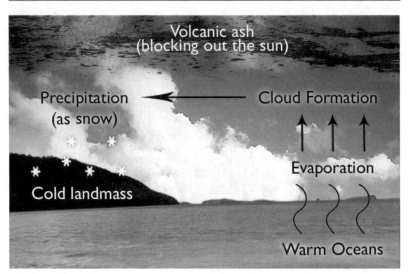

The Flood and its aftermath would provide the warm oceans and cold continents to produce an 'Ice Age'.

be cold, especially in the summer.[5,13–15] Warm oceans evaporate lots of water, which then moves over the land. Cold continents result in the water precipitating as snow rather than rain, and also prevent the snow from thawing during summer. The ice thus accumulates quickly.

Slow-and-gradual evolutionary scenarios[16] to explain the Ice Age do not work. Long-age theories involve a slow cooling down of the Earth, but this will not generate an ice age. If the oceans gradually cooled, along with the land, by the time everything was cold enough so that the snow didn't melt during summer, evaporation from the oceans would be insufficient to produce enough snow to generate the massive ice sheets.[17] A frozen desert would result, not an ice age.

However, the global Flood described in the Bible provides a simple mechanism for an ice age. We would expect warm oceans at the end of the global Flood, due to the addition of hot subterranean water to the pre-Flood ocean and heat energy released through volcanic activity.

13. Oard, M.J., 1979. A rapid post-Flood ice age. *Creation Research Society Quarterly* **16**(1):29–37.
14. Oard, M.J., 1986. An ice age within the biblical time frame. *Proc. First ICC*, Pittsburgh, PA **2**:157–166.
15. Wieland, C., 1997. Tackling the big freeze. *Creation* **19**(1):42–43.
16. Oard, Ref. 5, pp. 1–22.
17. The higher the water temperature the more the evaporation, because evaporation requires a lot of heat energy.

Oard and Vardiman point to evidence that the ocean waters were in fact warmer just before the Ice Age, as recorded by the oxygen isotopes in the shells of tiny marine animals called foraminifera.[18–20]

Large amounts of volcanic dust and aerosols from residual volcanic eruptions at the end of and after the Flood would have reflected solar radiation back into space, causing low temperatures over land, and especially causing the summers to be cold.[21] Dust and aerosols slowly settle out of the atmosphere, but continued post-Flood volcanism would have replenished these for hundreds of years following the Flood. In support of this, there is evidence of continued widespread volcanism in the large quantities of volcanic rocks among so-called 'Pleistocene' sediments, which probably formed soon after the Flood.

Vardiman[19,20] has shown, using standard knowledge of atmospheric circulation, that the warm oceans after the Flood, and the large rates of cooling at the poles, would have driven extreme atmospheric convection. This would have created an enormous polar hurricane-like storm system

Charcoal by Robert Smith.

The polar bear is a species of the bear kind adapted to cold conditions.

18. Vardiman, L., 1993. *Ice Cores and the Age of the Earth*, Technical Monograph, Institute for Creation Research, El Cajon, California.
19. Vardiman, L., 1994. A conceptual transition model of the atmospheric global circulation following the Genesis Flood. *Proc. Third ICC*, Pittsburgh, PA, pp. 569–579.
20. Vardiman, L., 1994. An analytical young-Earth flow model of ice sheet formation during the 'Ice Age'. *Proc. Third ICC*, Pittsburgh, pp. 561–568.
21. Oard, Ref. 5, pp. 33–38.

covering a large portion of the Arctic. This, he suggests, could have functioned for much of the 500-year period up to the glacial maximum (see next section). Such circulation patterns would have delivered to the higher latitudes the vast amounts of snow that would have quickly become ice sheets, spreading firstly over the continents, and then later over the oceans as the water cooled down towards the end of the glacial period.

How long an ice age?

Meteorologist Michael Oard[22] has estimated that it would have taken only about 700 years to cool the polar oceans from a uniform temperature of 30°C at the end of the Flood to the temperatures observed today (average 4°C). This 700-year period represents the duration of the Ice Age. The ice would have started accumulating soon after the Flood. By about 500 years after the Flood, the average global ocean temperature would have cooled to about 10 °C, and the resulting reduced evaporation would have caused much less cloud cover. This, combined with the clearing of the volcanic dust from the atmosphere, would have allowed more radiation to penetrate to the Earth's surface, progressively melting the ice sheets. Thus the glacial maximum would have been about 500 years after the Flood.

Interestingly, there seem to be certain references to this Ice Age in the ancient book of Job (37:9–10, 38:22–23, 29–30), who perhaps lived in its waning years. (Job lived in the land of Uz, Uz being a descendant of Shem [Gen. 10:23], so that most conservative Bible scholars agree that Job probably lived at some time between the Tower of Babel and Abraham.) God questioned Job from a whirlwind, *'Out of whose womb came the ice? And the frost of the heavens, who fathered it? The waters are hidden like stone, and the face of the deep is frozen'* (Job 38:29–30).

Such questions presuppose Job knew, either firsthand or by historical/family records, what God was talking about. This is probably a reference to the climatic effects of the Ice Age—effects not now seen in the Middle East.

In recent years the conventional age estimate for the Ice Age has been seemingly reinforced by claims that ice cores drilled from the Antarctic and Greenland ice sheets contain many thousands of annual layers. Layering is certainly visible in the uppermost section of such ice cores, but it only correlates with an annual pattern in the past few

22. Oard, Ref. 5, pp. 109–119.

thousand years, as it should if it represents annual snow deposits since the end of the Ice Age. Lower down in the ice cores, the so-called annual layers become less distinct and can be understood as being caused by other mechanisms, such as individual storms.

Vardiman[18–20] has demonstrated that the ice core data support a long-age model only if they are interpreted that way. The ice core data readily fit a young-Earth model, with the bulk of the ice sheet thickness having been deposited by the hurricane-like circulation in the relatively brief 500-year period following the Flood. In this understanding, the oxygen isotope variations, for example, do not represent annual seasons but individual storms from different directions depositing water evaporated from oceans differing in temperature.[23]

The riddle of the frozen mammoths

The remains of hundreds of thousands of woolly mammoths are found across northern Europe, Siberia and Alaska. There was a lucrative trade in mammoth ivory for many years. At least a million mammoths must have lived in Siberia and Alaska.[24] But how could the frozen wastes of Siberia have ever produced enough food for the mammoths? Woolly rhinoceros, bison, horses and antelopes also lived there in abundance. Even if the animals migrated there in summer, there would not have been enough food for them.

Furthermore, what did animals such as woolly mammoths, rhinoceros, bison and horses drink during the frozen winters? Such animals need large quantities of liquid water.

Evolutionists, with their eons of time and multiple ice ages, believe that Siberia and Alaska are relatively warm at present,[25] compared with the time when mammoths lived there. So, how could these large populations of animals have lived in these areas?

Many carcasses or partial carcasses may still exist. The vast majority show

Image by Steve Cardno

---

23. The oxygen isotope concentrations of snow vary with the temperature of the ocean from which the water was originally evaporated.
24. Oard, Ref. 5, p. 88.
25. Evolutionists consider that we are presently in a warm 'interglacial' period.

The musk ox, probably of the cattle kind, is adapted to the cold.

Charcoal by Robert Smith.

signs of substantial decay before they were buried and frozen, though about a half-dozen intact frozen carcasses have been found.

Some of the intact carcasses have been found with their stomach contents largely undigested. Some have claimed that an extraordinary snap-freeze would be needed to preserve such stomach contents. However, undigested stomach contents have been found in non-frozen mastodon remains in Ohio, USA. Studies of elephant digestion show that the stomach acts as a storage vat for food, with fermentation and digestion occurring in the hindgut (as with horses). Consequently, an elephant's stomach contents remain largely undigested. Mammoths would almost certainly be similar. So a snap freeze is not necessary to explain this observation.

Most of the mammoth remains show that they were in various states of decay, some with pupae of carcass-consuming flies, others showing signs of scavenging, indicating that this was no instantaneous regional freeze.

Some of the plant species identified in the stomach of the famous Beresovka mammoth now grow only in warmer climates. The evidence thus suggests a change in climate in northern Siberia / Alaska. The mammoths lived there because the climate was much warmer, with more precipitation, than today. Mammoth remains have been found as far south as Mexico, showing that they were probably adapted to a wide range of climates.

Cave paintings of mammoths were obviously done by people living after the Flood.[26] Furthermore, since the mammoth remains are frozen in silt on top of sediments laid down in the Flood, they must have been frozen there at some time during the Ice Age, after the Flood.[27]

The burial and freezing of these mammoths cannot be accounted for with uniformitarian / evolutionary explanations of a slow-and-gradual onset of the Ice Age over many thousands of years, and its slow waning over a similarly long period. However, while the mammoths are a big mystery to evolutionists, the biblical Flood / Ice Age model provides a framework for understanding the mammoths.

Michael Oard proposes that the mammoths were buried and frozen towards the end of the post-Flood Ice Age.[27,28] Note that because of the warm Arctic Ocean after the Flood, the ice sheets did not cover the sea, nor the lowlands near the sea, resulting in a relatively temperate climate near the sea. Significantly, mammoth remains are most abundant close to the Arctic Ocean and in the islands off the coast. Mammoth remains are also found south of the maximum southern limits of the ice sheets, indicating that the distribution of the ice sheets determined where the mammoths lived and died. It was at the end of the Ice Age that the sea froze over and the lowlands became permafrost. This coincided with the demise of the mammoths.

As the oceans cooled in the hundreds of years following the Flood, the humidity of the air over the oceans reduced and the climate of the Arctic coast dried out. Droughts developed. The ice sheets melted back exposing the land, allowing massive dust storms of sand and silt to bury the mammoths, suffocating some of them. This explains why the carcasses are found in what's known as yedoma or 'muck', which comprises *loess*, or wind-blown silt. Some were entombed in a standing

---

26. Distinctly mammoth-like elephants were recently discovered living in Nepal, suggesting that mammoths have not been extinct for as long as is commonly believed. See Wieland, C., 1997. 'Lost world' animals—found! *Creation* 19(1):10–13.

27. Oard, M.J., 2000, The extinction of the woolly mammoth: was it a quick freeze? *Journal of Creation* 14(3):24–34.

28. This means that there would be some 600 years for the populations of animals, including mammoths, to build up after the Flood. With a conservative population doubling time of 17 years, consistent with living elephant generation times, a pair of mammoths off the Ark could produce a population of over a **billion** in 500 years.

position. As the climate got colder, the oceans froze over and permafrost developed on the land, resulting in the carcasses buried in the sand and silt being frozen, where they are found today.

The aftermath

Animals coming off the Ark multiplied in the centuries following the Flood. But with the development of the Ice Age and the onset of permanent climate change towards its end, many animals were unable to cope and became extinct. Some, like the woolly mammoths, died in catastrophes and climate change and from loss of habitat associated with these drastic changes. As the ice retreated and the rainfall patterns changed yet again, many of the well-watered regions became arid, and so even more animals died out. The great cataclysm of the Flood, followed by the smaller related catastrophes of glaciation, volcanism, and eventual desiccation (drying out), drastically changed the character of the Earth and its inhabitants to what we see today.

Chapter 17

How did animals get from the Ark to places such as Australia?

- How did the animals get from remote countries to the Ark?
- After the Flood, did kangaroos hop all the way to Australia?
- What did koalas eat on the way?

LET us begin by reaffirming that God's Word does indeed reveal, in the plainest possible terms, that the whole globe was inundated with a violent, watery cataclysm—Noah's Flood. All land-dwelling, air-breathing creatures not on the Ark perished and the world was repopulated by those surviving on the Ark (see Chapter 10, *Was the Flood global?* pp. 141 ff.).

How did the animals get to the Ark?

Sceptics paint a picture of Noah going to countries remote from the Middle East to gather animals such as kangaroos and koalas from

Australia, and kiwis from New Zealand. However, the Bible states that the animals came to Noah; he did not have to round them up (Gen. 6:20). **God** apparently caused the animals to come to Noah. The Bible does not state how this was done.

Neither do we know what the geography of the world was like before the Flood. If there was only one continent at that time (see later in this chapter), then questions of getting animals from remote regions to the Ark are not relevant.

Animal distribution after the Flood

There are severe practical limitations on our attempts to understand the hows and whys of something that happened once, was not recorded in detail, and cannot be repeated.

Difficulties in our ability to explain every single situation in detail result from our limited understanding. We cannot go back in a time machine to check what happened, and our mental reconstructions of what the world was like after the Flood will inevitably be deficient. Because of this, the patterns of post-Flood animal migration present some problems and research challenges for the biblical creation model. However, there are clues from various sources which suggest answers to the questions.

Clues from modern times

When Krakatoa erupted in 1883, the island remnant remained lifeless for some years, but was eventually recolonized by a surprising variety of creatures, including not only insects and earthworms, but birds, lizards, snakes, and even a few mammals. One would not have expected some of this surprising array of creatures to have crossed the ocean, but they obviously did. Even though these were mostly smaller than some of the creatures we will discuss here, it illustrates the limits of our imaginings on such things.

Land bridges

Evolutionists acknowledge that men and animals could once freely cross the Bering Strait, which separates Asia and the Americas.[1] Before the

---

1. Elias, S.A., Short, S.K., Nelson, C.H. and Birks, H.H., 1996. Life and times of the Bering land bridge. *Nature* **382**:60–63.

idea of continental drift became popular, evolutionists depended entirely upon a lowering of the sea level during an ice age (which locked up water in the ice) to create land bridges, enabling dry-land passage from Europe most of the way to Australasia, for example.

The existence of some deep-water stretches along the route to Australia is still consistent with this explanation. Evolutionist geologists themselves believe there have been major tectonic upheavals, accompanied by substantial rising and falling of sea-floors, in the time-period with which they associate an ice age. For instance, parts of California are believed to have been raised many thousands of feet from what was the sea-floor during this ice age period, which they call 'Pleistocene' (one of the most recent of the supposed geological periods). Creationist geologists generally regard Pleistocene sediments as post-Flood, the period in which these major migrations took place.

In the same way, other dry-land areas, including parts of these land bridges, subsided to become submerged at around the same time.[2]

There is a widespread, but mistaken, belief that marsupials are found only in Australia, thus supporting the idea that they must have evolved there. However, living marsupials, opossums, are found also in North and South America, and fossil marsupials have been found on every continent. Likewise, monotremes were once thought to be unique to Australia, but the discovery in 1991 of a fossil platypus tooth in South America stunned the scientific community.[3] Therefore, since evolutionists believe all organisms came from a common ancestor, migration between Australia and other areas must be conceded as possible by all scientists, whether evolutionist or creationist.

Creationists generally believe there was only one Ice Age after, and as a consequence of, the Flood.[4] The lowered sea level at this time made it possible for animals to migrate over land bridges for centuries. Some creationists propose a form of continental break-up after the Flood,[5] in the days of Peleg. This again would mean several centuries for animals to disperse, in this instance without the necessity of land bridges. However, continental break-up in the time of Peleg is not widely accepted in creationist circles (see Chapter 11).

2. Note that the region around the north of Australia to Southeast Asia is a tectonically active part of the world.
3. Anon., 1992. Platypus tooth bites hard into long-held beliefs. *Creation* **14**(1):13, based on an article in *New Scientist,* August 24, 1991. A platypus is a monotreme (an egg-laying mammal).
4. See Chapter 16, *What about the Ice Age?* pp. 201 ff.
5. See Chapter 11, *What about continental drift?* pp. 161 ff.

Did the kangaroo hop all the way to Australia?

How did animals make the long journey from the Ararat region? Even though there have been isolated reports of individual animals making startling journeys of thousands of kilometres, such abilities are not even necessary. Early settlers released a very small number of rabbits in Australia. Wild rabbits are now found at the very opposite corner (in fact, every corner) of this vast continent. Does that mean that an individual rabbit had to be capable of crossing the whole of Australia? Of course not. Creation speakers are sometimes asked mockingly, 'Did the kangaroo hop all the way to Australia?' We see by the rabbit example that this is a somewhat foolish question.

Populations of animals may have had centuries to migrate, relatively slowly, over many generations. Incidentally, the opposite question (also common), as to whether the two kangaroos hopped all the way **from** Australia to the Ark, is also easily answered. The continents we now have, with their load of Flood-deposited sedimentary rock, are not the same as whatever continent or continents there may have been in the pre-Flood world.

We also lack information as to how animals were distributed before the Flood. Kangaroos (as is true for any other creature) may not have been on an isolated landmass. Genesis 1:9 suggests that there may have been only one landmass. *('Let the waters under the heavens be gathered*

*together into one place, and let the dry **land** appear.')* For all we know, kangaroos might have been feeding within a stone's throw of Noah while he was building the Ark.

It may be asked, if creatures were migrating to Australia over a long time (which journey would have included such places as Indonesia, presumably) why do we not find their fossils *en route* in such countries?

Fossilization is a rare event, requiring, as a rule, sudden burial (as in the Flood) to prevent decomposition. Lions lived in Israel until

Charcoal by Robert Smith

relatively recently. We don't find lion fossils in Israel, yet this doesn't prevent us believing the many historical reports of their presence. The millions of bison that once roamed the United States of America have left virtually no fossils. So why should it be a surprise that small populations, presumably under migration pressure from competitors and/or predators, and thus living in any one area for a few generations at most, should leave no fossils?

Unique organisms

Another issue is why certain animals (and plants) are uniquely found in only one place. Why is species x found only in Madagascar and species y only in the Seychelles? Many times, questions on this are phrased to indicate that the questioner believes that this means species y headed only in that one direction, and never migrated anywhere else. While that is possible, it is not necessarily the case at all. All that the present situation indicates is that these are now the only places where x or y **still survive**.

The ancestors of present-day kangaroos may have established daughter populations in several parts of the world, but most of these populations subsequently became extinct. Perhaps those marsupials only survived in Australia because they migrated there ahead of the placental mammals (we are not suggesting anything other than 'random' processes in choice of destination), and were subsequently isolated from the placentals and so protected from competition and predation.

Palm Valley in central Australia is host to a unique species of palm, *Livingstonia mariae*, found nowhere else in the world. Does this necessarily mean that the seeds for this species floated only to this one little spot? Not at all. Current models of post-Flood climate indicate that the world is much drier now than it was in the early post-Flood centuries. Evolutionists themselves agree that in recent times (by evolutionary standards) the Sahara was lush and green, and central Australia had a moist, tropical climate. For all we know, the *Livingstonia mariae* palm may have

Photo by Carol Drew

Livingstonia *palms in Palm Valley, central Australia.*

been widespread over much of Australia, perhaps even in other places that are now dry, such as parts of Africa.

The palm has survived in Palm Valley because there it happens to be protected from the drying out which affected the rest of its vast central Australian surrounds. Everywhere else, it died out.

Incidentally, this concept of changing vegetation with changing climate should be kept in mind when considering post-Flood animal migration—especially because of the objections (and caricatures) which may be presented. For instance, how could creatures that today need a rainforest environment trudge across thousands of kilometres of parched desert on the way to where they now live? The answer is that it wasn't desert then!

Photo by Cathy Christiansen

The koala's preference for euca-lyptus leaves is apparently due to an addiction. Young ones can be raised to eat other types of leaves.

The koala and other specialized types

Some problems are more difficult to solve. For instance, there are creatures that require special conditions or a very specialized diet, such as the giant panda of China and Australia's koala. We don't know, of course, that bamboo shoots or blue gum leaves[6] were not then flourishing all along their eventual respective migratory paths. In fact, this may have influenced the direction they took.

But, in any case, there is another possibility. A need for unique or special conditions to survive may be a result of specialization, a downhill change in some populations. That is, it may result from a loss in genetic information, from thinning out of the gene pool or by degenerative mutation. A good example is the many modern breeds of dog, selected by man (although natural conditions can do likewise), which are much less hardy in the wild than their 'mongrel' ancestors. For

---

6. Actually, the koala can eat other types of gum leaves. Australia has around 500 species of eucalypt (gum) trees. Koalas eat the leaves of about 20 species, with the blue gum a favourite. Recent work has shown that the koala's insistence on eucalypt is actually an **addiction** to certain chemicals in the leaf which it first eats in the mother's milk. Bottle-raised koalas can survive on a non-eucalypt diet (see *Journal of Creation* **8**(2):126). Also, the giant panda, which normally only eats bamboo shoots, has been known to eat small animals occasionally.

example, the St Bernard carries a mutational defect, an overactive thyroid, which means it needs to live in a cold environment to avoid overheating.

This suggests that the ancestors of such creatures, when they came off the Ark, were not as specialized. Thus they were more hardy than their descendants, who carry only a portion of that original gene pool of information.[7]

Iguanas have travelled hundreds of kilometres on rafts of vegetation torn off by storms.

In other words, the koala's ancestors may have been able to survive on a much greater range of vegetation. Such an explanation has been made possible only with modern biological insights. Perhaps as knowledge increases some of the remaining difficulties will become less so.

Such changes do not require a long time for animals under migratory pressure. The first small population that formed would tend to break up rapidly into daughter populations, going in different directions, each carrying only a portion of the gene pool of the original pair that came off the Ark.

Sometimes all of a population will eventually become extinct; sometimes all but one specialized type. Where all the sub-types survive and proliferate, we find some of the tremendous diversity seen among some groups of creatures which are apparently derived from one created kind. This explains why some very obviously related species are found far apart from each other.

The sloth, a very slow-moving creature, may seem to require much more time than Scripture allows to make the journey from Ararat to its present home. Perhaps its present condition is also explicable by a similar devolutionary process. However, to account for today's animal distribution, evolutionists themselves have had to propose that certain primates have travelled across hundreds of miles of open ocean on huge rafts of matted vegetation torn off in storms.[8]

---

7. See Chapter 18, *How did all the different 'races' arise?* for an example of the way in which a very light-skinned 'race' deriving from a mid-brown one is missing some of the information in the parent population.

8. Anon., 1993. Hitch-hiking lemurs. *Creation* **15**(4):11, commenting on Tattersall, J., 1993. Madagascar's Lemurs. *Scientific American* **268**(1):90–97.

Indeed, iguanas have recently been documented travelling hundreds of kilometres in this manner between islands in the Caribbean.[9]

The Bible suggests a pattern of post-Flood dispersal of animals and humans that accounts for fossil distributions of apes and humans, for example. In post-Flood deposits in Africa, ape fossils are found below human fossils. Evolutionists claim that this arose because humans evolved from the apes, but there is another explanation. Animals, including apes, would have begun spreading out over the Earth straight after the Flood, whereas the Bible indicates that people refused to do this (Gen. 9:1, 11:1–9). Human dispersal did not start until Babel, some hundreds of years after the Flood. Such a delay would have meant that some ape fossils would be found consistently below human fossils, since people would have arrived in Africa after the apes.[10]

We may never know the exact answer to every one of such questions, but certainly one can see that the problems are far less formidable than they may at first appear.[11] Coupled with all the biblical, geological, and anthropological evidence for Noah's Flood, one is justified in regarding the Genesis account of the animals' dispersing from a central point as perfectly reasonable.[12] Not only that, but the biblical model provides an excellent framework for the scientific study of these questions.

9. Anon., 1999. Surfing lizards wipe out objections. *Creation* **21**(2):8.
10. Dr Sigrid Hartwig-Scherer, paleoanthropologist, on the DVD, *The Image of God,* Keziah Videos.
11. In recent literature about some of the problems of animal distribution, even within an evolutionary framework, there has been an occasional suggestion that early man may have been a much better boat-builder and navigator than previously thought. Various types of animals may thus have accompanied people on boats across the sea. This should be kept in mind as a possibility in some instances. Animals brought in this way to a new continent may have prospered, even though the accompanying people did not stay, or perished.
12. For further reading: Whitcomb, J. and Morris, H., 1961. *The Genesis Flood,* Presbyterian and Reformed Publ. Co., Phillipsburg, New Jersey. Woodmorappe, J., 1990. Causes for the Biogeographic Distribution of Land Vertebrates After the Flood. *Proc. Second ICC,* Pittsburg, pp. 361–367.

Chapter 18

How did all the different 'races' arise (from Noah's family)?

- What is a 'race'?
- How did different skin colours come about?
- Are black people the result of a curse on Ham?
- What about 'Stone Age' people?
- What are the consequences of false ideas about the origin of 'races'

ACCORDING to the Bible, all humans descended from Noah and his wife, his three sons and their wives, and before that from Adam and Eve (Genesis 1–11). But today we have many 'races', with what seem to be greatly differing features; the most obvious of these is skin colour. Many see this as a reason to doubt the Bible's record of history, believing that the various groups could have arisen only by evolving separately over tens of thousands of years.

The Bible tells us how the population that descended from Noah's family had one language and by living in one place were disobeying God's command to *'fill the earth'* (Genesis 9:1, 11:4). God confused their language, causing a break-up of the population into smaller groups that scattered over the Earth (Genesis 11:8–9). Modern genetics shows how, following such a break-up of a population, variations in skin colour, for example, can develop in only a few generations. There is good evidence that the various people groups we have today have **not** been separated for huge periods of time.[1]

What is a 'race'?

There is really only one race—the human race. The Bible teaches us that God has '*made from one man all nations of mankind*' (Acts 17:26). Scripture distinguishes people by tribal or national groupings, not by skin colour or physical features. Clearly, though, there are groups of people who have certain features (e.g., skin colour) in common, which distinguish them from other groups. We prefer to call these 'people groups' rather than 'races', to avoid the unfortunate evolutionary connotations associated with the word 'race'.

All people can interbreed and produce fertile offspring. This shows that the biological differences between the 'races' are small. In fact, the DNA differences are almost trivial. The DNA of any two people in the world typically differs by just 0.2%.[2] Of this, only 6% (i.e. a minuscule 0.012%) can be linked to 'racial' categories; the rest is 'within race' variation.

Anthropologists often classify people into several main racial groups: Caucasoid (European or 'white'),[3] Mongoloid (which includes the Chinese, Inuit or Eskimo, and Native Americans), Negroid (black Africans), and Australoid (Australian Aborigines).

Virtually all evolutionists would now say that the various people groups did not have separate origins. That is, different people groups

---

1. World-wide variations in mitochondrial DNA (the 'Mitochondrial Eve' story) were claimed to show that all people today trace back to a single mother (living in a small population) 70,000 to 800,000 years ago. Subsequent findings on the rate of mitochondrial DNA mutations shortened this period drastically to put it within the biblical time-frame. See Loewe, L. and Scherer, S., 1997. Mitochondrial Eve: the plot thickens. *Trends in Ecology and Evolution* 12(11):422–423; Wieland, C., 1998. A shrinking date for Eve. *Journal of Creation* 12(1):1–3; <creation.com/eve>
2. Gutin, J.C., 1994. End of the rainbow. *Discover*, November, pp. 71–75.
3. However, people inhabiting the Indian subcontinent are mainly Caucasian and their skin colour ranges from light brown to quite dark. Even within Europe, skin colour ranges from very pale to brown.

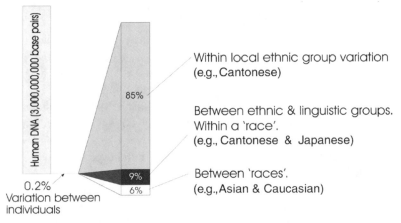

Human DNA (3,000,000,000 base pairs)

85%

0.2%
Variation between
individuals

9%
6%

Within local ethnic group variation
(e.g., Cantonese)

Between ethnic & linguistic groups.
Within a 'race'.
(e.g., Cantonese & Japanese)

Between 'races'.
(e.g., Asian & Caucasian)

The variation in DNA between human individuals shows that racial differences are trivial.

did not each evolve from different groups of animals. So they would agree with the biblical creationist that all people groups have come from the same original population. Of course, they say that such groups as the Aborigines and the Chinese have had many tens of thousands of years of separation. Most people believe that there are such vast differences between groups that there *had* to be many years for these differences to develop.

One reason for this is that many think that the differences arise from some people having unique features in their hereditary make-up that others lack. This is an understandable but incorrect idea. For example, it is easy to think that since different groups of people have 'yellow' skin, 'red' skin, black skin, 'white' skin, and brown skin, there must be many different skin pigments. Different chemicals for colouring would mean different codes in the DNA for each people group, so it appears to be a problem. How could those differences develop within a short time?

However, we all have the same colouring pigment in our skin, melanin. This is a dark-brown pigment that is produced in different amounts in special cells in our skin. If we had **none** (as do albino people, who inherit a mutation-caused defect, and cannot produce melanin), then we would have a very 'white' or pink skin colouring. If we produced a little melanin, we would be 'white'. If our skin produced a lot of melanin, we would be 'black'. And in between, of course, are all shades of brown.[4] So the most important factor in determining skin colour is the amount of melanin produced.

Generally, whatever feature we may look at, no people group has anything that is essentially different from that possessed by another. For example, the Asian, or almond, eye differs from a typical Caucasian eye in having a tiny ligament that pulls the eyelid down a little (see Figure 1). All babies are born with the ligament, but non-Asians usually lose it before 6 months of age. Some retain the ligament and thus have almond-shaped eyes like Asians, and some Asians lose the ligament and so have round eyes like most Caucasians.

Melanin protects the skin from damage by ultraviolet light from the sun. Too little melanin in a sunny environment leads to sunburn and skin cancer. A lot of melanin where there is little sunshine will make it harder to get enough vitamin D (which needs sunshine for its production in the skin). Vitamin D deficiency can cause a bone disorder such as rickets and has been linked with higher incidence of some cancers.

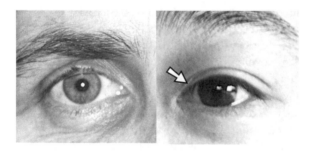

Figure 1. Caucasian and Asian eyes differ in the amount of fat around the eye, as well as a ligament that is lost in most non-Asian babies at about six months of age (arrow).

4. Other substances can in minor ways affect skin shading, such as the coloured fibres of the protein elastin and the pigment carotene. However, once again we all share these same compounds, and the principles governing their inheritance are similar to those outlined here. Factors other than pigment in the skin may influence the shade perceived by the observer in subtle ways, such as the thickness of the overlying (clear) skin layers, the density and positioning of the blood capillary networks, etc. In fact, 'melanin', which is produced by cells in the body called melanocytes, consists of two pigments, which also account for hair colour. Eumelanin is very dark brown, phaeomelanin is more reddish. People tan when sunlight stimulates eumelanin production. Redheads, who are often unable to develop a protective tan, have a high proportion of phaeomelanin. They have probably inherited a defective gene which makes their pigment cells 'unable to respond to normal signals that stimulate eumelanin production'. See Cohen, P., 1995. Redheads come out of the shade. *New Scientist* **147**(1997):18.

Scientists have also discovered that UV light destroys folate, an important vitamin in preventing spina bifida. Melanin protects folate, so this is a further advantage of having dark skin in areas with high UV levels (the tropics and at high altitudes).[5] Melanin also protects against tropical skin ulcers.

We are born with a genetically fixed *potential* to produce a certain amount of melanin, and the amount increases up to that potential in response to sunlight—skin 'tanning'.

Could many different shades of skin colour arise in a short time? If a person from a black people group marries someone from a very white group, their offspring are mid-brown. It has long been known that when such brown-skinned people marry each other, their offspring may be virtually any 'colour', ranging from very dark to very light. This suggests an answer to our question, but first we must look at some basic principles of heredity.

Heredity

Each of us carries information in our body that describes us, like plans and specifications that describe a complex building. It determines not only that we will be human beings, rather than bananas, but also that we will have brown eyes, short nose, etc. When a sperm fertilizes an egg, **all** the information that specifies how the person will be built (ignoring such factors as exercise and diet) is already present. Most of this information is in coded form in our DNA.[6]

This is by far the most efficient information storage system known, greatly surpassing foreseeable computer technology.[7] This information is copied (and

5. Jablonski, N.G., 1992. Sun, skin and spina bifida. In: Bruce, N.W. (Ed.), *Proc. 5th Annual Conf. Austral. Soc. Human Biol.*. Perth, Centre for Human Biology, pp. 455–462.
6. Most of this DNA is in the nucleus of each cell, but some is contained in mitochondria, which are outside the nucleus in the cytoplasm. Sperm contribute only nuclear DNA when the egg is fertilized. Mitochondrial DNA is inherited only from the mother, via the egg.
7. Gitt, W., 1997. Dazzling design in miniature. *Creation* **20**(1):6; <creation.com/dna>

reshuffled) from generation to generation as people reproduce.

'Gene' refers to a small part of that information that carries the instructions for only one type of enzyme, for example.[8] For example, a gene carries the instructions for making hemoglobin, the protein that carries oxygen in your red blood cells. If that gene has been damaged by mutation (such as copying mistakes during reproduction), the instructions will be faulty, so it will make a crippled form of hemoglobin, if any. (Diseases such as sickle-cell anemia result from such mistakes.)

Genes come in pairs, so in the case of hemoglobin, for example, we have two sets of code (instruction) for hemoglobin manufacture, one coming from the mother and one from the father. An egg that has just been fertilized gets one set of genes from the father (carried in the sperm), and another set from the mother (carried in the egg).

This is a very useful arrangement, because if you inherit a damaged gene from one parent that could instruct your cells to produce defective hemoglobin, you are still likely to get a normal one from the other parent that can continue to give the right instructions. (In fact, each of us inherits hundreds of genetic mistakes from one or the other of our parents, but these are often 'covered up' by being matched with a normal gene from the other parent—see the *Who was Cain's wife?* booklet).

Skin colour

Skin colour is governed by more than one pair of genes. For simplicity, let's assume there are only two,[9] located at positions A and B on the chromosomes. One form of the gene, 'M', 'says' make lots of melanin; another form of the gene,[10] 'm', says only make a little melanin. At position A we could have a pair such as $M_A M_A$, $M_A m_A$ or $m_A m_A$[11] which would instruct the skin cells to make a lot, some, or little melanin.

---

8. Incredibly, the same stretch of DNA can be 'read' differently, to have more than one function, by starting the reading process from different points, or editing the result of the reading process. The creative intelligence behind such a thing is mind-boggling.

9. This simplification is not done to help our case—the more genes there are, the easier it is to have a huge range of 'different' colours. The principle involved can be understood by using two as an example.

10. Variant forms of a gene are called 'alleles', but that is not important here.

11. For the technically minded, this type of genetic expression, where allele dosage affects the trait, is called partial dominance.

Similarly, at position B we could have the gene pairs M_BM_B, M_Bm_B or m_Bm_B instructing cells to make a lot, some or little melanin. Thus very dark people could have $M_AM_AM_BM_B$ (see Figure 2). Since both the sperm and eggs of such people could only be M_AM_B (remember, only one from each A or B pair goes to each sperm or egg), they could only produce children with the same combination of genes as themselves. So the children will all be very dark. Likewise, very light people, with $m_Am_Am_Bm_B$, could only produce children like themselves (see Figure 3).

What combinations would result from brown-skinned parents with $M_Am_AM_Bm_B$ (the offspring of an $M_AM_AM_BM_B$ and $m_Am_Am_Bm_B$ union, for example; see Figure 4)? We can do this with a diagram called a 'punnet square' (see Figure 5). The left side shows the four different gene combinations possible in the sperm from the father and the top gives the combinations possible in the eggs from the mother (remember that a parent can only pass on one of each pair of genes to each sperm or egg). We locate a particular sperm gene combination and follow the row across to the column below a particular egg gene combination (like finding a location on a street map). The intersection gives the genetic makeup of the offspring from that particular sperm and egg union. For example, an M_Am_B sperm and an m_AM_B egg would produce a child with $M_Am_AM_Bm_B$, the same as the parents. The other possibilities mean that five levels of melanin (shades of colour) can result in the offspring of such a marriage, as roughly indicated by the level of shading in the diagram. If three gene pairs were involved, seven levels of melanin would be possible.

Thus a range of 'colours', from very light to very dark, can result in only **one generation**, beginning with this particular type of mid-brown parents.

If people with $M_AM_AM_BM_B$, who are 'pure' black (in the sense of having no genes for lightness at all), were to migrate to a place where their offspring could not marry people of lighter colour, all

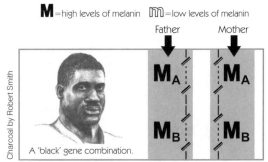

M = high levels of melanin   **m** = low levels of melanin

Father   Mother

M_A M_A

M_B M_B

Charcoal by Robert Smith

A 'black' gene combination.

Figure 2. A 'black' gene combination.

their descendants would be black—a pure 'black line' would result.

If 'white' people ($m_A m_A m_B m_B$) were to migrate to a place where their offspring could not marry darker people, a 'pure' (in the same sense) 'white line' would result—they would lose the genes needed to produce a large amount of melanin and so could not produce 'black' children.

It is thus easily possible, beginning with two middle-brown parents, to get not only all the 'colours', but also people groups with stable shades of skin colour.

But what about people groups that are permanently mid-brown, such as we have today? Again, this is easily explained. If those with genes $M_A M_A m_B m_B$ or $m_A m_A M_B M_B$ no longer intermarry with others, they will be able to produce only mid-brown offspring. (You can work this out with your own punnet square.)

If either of these lines were to interbreed again with the other, the process would be reversed. In a short time their descendants would show a whole range of colours, often in the same family.

If all people were to intermarry freely, and then break into random groups that kept to themselves, a whole new set of gene combinations could emerge. It may be possible to have almond eyes with black skin, blue eyes with black frizzy short hair, etc. We need to remember, of course, that the way in which genes express themselves is much more complex than this simplified picture. For example, sometimes certain genes are linked together.

Even today, within a particular people group you will often see a feature normally associated with another people group. For instance, you will occasionally see a European with a broad

A 'white' gene combination.

Figure 3. A 'white' gene combination.

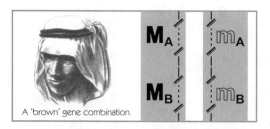
A 'brown' gene combination.

Figure 4. A 'brown' gene combination.

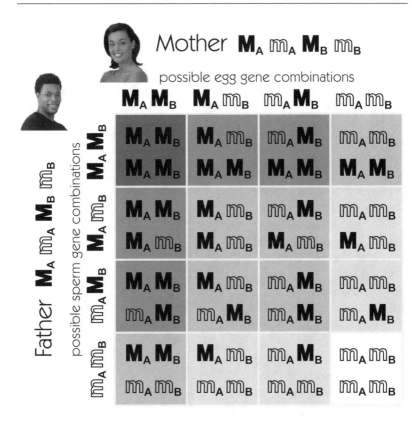

Figure 5. 'Punnet square' showing the possible offspring from brown parents with $M_A m_A M_B m_B$ genes.

flat nose, or a Chinese person with Caucasian eyes. Most scientists now agree that, for humans, 'race' has little or no biological meaning. This also argues strongly against the idea that the people groups have been separated for a long time.

What really happened?

We can now reconstruct the true history of the people groups, using:
- The information given by the Creator Himself in the book of Genesis.
- The background information given above.
- Some consideration of the effect of the environment.

God created the first man, Adam, from whom all other humans descended. 1656 years after Creation, a world-wide Flood destroyed all humans except Noah, his wife, his three sons, and their wives. This Flood greatly changed the environment. God commanded the survivors to multiply and fill the Earth (Genesis 9:1). The people disobeyed God and united to build a city, with the Tower of Babel as the focal point of rebellious worship.

Genesis 11 indicates that up to this time there was only one language. God judged the people's disobedience by imposing different languages, thus stopping their work against God and forcing them to scatter over the Earth as God intended. So all the people groups have come into existence since Babel.

Noah and his family were probably mid-brown, with genes for both dark and light skin, because a medium skin colour would seem to be the most generally suitable (dark enough to protect against skin damage and folate destruction, yet light enough to allow vitamin D production). Adam and Eve would most likely have been mid-brown as well, with brown eyes and brown (or black) hair. In fact, most of the world's population today is mid-brown.

Figure 6. 'Britain's amazing twins'.

After the Flood, until Babel, there was only one language and one culture group. Thus, there were no barriers to marriage within this group. This would tend to keep the skin colour of the population away from the extremes. Very dark and very light skin would appear, of course, but people tending in either direction would be free to marry someone lighter or darker than themselves, ensuring that the average colour stayed roughly the same.

The same would be true of characteristics other than skin colour. Under these sorts of circumstances, distinct differences in appearance will never emerge. To obtain such separate lines, you would need to break a large breeding group into smaller groups and keep them separate; that is, prevent interbreeding between groups. This is true for animal as well as human populations, as every biologist knows.

The effects of Babel

This actually happened at Babel. God's imposition of separate languages created instant barriers. Not only would people tend not to marry someone they couldn't understand, but groups that spoke the same language would have difficulty relating to and trusting those that did not. Thus, they would move away from each other, into different environments. God intended this so they would 'fill the earth'.

It is unlikely that every small group would carry the same broad range of skin colours as the original, larger group. One group might have more dark genes, on average, while another might have more light genes. The same thing would occur with other characteristics: nose shape, eye shape, etc. And since they would intermarry only within their own language group, these differences would no longer be averaged out as before.

As these groups migrated away from Babel, they encountered new environments. Consider a group of people who moved to a region with little

What was Adam and Eve's skin colour?

Image by Keaton Halley

sunlight. Here, the dark-skinned folk would not be able to produce enough vitamin D, and thus would be less healthy and have fewer children. So, in time, the light-skinned members would predominate.

If several different groups went to such an area, and if one group happened to be carrying few genes for lightness, this particular group could in time die out. Thus, natural selection acts on the characteristics *already present*, and does not create new ones.

The Neandertals of Europe, now extinct but recognized as fully human, show evidence of rickets, a symptom of vitamin D deficiency.

In fact, this, plus evolutionary prejudice, caused them to be classified as 'ape-men' for a long time. They could well have been dark-skinned people who were unfit for the environment into which they moved because of the skin colour genes *they began with.* Notice (again) that this natural selection, as it is called, does not *produce* skin colours, but only acts on the created capacity for making skin pigment that is *already* there.[12]

Conversely, fair-skinned people in sunny regions could suffer from skin ulcers, skin cancer and folate deficiency. Thus, in these regions dark-skinned people would come to predominate.

So we see that the pressure of the environment can (a) affect the balance of genes within a group, and (b) even eliminate entire groups. This is why, to a large extent, the physical characteristics of people tend to match the environment where they live (e.g., Nordic people with pale skin, equatorial people with dark skin).

But this is not always so. The Inuit (Eskimo) have brown skin, yet live where there is not much sun. Presumably they all have a genetic makeup such as $M_A M_A m_B m_B$, which would not be able to produce lighter or darker skin. The Innuit fish diet provides plenty of vitamin D. On the other hand, native South Americans living on the equator do not have black skin. These examples confirm that natural selection does not create new information—if the genetic makeup of a group of people does not allow variation in colour toward that colour desirable for that environment, natural selection cannot create such variation.

Pygmies live in a hot area, but rarely experience strong sunshine in their dense jungle environment; yet they have dark skin. Pygmies may be a good example of another factor that has affected the racial history of man: discrimination. People different from the 'norm' (e.g., a very light person in a dark people group) have historically been regarded as abnormal and rejected by the group. Such a person could fail to get a marriage partner. This would further tend to eliminate light genes from a dark people, and vice versa. In this way, groups have tended to 'purify' themselves.

---

12. Indeed a mutant form of the MC1R gene has been found in Neandertal fossils—a mutation that causes red hair due to depressed production of normal brown melanin. So it seems that at Neandertals could have had the range of colouration seen in Europeans today. See Carles Lalueza-Fox, C., *et al.*, 2007. A melanocortin 1 receptor allele suggests varying pigmentation among Neanderthals. Science 318:1453–1455; DOI: 10.1126/science.1147417.

Also, in some instances, breeding within a small group can accentuate a commonly occurring unusual feature that would otherwise be swamped by marriage outside the group. There is a tribe in Africa whose members all have grossly deformed feet from such inbreeding.

If people possessing genes for short stature were discriminated against, a small group of them might seek refuge in the deepest forest. By marrying only each other they would ensure a pygmy 'race' developed. The fact that pygmy tribes speak dialects of neighbouring non-pygmy tribal languages suggests that this happened.

Certain genetic characteristics may have influenced people groups to make deliberate (or semi-deliberate) choices concerning the environments to which they migrated. For instance, people with genes for a thicker, more insulating layer of fat under their skin would tend to leave areas that were uncomfortably hot.

Common memories

The evidence for the Bible's account of human origins is more than just biological and genetic. Since all peoples have descended from Noah's family a relatively short time ago, we would expect to find some memory of the catastrophic Flood in the stories of many people groups. In fact, an overwhelming number of cultures do have accounts of a world-destroying flood. Often these have striking parallels to the true, original account, such as: eight people saved in a boat, the sending out of birds, a rainbow, and more.

Conclusion

The dispersion at Babel broke up a large interbreeding group into small inbreeding groups. This ensured that the resultant groups would have different mixes of genes for various physical features. By itself, this dispersion would ensure, in a short time, that there would be certain fixed differences in some of these groups, commonly called 'races'. In addition, the selection pressure of the environment would modify the existing combinations of genes so that the physical characteristics of each group would tend to suit their environment.

There has been no simple-to-complex evolution of any genes, for the genes were present already. The dominant features of the various people groups result from different combinations of previously existing created genes, plus some minor degenerative changes, resulting from mutation (accidental changes which can be inherited). The originally created (genetic) information has been either reshuffled or has degenerated, but has not been added to.

Consequences of false beliefs about the origin of races

Rejection of the Gospel

The accuracy of the historical details of Genesis is crucial to the trustworthiness of the Bible and to the whole Gospel message. So the popular belief that people groups evolved their different features, and could not all have come from Noah's family (contrary to the Bible), has eroded belief in the Gospel of Jesus Christ.[13]

Racism

One of the biggest justifications for racial discrimination in modern times is the belief that people groups have evolved separately. So, different groups would be at different stages of evolution, with some more backward than others. Therefore, the other person may not be as fully human as you. This sort of thinking inspired Hitler's gas chambers, aiming to establish the 'master race'.[13] Sadly, some Christians have been infected with racist thinking through evolutionary indoctrination that people of a different 'colour' are inferior because they are supposedly closer to the animals. Such attitudes are completely unbiblical (e.g. Acts 17:26, Col. 3:11), although out-of-context Bible verses are sometimes misused to justify racist views (see Appendix 1).

Bad influence on missionary outreach

The spread of evolutionary belief has negatively impacted missionary activity. The idea of savage, half-evolved inferior peoples somehow does not evoke the same missionary urgency as the notion that our 'cousins', closely linked to us in time and heredity, have yet to hear the Gospel.[14] Even many of the finest

---

13. Bergman, J., 1999. Darwinism and the Nazi race holocaust. *Journal of Creation* **13**(2):101–111; <creation.com/holocaust>
14. For example, Grigg, R., 1999. Darwin's quisling. *Creation* **22**(1):50–51. See <creation.com/racism>

of today's missionary organizations have been influenced, often unconsciously, by deeply ingrained evolutionary ideas about the origin of other peoples and their religions.

All tribes and nations are descendants of Noah's family!

The Bible makes it clear that any newly discovered tribe ultimately goes back to Noah. Thus their culture began with (a) a knowledge of God, and (b) technology at least sufficient to build a boat of ocean-liner size. Romans Chapter 1 suggests the major reason for this technological loss and cultural degeneration (see Appendix II). It is linked to the deliberate rejection by their ancestors of the worship of the living God. So the first priority in helping a 'backward' people group should not be secular education and technical aid, but first and foremost the Gospel.

In fact, most 'primitive' tribes still have a memory that their ancestors turned away from the living God, the Creator. Don Richardson, missionary of *Peace Child* fame, has shown that a missionary approach unblinded by evolutionary bias, and thus looking for this link and utilizing it, has been very effective in rescuing people from the squalor of animism, for example.[15]

Jesus Christ, God's reconciliation in the face of man's rejection of the Creator, is the only truth that can set men and women of every culture, people group or colour truly free (John 8:32; 14:6).

Appendix I.
Is black skin due to the curse on Ham?

'Black' (really dark-brown) skin is merely one particular combination of inherited factors. These factors, though not in that combination, were originally present in Adam and Eve. The belief that the skin colour of black people is a result of a curse on Ham and his descendants is *nowhere taught in the Bible*. Furthermore, it was not *Ham* who was cursed, but his son, Canaan (Genesis 9:18,25; 10:6). And Canaan's descendants were probably mid-brown skinned (Genesis 10:15–19), not black. False teaching about Ham has been used to justify slavery and other non-biblical racist practices. It is

---

15. Richardson, D., 1986. *Eternity in Their Hearts*, Regal Books, Division of Gospel Light, Ventura, California, USA.

traditionally believed that the African nations are largely Hamitic, because the Cushites (Cush was a son of Ham: Genesis 10:6) are thought to have lived where Ethiopia is today. Genesis suggests that the dispersion was probably along family lines, and it may be that Ham's descendants were on average darker than, say, Japheth's. However, it could just as easily have been the other way around.

Rahab, mentioned in the genealogy of Jesus in Matthew 1, was a Canaanite. A descendant of Ham, she must have married an Israelite. God approved of this union, which shows that the particular 'race' she came from was not important—it mattered only that she trusted in the true God. Ruth, a Moabitess, also features in the genealogy of Christ. She expressed faith in God before her marriage to Boaz (Ruth 1:16). The only marriages God warns against are same sex 'marriages' and God's people marrying unbelievers.[16]

Appendix II.
'Stone Age' people?

Archaeology shows that there have been people who lived in caves and used stone tools. There are still people who do the same. We have seen that all people on Earth today descended from Noah and his family. Before the Flood, Genesis indicates, people had enough technology to make musical instruments, farm, forge metal implements, build cities, and build a huge seaworthy vessel. After the dispersion from Babel, the hostilities induced by the new languages may have forced some groups to scatter rather rapidly, finding shelter wherever they could.

In some instances, stone tools may have been used temporarily, until

Image by Donna Nicholls

Contrary to popular stereotypes of cavemen, people who dwelt in caves were not brutish, ape-like or unintelligent. They simply lacked the knowledge or technological infrastructure to do otherwise. In a harsh climate, such as during the Ice Age, cave-dwelling makes sense.

---

16. Ham, K., 1999. Inter-racial marriage: is it biblical? *Creation* **21**(3):22–25; <creation.com/interracial>

their settlements were fully
established and they found
and exploited metal deposits,
for example. In others, the
original diverging group may
not have taken the relevant
knowledge with them. Ask an
average family group today
how many of them, if they had
to start again, would know how
to find, mine, and smelt metal-
bearing deposits? Obviously,

there has been technological (cultural) degeneration in many post-
Babel groups.

In some cases, harsh environments may have contributed. The
Australian Aborigines have a technology and cultural knowledge
which, in relation to their lifestyle and need to survive in the dry
outback, is appropriate. This includes the aerodynamic principles used
in making boomerangs (some of which were designed to return to the
thrower, while others were not).

Sometimes we see evidence of degeneration that is hard to explain.
For instance, when Europeans arrived in Tasmania, the Aborigines
there had the simplest technology known. They caught no fish, and
did not usually make clothes. Yet recent archaeological discoveries
suggest that earlier generations had more knowledge and equipment.
Archaeologist Rhys Jones believes that in the Tasmanian Aborigines'
distant past these people had equipment to sew skins into complex
clothes. This contrasts with the observations in the early 1800s that
they just slung skins over their shoulders. It also appears that they
were in fact catching and eating fish in the past, but when Europeans
arrived, they had not been doing this for some time.[17,18] So technology
is not always retained and built upon, but can be lost or abandoned.
Animist peoples live in fear of evil spirits and often invent taboos
against healthy practices like washing, and eating various nutritious
foods. Again this illustrates how loss of knowledge of the true
Creator-God leads to degradation (Romans 1:18–32).

---

17. Jones, R., 1987. Tasmania's Ice-Age hunters. *Australian Geographic*, No. 8,
    (Oct.–Dec.), pp. 26–45.
18. Jones, R., 1977. The Tasmanian paradox. In: Wright, R.S.V. (ed.), *Stone Tools as
    Cultural Markers*, Australian Institute of Aboriginal Studies, Canberra.

Chapter 19

What about dinosaurs?

- Was there an 'age of dinosaurs' long before people came on the scene?
- What does the Bible say about dinosaurs?
- What were the dragons of history?
- What do dinosaur fossils tell us?
- What happened to the dinosaurs?

WE hear and see it everywhere. Via newspapers, radio broadcasts, television documentaries, museum displays, university courses, school textbooks and even in picture books for toddlers, the message is unrelenting: *millions of years ago there was an 'age of dinosaurs', but they became extinct long before man appeared on this planet.*

However, a straightforward reading of the Bible contradicts this utterly. Dinosaurs were created by God alongside man (Genesis 1:24–31) only around 6,000 years ago, and as there was no death before Adam sinned (Genesis 2:16–17; 3:6); *humans and dinosaurs once lived together, in recent history.*

The basis of the conflict

As we saw in Chapter 1, the way you view the world—including the whole issue of dinosaurs—depends upon your starting assumptions.

A basic idea of evolutionary theory, as taught in science textbooks, is that humans have appeared 'only' in the last 100,000 years or so. Therefore, given that no-one was around before then to observe and record what happened, scientists can only reconstruct history (i.e. what they define as 'pre-history') on the basis of fossil evidence, and assumptions. This scenario posits that sedimentary rock layers around the world were deposited over a very long time—*billions* of years. Thus, looking at the 'progression' of organisms from the lowest ('oldest') layers to the uppermost ('youngest') layers provides the order of evolutionary appearance and extinction, over many millions of years.

In contrast, the Christian's starting assumptions are (or ought to be) very different. For starters, Christians believe in a Creator, and that He has spoken through His prophets (Hebrews 1:1), for our benefit (2 Timothy 3:16). And Christians know (or ought to know) the biblical emphasis on eyewitness accounts (Deuteronomy 19:15; 2 Corinthians 13:1), without which we cannot know definitively what happened before we were born (Job 38:4,21).

Secular/evolutionary paleontologists, biologists and anthropologists are at an enormous disadvantage in trying to reconstruct history without reference to an eyewitness account. (See the section on experimental versus 'historical' science in Chapter 1, pp. 16–17.) Conversely, if the Bible's claim to be an eyewitness account of history from the very beginning is true, then the dinosaur fossil evidence found around the world ought to make much better sense from the perspective of 'young-earth' biblical history than from the claimed long-age evolutionary 'history'. And it does.

Lots and lots of dinosaur fossils!

As discussed in Chapter 10, the Bible speaks of a cataclysmic global Flood around 4,500 years ago—such was its impact that Noah and his family and animal/bird 'cargo' remained on board for over a year. Multiple layers of water-borne sediments, now hardened into rock, right around the world, are powerful evidence of the geography-rearranging forces at work during that Flood. These sedimentary rock layers contain billions of fossils (see Chapter 15), with many of them so well-preserved that those creatures must have been buried *quickly* under *loads* of sediment—neither scavengers nor the ravages of oxygen-facilitated decay have left their mark.

Among those billions of fossils, researchers have found and documented many *dinosaur*[1] fossils. (Occasionally one hears of people claiming that dinosaurs never existed—but such claims are completely untenable, given the abundant fossil evidence.) Dinosaur fossil 'graveyards' have been found at many places around the world.

One such 'mass fossil graveyard'[2] in Patagonia, South America, has yielded a great many dinosaur fossils. Some of the fossils are of quite large creatures indeed, such as the *T. rex*-like *Giganotosaurus* (Greek *gigas* [giant] and *notos* [south]), measuring up to 14 m (47 ft) long. Many small dinosaurs are found there, too. But whether big or small, the excellent preservation of these fossils is consistent with the animals

Dinosaur graveyards testify to catastrophic burial conditions, consistent with the Flood.

1. In popular culture, extinct flying reptiles such as the pterosaurs and aquatic (swimming) reptiles such as plesiosaurs are often called dinosaurs. However, scientists, despite some variation in the formal definition of 'dinosaur', generally exclude flying and swimming reptiles. Thus 'true dinosaurs' are described as being 'chiefly terrestrial'. They are reptiles with column-like legs beneath the body, rather than having splayed-out legs like a crocodile or lizard.
2. Owen, J., for *National Geographic News*, 2006. Meat-eating dinosaur was bigger than T. rex, <news.nationalgeographic.com/news/20067/04/0417_060417_large_dino.html>.

having perished and been covered over during the Flood of Noah's day. For example, one 'family' of six fossilized dinosaurs—one adult, two smaller adults, two juveniles and a 'baby'—were found buried together, with no evidence of their having been attacked or scavenged by other animals.[3] Secular paleontologists theorized that this group of dinosaurs therefore 'may have perished in a flood'.[4]

Time and again, paleontologists speak of dinosaur fossil finds as having been formed 'on the floor of an ancient lake or sea' or 'in an old riverbed'. When seven fossilized dinosaurs, all identified as being of one species, *Mapusaurus roseae*, were found in a single deposit in Patagonia, they 'showed no sign of disease, so the animals were apparently victims of some catastrophic event.'[5,6] It must, indeed, have been quite some catastrophic event to have suddenly buried a group of such large—up to 12.5 m (40 ft) long—monsters.

Similar fossil finds around the world are consistent with the *global* catastrophic Flood event that the Bible describes (Genesis 6–9, 1 Peter 3:20), yet secular paleontologists apparently can't see it (2 Peter 3:5–6), despite encountering the evidence in their daily work. One such person is Montana State University paleontologist Jack Horner. He is very familiar with dinosaur fossil 'graveyards'—on an expedition to Mongolia's Gobi Desert he and his team set a new 'record' for dinosaur discovery—67 skeletons in one week![7] An expedition to the same area the previous year had yielded 30 skeletons.

And evidence of *rapid* burial is often unmistakeable. For example: from Oxfordshire, UK, sauropod *footprints*,[8] which require rapid burial for preservation. From China's Jiangxi province, an oviraptor dinosaur fossil with two *eggs* still visible in the body cavity—i.e. it died just before it was about to lay the eggs,[9] and must therefore have been buried *quickly*, before the eggs could decay.

3. Anon., 2000. Flood link to fossilized dino family, *Creation* 22(4):7; <creation.com/content/view/253>.
4. Niiler, E., 2000. A New Rex, *Scientific American* 282(5):17–18.
5. Ref. 2.
6. Coria, R., and Currie, P., 2006. A new carcharodontosaurid (Dinosauria, Theropoda) from the Upper Cretaceous of Argentina, *Geodiversitas* 28(1):71–118.
7. Boswell, E., 2006. MSU, Mongolian paleontologists find 67 dinosaurs in one week, *Montana State University News*, <www.montana.edu/cpa/news/nwview.php?article=4016>.
8. Day, J.J., Upchurch, P., Norman, D.B., Gale, A.S. and Powell, H.P., 2002. Sauropod trackways, evolution, and behaviour, *Science* 296(5573):1659.
9. Sato, T., Cheng, Y.-N., Wu, X.-C., Zelenitsky, D.K., and Hsiao, Y.-F., 2005. A pair of shelled eggs inside a female dinosaur, *Science* 308(5720):375.

The Bible *does* talk about dinosaurs

At this point, some may object: 'But the Bible doesn't mention anything about dinosaurs!' It's true that the word 'dinosaur' does not appear in the Bible. But 'dinosaur' is a modern word, coined by Sir Richard Owen in 1841. He derived it from the Greek words meaning 'terrible lizard' after seeing fossil bones of *Iguanadon* and *Megalosaurus*. It's understandable that 'dinosaur' does not appear in English translations of the Bible, because the tradition of English translation was set in the 1500s and 1600s with the Geneva Bible and the King James Version. However, the Bible does tell us important information about dinosaurs:

© Day6Designs.com

- The original dinosaur kinds were made during Creation Week, around 6,000 years ago.
- The land-based dinosaurs were created on Day 6 of Creation Week, along with man. If there were aquatic dinosaurs, they were created on Day 5, along with the swimming reptiles (like the plesiosaurs) and the flying reptiles (like the pterosaurs).
- There was no suffering and death before Adam sinned—dinosaurs from the beginning lived alongside man and all the other created kinds.
- The whole Creation (including dinosaurs) was cursed as a consequence of Adam's sin, and has been 'in bondage to decay' (Romans 8:21) ever since.
- All air-breathing vertebrate land animals (including dinosaurs) that were not aboard Noah's Ark perished in the global Flood around 4,500 years ago. But they did not become extinct at that time because pairs of each kind were preserved on the Ark.
- It was from the Ark's landing site in (what is today known as) the Near East, or commonly called the Middle East, ('the mountains of Ararat'—Genesis 8:4) that the air-breathing land animals (including dinosaurs) began to repopulate the Earth.
- From the end of the Flood, the 'fear and dread' of man fell upon all the animals (including dinosaurs), coinciding with man being given permission to now eat meat (Genesis 9:2–4).

Do 'dragons' = dinosaurs?

Applying the above biblical framework to our thinking in relation to dinosaurs, then, raises this question: As man, post-Flood, spread out after the fiasco at Babel (Genesis 11), surely he would have (re-)encountered dinosaurs?

Indeed, there are strong indications of exactly that. From Europe, across Asia and into China, historical references to 'dragons' abound, with the described features of those creatures often matching scientists' modern reconstructions of dinosaurs from fossil evidence.

For example, from a chronicle of 1405, in England: 'Close to the town of Bures, near Sudbury, there has lately appeared, to the great hurt of the countryside, a dragon, vast in body, with a crested head, teeth like a saw, and a tail extending to an enormous length. Having slaughtered the shepherd of a flock, it devoured many sheep.'[10] Such features as 'crested head' and 'tail extending to an enormous length', are consistent with this 'dragon' being a dinosaur-like creature.

St George and the dragon, Venice, Italy, c. 1500.

---

10. This and numerous other accounts of similar encounters between people and dinosaur-like creatures described as 'dragons' can be found in Cooper, B., 1995. *After the Flood—The early post-Flood history of Europe traced back to Noah*, New Wine Press, West Sussex, UK, pp. 130–161.

Brass engraving on the tomb of bishop Richard Bell, who died in 1496, Carlisle Cathedral, U.K.

An Irish writer around A.D. 900 recorded an encounter with a large animal with thick legs and strong claws and described it as having 'iron' nails on its tail—could that have been a *Stegosaurus*?[11]

And brass engravings dating from the 1400s at Carlisle Cathedral in Britain depict creatures that any 21st century child would instantly recognize as dinosaurs, along with depictions of various fish, a dog, a pig, a bird and other familiar animals.[12] How could the person engraving those depictions have known what dinosaurs looked like, given that he/she lived over three centuries before the fossil bones of such creatures were systematically dug up, described and named? Surely the answer is clear: people knew what such dinosaurs looked like because those creatures were alive at that time, and were as familiar to people as fish, dogs, pigs and birds.[13]

Descriptions of 'dragons' have a remarkable consistency, stretching from Britain (the emblem on the flag of Wales is a dragon) across Europe and India and into China. Chinese pottery, embroidery, carvings, etc., are famous for being prominently adorned with images of dragons.

Chinese character for 'dragon'.

---

11. Taylor, P.S., 1989. The great dinosaur mystery and the Bible, Chariot Victor Publishing, Colorado Springs, USA, p. 43.

12. Bell, P., 2003. Bishop Bell's brass behemoths! *Creation* **25**(4):40–44; <creation. com/brass_behemoth>.

13. Australian Aboriginal descriptions of a 'bunyip', recorded in a newspaper in 1845, bore a strong resemblance to what today are known as duck-billed dinosaurs. Note that the 1845 newspaper report appeared 13 years before the first duck-billed dinosaurs were described on the basis of fossil reconstructions. See (1) Anon, 1993. Bunyips and dinosaurs, *Creation* **15**(2):51, <creation.com/content/view/821> and (2) Anon, 2006. Settlers feared the bunyip, *Creation* **28**(2):11.

In the traditional (complex) Chinese script, the character for 'dragon' is seen as pictographically representing the creature—the right part of the character being the spines and tail of a dragon. There are also many sayings in Chinese that connect dragons with still-living animals, such as tigers.[14]

Furthermore, of the twelve symbols used in the Chinese lunar calendar cycle, eleven are real animals (pig, rat, rabbit, tiger, etc.), suggesting that the remaining one, the dragon, is equally real.

All of this is consistent with identifying dinosaurs with the dragons of history and as real animals that lived not too long ago. This contradicts the whole idea of an 'age of dinosaurs' millions of years before people existed, and further supports the biblical account of the real history of the world.

A dinosaur described in the Bible?

As well as possible oblique references in the Bible to creatures which may have been dinosaurs,[15] there is a detailed description of an animal in the book of Job which defies ready categorization as any of the animals known to be living today.

Within a few hundred years of the Flood, God spoke to a man called Job, and reminded him of how great He was as Creator, by pointing to a particularly massive creature He had made:

'Look now at the behemoth, which I made along with you; he eats grass like an ox. See now, his strength is in his hips, and his power is in his stomach muscles. He moves his tail like a cedar; the sinews of his thighs are tightly knit. His bones are like beams of bronze, his ribs like bars of iron. He is the first of the ways of God; only He who made him can bring near His sword.' (Job 40:15–19)

One difficulty facing Bible scholars is trying to identify just what this 'behemoth' could be. Obviously it was alive in Job's day, otherwise God's instruction would not have made sense. Some Bible translators, not being sure what the beast was, simply transliterated the Hebrew בהמות, *behemoth*. Others, noting the size and strength of the creature, and that it ranks 'first among the ways of God', thought it must be the

---

14. Batten, D., 2001. Crouching tiger, hidden dinosaur? *Creation* 23(4):56; <creation.com/content/view/407/>.

15. In the Old Testament, the Hebrew word תנין, *tanniyn*, appears some 15 times—some modern English translations translate it as 'monster', 'serpent' or 'jackal', while in the King James Bible the word 'dragon' is used. *Tanniyn* could refer, at least in some contexts, to large reptiles/dinosaurs.

Was 'behemoth', seen by Job, one of the big dinosaurs?

largest land animal alive today, namely the elephant, or alternatively (noting its capacity to occupy streams/marshlands—vv. 21–23) the hippopotamus. This idea was indicated either in a footnote or, in some instances, in the translation itself.

However, besides the fact that the elephant and the hippo were not the largest land animals that God made (fossils show that certain dinosaurs completely dwarfed anything the size of an elephant), such an interpretation does not make sense, since the tail of a behemoth is compared to a cedar tree (v. 17). Neither the cord-like tail of an elephant nor the hippo's tail in any way justify comparison with a cedar tree. But paleontologists' reconstructions of *Brachiosaurus*, based on the fossils, look very much like God's description of behemoth to Job.[16]

How could dinosaurs have fitted on the Ark?

Given the many different dinosaur species that have been identified, and the huge size of some of them (e.g. *Seismosaurus*, on the basis of fossil reconstructions, attained lengths of 45 metres (150 ft)), some people might wonder how Noah could have taken all the dinosaur kinds onto the Ark. However, when one considers the following, there is no problem.

16. Steel, A., 2001. Could Behemoth have been a dinosaur? *Journal of Creation* **15**(2):42–45, <creation.com/behemoth>

1. Only around 55 dinosaur 'kinds'

In Chapter 13, we discussed how Noah did not need to take all *species* (a notoriously flexible concept) on board the Ark, but only pairs of each created *kind*. The same principle applies to dinosaurs. So Noah's Ark did not have to carry the 668 or so named species of dinosaurs; rather, just the representative 'kinds' (Genesis 6:20)—of which it has been estimated there were only 55.[17]

Photos by Don Batten

Skulls given different genus names Apatosaurus *(top) and* Diplodocus *(bottom) which are clearly the same biblical kind.*

And although it's the immense dinosaurs that capture public attention (and are given media prominence), most dinosaur kinds were actually a lot smaller—for example, *Compsognathus* was only as big as a chicken. In fact, the average size of all known dinosaurs was that of a small sheep.

2. The Ark was huge

According to Genesis 6:14–16, the Ark was huge—nothing like the 'bathtub' caricature often portrayed by modern artists.[18] It was more

---

17. Paleontologists are beginning to see that there are many duplicate names for dinosaurs, so that the number of species is greatly inflated. See: Bye bye "Hogwarts dinosaur"? New analyses of dinosaur growth may wipe out one-third of species; <www.physorg.com/news176132721.html>; 30 Oct., 2009. See also Sarfati, J., 2004. *Refuting Compromise*, chapters 7–8.

18. Naval architects concluded that the Ark would have had a capacity of 15,000 tonnes and been stable in the roughest seas. See Hong, S.W., Na, S.S., Hyun, B.S., Hong, S.Y., Gong, D.S., Kang, K.J., Suh, S.H., Lee, K.H. and Je, Y.G., 1994. Safety investigation of Noah's Ark in a seaway, *Journal of Creation* **8**(1):26–36; <creation.com/arksafety>.

than large enough to carry the requisite number of animals.[19] (See also Chapter 10.)

3. No need for fully-grown dinos on the Ark

Even considering the actual (voluminous) size of the Ark,[18] dinosaurs as large as the huge fossil specimens that have been discovered would not likely have fitted through the Ark door. But this does not mean that those very large dinosaur kinds were not represented. Rather, juveniles could have easily been taken on board—and this makes more sense than taking 'grandma and grandpa brachiosaur'[20] onto the Ark, given the need for actively reproducing pairs after the Flood, necessary to repopulate the Earth. Note that it was God who selected which pairs would represent each kind and brought them to Noah (Genesis 6:20)— Noah did not need to 'round up' the dinosaurs (and other animals and birds), in contrast to the taunts of some Bible sceptics.

Some might ask: 'But some dinosaurs were huge—doesn't that mean their "babies" were big, too?' In fact, no. Lots of dinosaur eggs have been discovered at various places around the world, but the largest

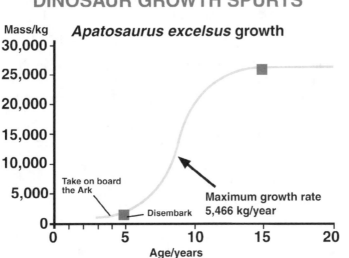

DINOSAUR GROWTH SPURTS

Apatosaurus excelsus growth

Mass/kg vs Age/years

Take on board the Ark — Disembark

Maximum growth rate 5,466 kg/year

---

19. Woodmorappe, J., 1996. *Noah's Ark—A Feasibility Study*, Institute for Creation Research, California, USA.
20. As reptiles have the potential to grow as long as they live, the large fossil dinosaur specimens that have been discovered were probably older ones. See ref. 23.

is about 50 cm (20 inches) long. So, immediately after hatching out, the juveniles of even the largest dinosaurs were less than 1 metre tall (about 3 ft).

What about the possible problem of dinosaurs, taken onto the Ark as small juveniles, growing too big (during the subsequent year aboard the Ark) to go out of the door when it was time to disembark? Growth studies of dinosaur bones show that this would not have been a problem either (provided the juveniles were at the correct stage of growth when selected to go on board). Researchers who studied growth rings in dinosaur bones showed that dinosaurs had a type of 'adolescent growth spurt'.[21,22,23] For example, in the huge *Apatosaurus*, the spurt started at the age of about five years, when the dinosaur was only one tonne (bullock-sized). During the spurt, it grew at over five tonnes per year, then the growth levelled off at the age of 12–13, when it was about 25 tonnes. (See graph previous page.) Other dinosaurs such as the 1700 kg (3700 lb) *Maiasaura* and the much smaller 20 kg (44 lb) *Syntarsus* and *Psittacosaurus* had the same sigmoid ('S'-shaped) growth pattern.

These studies suggest a means of fitting the animals on board. God could well have chosen specimens He knew would undergo their growth spurt as soon as they left the Ark. This would solve the common sceptical objections of fitting and feeding huge dinosaurs on the Ark. That is, the dinosaurs weren't actually that huge while they were on board. The growth spurt just after leaving the Ark would also mean that they could quickly outgrow potential predators.

To summarize, Noah would have easily been able to fit all the dinosaur kinds on the Ark because:

- Most dinosaur kinds were small—the average size being that of a sheep.
- Even the big dinosaur kinds were small before their teenage growth spurt.
- There were comparatively few kinds of dinosaur (likely around 50 or so) compared to the number of named 'species'.
- The Ark was big enough!

21. Erickson, G., Rogers, K., and Yerby, S., 2001. Dinosaurian growth patterns and rapid avian growth rates, *Nature* **412**(6845):429–433.
22. Erickson, G., Makovicky, P., Currie, P., Norell, M., Yerby, S., and Brochu, C., 2004. Gigantism and comparative life-history parameters of tyrannosaurid dinosaurs, *Nature* **430**(7001):772–775.
23. Sarfati, J., 2005. How did dinosaurs grow so big? *Creation* **28**(1):44–47; <creation.com/dinogrowth>.

Dinosaurian challenges
to evolutionary theory

In Chapter 15, we saw how, according to an evolutionary long-age interpretation of the fossil record, many fossils are 'out of place'. That is, they do not fit the supposed bottom-to-top progressive order of appearance claimed by evolutionists.

'Out-of-sequence' fossils are a challenge to theories of dinosaur evolution, too. For example:

- The fossilized remains of a small dinosaur (psittacosaur) have been found in the belly of a fossil mammal named *Repenomamus robustus*.[24,25] This specimen, and another newly-discovered large *Repenomamus* fossil, are a real surprise for evolutionists because evolutionary assumptions say that mammals living during the so-called 'age of the dinosaurs' had to be small to avoid the huge reptiles. While a surprise for evolutionists, it's no shock to creationists—mammals, dinosaurs and man originally lived at the same time.

- Another evolutionary idea that only tiny, shrew-like mammals lived with the dinosaurs was overturned when a fossil of a beaver-like mammal unearthed in Inner Mongolia was dated by evolutionists to 164 million years.[26,27] By evolutionary reckoning, that is around 100 million years *before* dinosaurs are said to have died out.

- Dinosaur fossils are often found in rock strata containing few plant fossils, yet there must have been huge amounts of vegetation to feed the large herbivorous dinosaurs such as *Brachiosaurus*. However, from a creationist perspective, there's no mystery. The dinosaur-bearing strata do not represent a buried ecosystem or dinosaurian 'age'—rather, dinosaur-bearing strata are simply rocks that have hardened around dinosaurs buried during the Flood. One might expect that the mobility of the dinosaurs compared to the plants would mean that they were not buried together—the dinosaurs would try to escape the rising floodwaters, whereas the plants could not.

24. Weil, A., 2005. Living large in the Cretaceous, *Nature* **433**(7022):116–117.
25. Hu, Y., Meng, J., Wang, Y., and Li, C., 2005. Large Mesozoic mammals fed on young dinosaurs, *Nature* **433**(7022):149–152.
26. Martin, T., 2006. Early Mammalian Evolutionary Experiments, *Science* **311**(5764):1109–1110.
27. Ji, Q., Luo, Z.-X., Yuan, C.-X., and Tabrum, A.R., 2006. A Swimming Mammaliaform from the Middle Jurassic and Ecomorphological Diversification of Early Mammals, *Science* **311**(5764):1123–1127.

- Evolutionary researchers who discovered the remains of at least five types of grasses in dinosaur coprolites (fossilized dung[28]) say 'it was a complete shock'.[29,30,31,32] It was a shock because according to the standard evolutionary line, based on a long-age fossil record 'chronology', grasses evolved around 55 million years ago, which would be 10 millions years *after* the extinction of the dinosaurs (supposedly) around 65 million years ago. But the discovery that dinosaurs ate grass left evolutionists with a dramatic grassy 'time-travel' conundrum: how could dinosaurs have eaten something that supposedly hadn't yet evolved?

- The popular evolutionary idea that dinosaurs were the ancestors of birds contradicts itself, as, according to their own dating, fossils of 'bird-like dinos' (the supposed precursors of birds) are millions of years younger than the famous fossil *Archaeopteryx*, which was a fully developed flying *bird*. Even fossils of the beaked bird *Confuciusornis*[33] are older than its supposed ancestors.

- The extinction of the dinosaurs is a great mystery for secular science. Little wonder, then, that it has so captured the attention of popular culture. Various evolutionary theories have been mooted as explanations for the demise of the dinosaurs, e.g. mammals appeared and ate dinosaur eggs; new narcotic plants evolved; and global cooling/warming. However, by far and away the most popular idea is that an asteroid impact was responsible. But that notion has insurmountable difficulties. For example, (evolutionary) extinction dates don't correlate with (evolutionary) crater dates;[34,35] and the

28. The fact that we find fossilized dung at all speaks of rapid burial in an oxygen-free environment—for how else could dung have been so preserved?
29. Prasad, V., Strömberg, C., Alimohammadian, H., and Sahni, A., 2005. Dinosaur Coprolites and the Early Evolution of Grasses and Grazers, *Science* **310**(5751):1177–1180.
30. Piperno, D., and Sues, H.-D., 2005. Dinosaurs Dined on Grass, *Science* **310**(5751):1126–1128.
31. Hecht, J., 2005. Dino droppings reveal prehistoric taste for grass, *New Scientist* **188**(2527):7.
32. According to the researchers, the spherical coprolites (fossilized feces/dung), which measured up to 10 cm across, were probably created by titanosaurs, the most common type of dinosaur represented in the rock layer holding the coprolites. Perkins, S., 2005. Ancient Grazers: Find adds grass to dinosaur menu, *Science News Online*, <www.sciencenews.org/articles/20051119/fob1.asp>.
33. See Sarfati, J., 2003. New four-winged feathered dinosaur?; <creation.com/4wings>.
34. *The Geological Society of America*, 2006. Far more than a meteor killed dinos, News Release 06-47; <www.geosociety.org/news/pr/06-47.htm>.
35. AFP, 2003. Dinos doomed before asteroid strike? *Discovery Channel News,* <dsc.discovery.com/news/afp/20030714/dinodead_print.html>.

famous iridium layer found in rocks worldwide—supposedly a key proof of meteor impact—is much less clearly defined than was once claimed.[36]

From a biblical perspective, there is no dinosaur extinction 'mystery'—the sedimentary rock layers containing fossils are not a 'record' of evolution and extinction over a millions-of-years timeframe, but rather a legacy of burial in the global Flood (around 4,500 years ago) and its aftermath. All the kinds of land animals (including dinosaurs) and birds survived aboard the Ark, repopulating the Earth afterwards. Since then, many creatures have gone extinct, not just dinosaurs, in an ongoing display of the Curse on Creation. Just as with the dodo, it's likely that some dinosaurs perished through human influence, e.g. because of being a direct threat to man's safety or because of loss of habitat (to agriculture or urban encroachment).

A modern parallel can be seen in that the tiger, the rhino and the elephant have either died out or are on the 'endangered species' list in many parts of South-East Asia through the ongoing post-Babel dispersion of man. Heroic accounts of brave young men in Indonesia slaying 'rogue' tigers and elephants bear a striking parallel with centuries-old stories of 'St George and the Dragon', Beowulf, etc, where the dragon-slayers were also protecting others.

Some might wonder how people could kill some of the larger dinosaurs without modern weapons. But people killed whales that were larger than any dinosaur, from sailing boats, using team work and hand-launched harpoons. And this on the whales' 'home turf'. Hunters have used such things as fire, traps and curare to capture/kill large animals.

The drying out of the continents after the Flood—all continents once had extensive inland seas—could also have been a factor in the demise of the dinosaurs. It seems that dinosaurs were like hippos, inhabiting areas with plenty of water, and the drying out of the land resulted in a contraction of areas suitable for them. The wax and wane of the post-Flood Ice Age (Chapter 16) would have also impacted dinosaur survival.

Thus dinosaur extinction is readily understandable from a biblical perspective.

---

36. Many evolutionists agree with creationists that iridium enrichment can be caused by massive volcanism. This would certainly have been a feature of the Flood year, associated with the breaking up of the 'fountains of the great deep' (Genesis 7:11). See Sarfati, J., 2001. Did a meteor wipe out the dinosaurs?—What about the iridium layer? <creation.com/iridium>.

Image by Steve Cardno

Beowulf and the dragon: a story from Scandinavia.

Interestingly, according to an evolutionary interpretation of the fossil layers, lots of other organisms became extinct millions of years ago, e.g. the coelacanth (sometimes referred to as the 'dinosaur fish' because it was said to have become extinct around 65 million years ago), and the Wollemi pine (also known as the 'dinosaur tree' for the same reason). But evolutionists were surprised when these, and many other 'living fossils'[37] or 'Lazarus taxa' were found to be still living today. Such discoveries did not surprise creationists. Similarly, it would not be a surprise if someone happens to find a live *dinosaur* today, e.g. in the remote jungles of the Congo or Papua New Guinea.[38] But for evolutionists, the shock would greatly exceed that experienced when the coelacanth and the Wollemi pine were discovered to be still living today.[39]

37. Scheven, J., 1993. Living fossils, *Creation* **15**(4):45; <creation.com/scheven>.
38. Reports of sightings of dinosaur-like creatures in remote areas today periodically make their way into the news media, e.g. (1) *ABC News Online*, 2004. PNG hunts giant mystery creature, <www.abc.net.au/news/newsitems/200403/s1064948.htm>; (2) Catchpoole, D., 1999. Mokele-Mbembe: a living dinosaur? *Creation* **21**(4):24–25, <creation.com/content/view/326>; (3) Anon, 2000. A living dinosaur? *Creation* **23**(1):56; <creation.com/live_dino>.
39. See, e.g., Anon., 1995. Sensational Australian tree ... like 'finding a live dinosaur' *Creation* **17**(2):13; <creation.com/woll>.

Dinosaur bones—*not* millions of years old!

Many dinosaur fossils are not completely mineralized—in fact, dinosaur bones with blood cells, hemoglobin and soft tissue such as blood vessels have been found. This is enormously confronting for evolutionists, because how could such bones possibly be 65 million years old? As one of the researchers involved in the discovery of dinosaur blood cells, Dr Mary Schweitzer, said: 'If you take a blood sample, and you stick it on a shelf, you have nothing recognizable in about a week. So why would there be anything left in dinosaurs?'[40]

Why indeed? Unless of course they haven't been extinct for millions of years, and their remains were preserved quickly under catastrophic conditions a few thousand years ago, or even more recently.

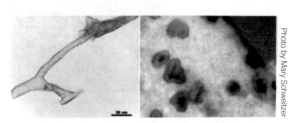

Photo by Mary Schweitzer

A stretch? T.rex *bone yielded flexible, branching vessels (left), some of which contained red blood cells (right). How could they be millions of years old?*

But so entrenched is the evolutionary paradigm in the scientific community, that it soon became known that Dr Schweitzer 'was having a hard time' trying to get her results published in scientific journals.

'I had one reviewer tell me that he didn't care what the data said, he knew that what I was finding wasn't possible,' says Schweitzer. 'I wrote back and said, "Well, what data would convince you?" And he said, "None."'

Schweitzer recounts how she noticed that a *T. rex* skeleton (from Hell Creek, Montana) had a distinctly cadaverous odour. When she mentioned this to long-time paleontologist Jack Horner (see p. 242, earlier in this chapter), he said 'Oh yeah, all Hell Creek bones smell.' But so ingrained is the notion among paleontologists that dinosaur bones must be millions of years old that the 'smell of death' didn't even register with them—despite the evidence being right under their noses.[41] Schweitzer herself does not seem able or willing to escape the

---

40. Yeoman, B., 2006. Schweitzer's Dangerous Discovery, *Discover* **27**(4):37–41, 77.
41. For more on this see: Catchpoole, D. and Sarfati, J., 2006. 'Schweitzer's dangerous discovery', <creation.com/schweit>.

long-age paradigm.

Dinosaurs—a key witnessing tool

© Day6Designs.com

for Christians

Given the evolutionists' difficulty in facing up to such confronting (to them) evidence, you'd think that the church in general would be proclaiming it loudly in the quest to reach out to the many who think that evolution is true. ('Evolution is true' means the Bible is wrong in saying Christ is Creator, and therefore, by definition, there can be no salvation in Christ.) In the light of the Bible, the supposed dinosaur 'mystery' completely disappears.

Sadly, however, many Christians are not actively using dinosaurs as a witnessing tool, for a variety of reasons. For some, it is because they are unaware of just how powerful addressing the dinosaur issue can be when witnessing to a culture bombarded by evolutionary teaching about dinosaurs. Children in particular are being indoctrinated in evolution with its millions of years through captivating their imaginations using dinosaurs.

For others, it is because they think the contradictions between 'science' and the Bible are solved through adopting one of the oft-taught 'compromise' positions, e.g. Gap Theory (which of course doesn't solve anything—see Chapter 3). Such Christians can be gently 'won over' by pointing out examples of Curse-affected dinosaurs—e.g. fossilized dinosaurs that died from cancerous tumours similar to those that afflict people today,[42,43] or that were cannibalized by their own kind[44,45,46]— then asking them the question: 'Did this dinosaur die such a terrible death in the 'very good' world *before* Adam sinned, or *after* he sinned?' Of course, there was no cancer in the pre-Fall world, and God said that the animals (including dinosaurs) were to *reproduce* 'after their kind', not to *eat* their own kind!

There is no need for the church to be silent regarding dinosaurs. Nor is there any excuse, given the increasingly abundant creationist resource materials, such as this book, which can help equip Christians to boldly proclaim Christ, no matter how 'evolutionized' the culture. And if more and more Christians, thus equipped and emboldened, are ready to do just that, what a difference that could make—as we'll see in Chapter 20.

42. Scientists find first dinosaur brain tumor, Yahoo News, <story.news.yahoo.com/news?tmpl=story&u=/nm/20031023/sc_nm/science_dinosaur_dc>, 28 October 2003.

43. Wieland, C., 2004. First-ever dinosaur brain tumour found, *Creation* **26**(2):21; <creation.com/dinotumour>.

44. Pilcher, H.R., 2003. Dinosaurs ate each other, *Nature Science Update*, <www.nature.com/nsu/030331/030331-7.html>.

45. Rogers, R.R., Krause, D.W. and Rogers, K.C., 2003. Cannibalism in the Madagascan dinosaur *Majungatholus atopus*, *Nature* **422**(6931):515–518.

46. Catchpoole, D., 2004. Grotesque dinosaur cannibals! *Creation* **26**(4):34–35; <creation.com/grotesque>.

Chapter 20

What can I do?

MAYBE, having read *The Creation Answers Book,* you have realized for the first time that the Bible is indeed the written revelation of Almighty God to man—it is our Creator's message to us, His creatures.

As His creatures, He owns us and we are accountable to Him for how we live our lives (Romans 14:12, Hebrews 9:27). The Bible tells us that we all, like Adam, have departed from God's ways; we have gone our own way, living life as if we were God, in effect. This, the Bible calls 'sin'. We have all sinned (Romans 3:23).

The Bible also tells us that God will hold us accountable for our sin. Like Adam, we all deserve God's judgment for our sin. As descendants of Adam, we all suffer physical death at the end of this earthly life. The Bible calls this death a curse and 'the last enemy' (Genesis 3:19, 1 Corinthians 15:26). It came about because of Adam's sin, when he by his actions effectively told God that He was not needed—Adam was going to be his own god. However, each one of us has effectively endorsed Adam's action, in ourselves rejecting God's rule over us (Romans 5:12).

The Good News is that God has provided a way of escape from the curse of death and the judgment to come. *'For God so loved the world that He gave his only begotten Son, that whoever believes in Him should not perish, but have everlasting life.'* (John 3:16)

Jesus Christ came into the world, born of a woman, to take upon Himself the Curse and penalty for our sins. As God in the flesh (Colossians 2:9), the God-man Jesus lived a sinless life (Hebrews 4:15) and willingly gave Himself to suffer death for us, in our place (Romans 5:8, 1 Peter 3:18). He took upon Himself the punishment for our sins. As He was God (as well as man), His life was of sufficient value to pay for the sins of any number of people.

God offers this free gift of salvation to all who will receive it. He calls upon all to turn away from their sinful ways and trust in what Christ has done for us. There is nothing we can do to remove our guilt before God. Doing good things does not remove our sin, and since we are all sinners, nothing we can do can undo that; it is only by the mercy of God that we can be saved through what He has done (Ephesians 2:8, 9).

On the other hand, whoever spurns God's offer will suffer His wrath in the judgment to come, which the Bible clearly warns. This is a terrifying prospect (2 Thessalonians 1:8–9). Jesus spoke much of this, warning people of their fate. The book of Revelation uses graphic imagery to depict the dreadful future of those who reject God's mercy here and now.

How can I be saved?

If God has shown you that you are an unworthy sinner, deserving of God's condemnation, in need of His forgiveness, then the Bible says that you must have *'repentance toward God and faith toward our Lord Jesus Christ'* (Acts 20:21). *Repentance* means a complete change of heart and mind regarding sin—that you agree with God about your sin and now want to live a life pleasing to Him. *Faith* in Jesus Christ entails accepting who He is, *'the Son of the living God'*, that *'Christ died for the ungodly'* and that He conquered death in His resurrection (1 Corinthians 15:1–4, 21, 22). You must believe that He is able to save you, and you must put your trust in Christ alone to make you right with God.

If God has shown you your need and given you the desire to be saved, then turn to Christ now. Speak to Him, admitting that you are a guilty, helpless sinner, and ask Him to save you and be Lord of your life, helping you to leave behind your sinful ways and live for Him. The Bible says, *'if you confess with your mouth the Lord Jesus, and believe in your heart that God raised Him from the dead, you shall be saved'* (Romans 10:9).

If you have prayed in this manner, then you should find some Christians who hold to the Bible as God's Word (as the authors of this book do) and ask them to help you as you learn to live as God wants you to live. Perhaps someone gave you this book to read—that person might be able to advise you as to how to contact a group of such Christians.

How can I spread the Creation/Gospel message?

- *Use* **Creation** *magazine to keep informed*—subscribe for yourself and keep up to date with what is happening so that you are ready to share with anyone who *'asks you a reason for the hope that is in you'* (1 Peter 3:15). Many a person has been converted through a friend sharing things learned from *Creation* magazine. It encourages and equips Christians, and challenges non-Christians as to where they stand with Christ. The magazine helps both young and old. Testimonies (children's to professors') show that it

is understandable, but also biblically and scientifically accurate. A special children's section caters for younger children. Schoolteachers find that *Creation* magazine gives them great up-to-date material, and illustrations, for the classroom. The magazine helps teachers to keep up to date so that the best of current science is being taught, and not outmoded arguments[1] (science is always changing). The evolutionists are always 'shifting the goal posts' and we need to keep redirecting our aim in sharing the Creation/Gospel message, so as to be most effective.

- *Lend* **Creation** *magazines* to your friends, relatives, workmates, pastor, youth leader, etc. If someone asks about something that *Creation* magazine has an article about, lend them the whole magazine, not just the photocopied article. They will almost certainly read the whole lot and be challenged. There are many testimonies of folk converted because someone gave them *Creation* magazines to read. Donate subscriptions to church leaders, church libraries, school libraries, local government libraries, friends, relatives, etc.

- *Put* **Creation** *magazines in waiting rooms* at doctors' surgeries, dentists, hairdressers, automotive repair shops, etc. People will read them—they are so colourful and attractive—instead of the shallow

---

1. For example, the Japanese 'plesiosaur', or lack of moon dust as evidence for a young creation.

magazines that are so often available to read in those places.

- **Lend, or give, someone a creation tract or a book.** Good books to give are *Stones and Bones* (Wieland) and *The Lie: Evolution* (Ham). The book *Refuting Evolution* (Sarfati) deals with the major scientific arguments in an excellent manner. Some testify to having been converted through *The Answers Book,* as they found answers to problems that they thought were insoluble (like *Who was Cain's wife?*). Of course, if you have read them first, you will be better able to know which book is suitable for the person you are trying to reach!

Good books are an excellent way to inform yourself and spread the message

- **Show DVDs.** Many people will not read much these days, but they might watch a DVD, especially if you invite them around to your home and show genuine hospitality. Some good DVDs are *Origins in the Modern World: Why it matters,* by Carl Wieland, which is good for awakening Christians to the issues. *Unlocking the Mystery of Life* is a good one-off DVD on evidences for creation and is particularly suitable for showing to non-Christians.

  There are many other DVDs suitable for various levels of interest. Check out the web store via <creation.com> for the most up-to-date DVDs. When presenting a DVD to a group of Christians, it is important to encourage them to obtain their own resources, particularly *Creation* magazine, so that they can also become equipped to share the message with others.

- **Sponsor a visiting speaker**—you could act as a local support person or organizer for a visiting speaker. Speak to your pastor about the possibility and then ask for a visiting speaker when one is available, distributing promotional material before the meeting. You may have to encourage your pastor to understand the importance of the issue—your own testimony can be powerful here, as well as videos that explain the foundational importance of the Genesis accounts of Creation, the Fall and the Flood.

- *Give creation talks*—this is recommended only if you really know the issues and you are able to teach. If those senior to you who know you best do not actively affirm that you are able to teach, please consider that your gifts may lie elsewhere. However, continue sharing the message on a one-on-one personal basis—everyone can do that. Jesus said,

All authority is given to me in heaven and on earth. Therefore go and teach all nations, baptizing them in the name of the Father and of the Son and of the Holy Spirit, teaching them to observe all things, whatever I commanded you. And, behold, I am with you all the days until the end of the world (Matt. 28:18–20).

Index

About the authors

Don Batten, B.Sc. (Hons), Ph.D.
(Contributing editor)

Don received both his B.Sc.Agr.(First Class Honours) and his Ph.D. from the University of Sydney. He worked for over 20 years as a research horticulturalist with the NSW Department of Agriculture. His research included environmental adaptation of tropical/ subtropical fruits such as mango, lychee and custard apple (*Annona*); floral biology, floral induction; breeding; environmental physiology (especially water requirements, effects of water deficits), plant taxonomy, and mineral nutrition. His research on floral induction of lychee and mango overturned long-held ideas which had been an impediment to the scientific understanding of these plants, as well as causing economic loss due to inappropriate management of these crops. He conducted a number of research projects that were externally funded and has published a dozen papers in scientific journals.

Don joined the ministry in Brisbane, Australia in 1994 and has spoken around the world on the creation issue, showing the errors in the evolutionary ideas he was taught. He is also co-author of *One Blood, Answers to the 4 Big Questions, 15 Reasons to Take Genesis as History*, and author of the booklets *Does Carbon Dating Disprove the Bible?* and *Is There Intelligent Life in Outer Space?* Don is also a co-editor of *Creation* magazine, and has written many articles for *Creation* as well as the in-depth *Journal of Creation* (formerly *TJ*).

David Catchpoole, Ph.D.

Dr Catchpoole graduated with B.Ag.Sc. (Hons) from the University of Adelaide and a Ph.D. from the University of New England (New South Wales, Australia). David's Ph.D. investigated nitrogen transfer between tree legumes, associated grass and ruminant animals (goats). This was undertaken in Indonesia as part of a joint Australia-Indonesia project in forage research, aimed at improving the quality and availability of animal feed.

David subsequently worked for the Queensland Department of Primary Industries as a plant physiologist. His work primarily focused on plant nutrition of tropical fruit trees (especially mango), and varietal selection. He also worked as a science educator at James Cook University, which included lecturing in tropical horticulture.

David was once an ardent atheistic evolutionist, before being challenged to look critically at the problems of evolution, and the scientific evidence for creation and the Bible. He now works full-time for *Creation Ministries International* (CMI) in Brisbane, Australia and is a popular speaker having lectured all over Australia and across the world. He has spoken widely on the issues of creation, in particular their importance to evangelism. He is a co-editor of *Creation* magazine, as well contributing articles for CMI's popular website, <creation.com>.

Jonathan D. Sarfati, B.Sc. (Hons), Ph.D., F.M.

Dr Sarfati was born in Ararat, Australia, but spent most of his life in New Zealand. He obtained a B.Sc. (Hons.) in chemistry (with two physics papers substituted) and a Ph.D. in physical chemistry from Victoria University of Wellington. He has co-authored papers in mainstream scientific journals on high temperature superconductors and selenium-containing ring and cage molecules. To help Christians defend the faith, Dr Sarfati was a co-founder of the Wellington Christian Apologetics Society. Since 1996, he has worked full-time for Creation Ministries International (CMI), as a research scientist, speaker and editorial consultant for *Creation* magazine and the associated *Journal of Creation*, and has written many articles for both. For most of this time, he was based in the CMI office in Brisbane, Australia, until transferring to the CMI-US office in Atlanta, Georgia, in early 2010 with his American-born wife, Sherry. He is also a former New Zealand Chess Champion, and represented New Zealand at the World Junior Champs and in three Chess Olympiads. Jonathan has written *Refuting Evolution, Refuting Evolution 2, Refuting Compromise* and *The Greatest Hoax on Earth? Refuting Dawkins on Evolution*.

Carl Wieland, M.B., B.S.

Carl is the Managing Director of *Creation Ministries International* (Australia), a position he has held since 1987, when it was called *Creation Science Foundation*, then *Answers in Genesis*. He was the founding editor of *Creation* magazine (in 1978) that now has subscribers in over 140 countries.

Carl's formal qualifications are in medicine and surgery, and he is a past president of the Christian Medical Fellowship of South Australia. He no longer practises medicine, having been in fulltime ministry since 1987. He is in great demand as a speaker on the scientific evidence for Creation and the Flood, and its relevance to Christianity. Able to hold both academic and lay audiences, he has lectured extensively in Australia and around the world, and has engaged in a number of public debates with prominent evolutionists.

He is also the co-author of *One Blood*, *Walking Through Shadows*, *Answers to the 4 Big Questions*, and author of *Dragons of the Deep: Ocean Monsters Past and Present*, *Stones and Bones* and *One Human Family*. These are among the most popular creation books of recent times, and have been translated into many languages. He has also authored numerous articles in both *Creation* magazine and the *Journal of Creation*.

RECOMMENDED READING

REFUTING EVOLUTION
Dr Jonathan Sarfati

Refuting Evolution is a hard-hitting critique of the most up-to-date arguments for evolution to challenge educators, students and parents. It is a powerful, yet concise summary of the arguments against evolution and for creation. It should stimulate much discussion and help students and teachers think more critically about origins. Over 500,000 in print. *176 pages.*

15 REASONS TO TAKE GENESIS AS HISTORY
*Drs Don Batten
and Jonathan Sarfati*

Many have been misled into thinking that the Genesis account of creation is not actual history, but is just some sort of theological argument ('polemic'). This small book succinctly shows why those who believe in the inspiration of Scripture have no intellectually honest choice but to take Genesis as straight-forward history, just as Jesus did. It powerfully challenges one of the major problems in the church today that affects the authority of the entire Bible. Read it, and give it to your pastor or particularly anyone contemplating theological training—it could save them from getting derailed by some of the misleading arguments common in theological academia. *32 pages.*

AUSTRALIA
*Creation Ministries
International (Australia)*
P.O. Box 4545
Eight Mile Plains, Qld 4113
Phone: (07) 3340 9888
Fax: (07) 3340 9889

CANADA
*Creation Ministries
International (Canada)*
300 Mill St, Unit 7,
Kitchener, ON, N2M 5G8
Phone: (519) 746–7616
Fax: (519) 746–7617

NEW ZEALAND
*Creation Ministries
International (NZ)*
P.O. Box 39005
Howick, Auckland 2145
Phone/Fax: (09) 537 4818
A Registered Charitable Trust

SINGAPORE
*Creation Ministries
International (Singapore)*
Clementi Central Post Office
P.O. Box 195
Singapore 911207
Phone: 9698 4292

SOUTH AFRICA
*Creation Ministries
International (SA)*
P.O. Box 3349
Durbanville 7551
Phone/Fax: (021) 979 0107

UK/EUROPE
*Creation Ministries
International (UK/Europe)*
15 Station Street, Whetstone
Leicestershire LE8 6JS,
United Kingdom
Phone: 0845-6800-264 (CMI)

USA
*Creation Ministries
International (USA)*
PO Box 350, Powder Springs,
GA 30127
Phone: 1-800-616-1264
Fax: (770) 439-9784

OTHER COUNTRIES
*Creation Ministries
International*
P.O. Box 4545
Eight Mile Plains, Qld 4113
Australia
Phone: +617 3340 9888
Fax: +617 3340 9889

Visit our website: CREATION.com